A BRUSH WITH MADNESS

by

Robin Plummer

Published by:

A Brush With Madness Ltd

A BRUSH WITH MADNESS
ISBN: 978-0-9567042-0-7

Originally published in Great Britain
by
A Brush With Madness Ltd

PRINTING HISTORY
A Brush With Madness Ltd 2010

Set in 10/14pt Times New Roman by
A Brush With Madness Ltd

Copies are published by
A Brush With Madness Ltd
2, Barkway Road, Royston, Herts SG8 9EA England

Copies may be obtained and contact details found at:
www.ABrushWithMadness.com
A Brush With Madness Ltd, Reg. No 7381781

Made and printed in Great Britain by
Print-Out
High Street, Histon, Cambridge CB24 9JE, England

Cover Design by Rebecca Parker

Dedications to:

Rachel Russell, whose love, support, and critical, editorial comment helped to bring this book to fruition.
Pat, who took our case to the Prime Minister,
Katy, Ross and Christopher, who suffered greatly,
Kate Adie, without whose presence we might still be there,
Terry Waite, without whose presence we might still be there,
Ian McClarence for all the aikido,
and
The author of the Jamahiriyah Calypso, who wishes to remain anonymous.

Acknowledgements:

My brothers, Barry and Andrew
My late, best friend, Alan Marr, and his wife Sue.
Kate Adie OBE
Amanda Goodman
Lord Howe of Aberavon (Sir Geoffrey Howe)
Free to Decide
Duke Ellington, Charles Mingus
Northampton Chronicle
Yevtushenko
Morihei Ueshiba
Derrick Wareham FIET
All our friends, neighbours and Neil, of the Royston Police, who supported Pat, the children and me during and after the situation
Dr Robert Runcie, Late Archbishop of Canterbury
Terry Waite CBE - Thank you.

PROLOGUE

One day, two men came to Robin's office.

As Graham, the office factotum, lifted the receiver in one more futile attempt to raise the company manager, the two men started to move towards Robin.

Robin started to back away.

"You must come now," said the senior man.

Robin attempted to stall. "I thought you said that you weren't the police."

"We aren't, but they are waiting below. If you do not come now, we will be in trouble."

Robin's heart bled for them.

"Mr Plummer!" barked the senior man.

Dorothy spoke. "I'll come too. They're usually better when there's a woman present."

This broke the tension to some extent because what she said was generally true. Robin relaxed a bit. If he had to go and see the police, a woman's presence could make a lot of difference.

Robin sighed. He breathed out to the office manager, "OK. Forget it Graham." But Graham continued feverishly to punch numbers into the telephone.

"No, no. It's quite alright old chap. I'll keep trying to get him."

"Thanks."

Robin spun on his heel. The room spun around his head. The world spun on its axis. And, as he walked out the door, nothing would ever be the same again.

*** *** ***

PART ONE
17th April to 14th May 1984

WPC Yvonne Fletcher slid silently to the ground. The clatter of machine gun fire echoed in her ears. A pool of blood ran towards the gutter and drained away, along with the echo of gunfire and her existence on this planet. Her mother would be destroyed. Colonel Gaddafi would later apologise.

Less than a quarter of a mile away Robin's lunch was superb but getting cold. Could the waiter heat it up for him? The chef had no time to reheat food, not even for favoured customers. So he sent a new meal instead.

Finishing the second steak with a matching bottle of red, Robin took the receipt, the stairs two at a time, and the fresh air, as he walked to the Tube.

There was yet one more piece of business to do before taking the train home to his beloved wife - a pint of Directors at King's Cross station.

As the Indian served an impeccable pint, Robin's thoughts of the morning's meeting with Chris Wright remained undisturbed.

Chris had told Robin that he could have his old London job back - provided that he returned from Libya in August as scheduled - or they would give the job to someone else. Chris, himself, had been an expatriate in Saudi Arabia for five months and had been given the option to stay there. Chris had told his bosses back in the UK that he would only return to the UK if they promoted him. The blackmail had worked. But Chris knew to watch for others trying the same trick. They shook hands. Robin left.

The train pulled out of King's Cross and the inevitable wifely welcome was a little over an hour away. Robin slept.

High over the Mediterranean, the second and last British Caledonian flight of the day to Libya was midway to Tripoli when the order came to return immediately to London. With more than faint relief, the pilot turned the aircraft around.

The Six O'Clock News brought the story that a woman police constable, patrolling a demonstration by dissident Libyans outside the Libyan High Commission in St James's Square, London, had died after being shot by bullets fired from, what is believed to have been, within the Libyan High Commission.

"Shit!" thought Robin, and turned to his wife. "And we've got to go back there. I hope to Christ nobody looks too closely at my passport and asks if I was in London that day. Christ alone knows what they'll think."

"Don't be ridiculous," said Pat. "You were only having a meeting." And she got on with cooking dinner.

"Yes," said Robin. "Less than a quarter of a mile from where this happened."

She tutted. "I don't want to go back to Libya."

The news of the return to Gatwick was relayed to British Caledonian's airport manager at Tripoli Airport, Doug Ledingham. Doug understood by the message that there had been technical difficulties of a nature that he knew could not be resolved at a place such as Tripoli Universal Airport. Nevertheless, it wouldn't go down too well with the Libyans that a prestige foreign airline had turned a ship around in mid-flight, no matter what the reason.

But Doug had spent long enough in Africa to expect the unexpected, so when he registered loud footfalls on the marble floor outside his office, he took no real notice and continued packing his brief case for the end of another day. After cracking his change of shirt to get the sand off it, he placed it neatly inside the case, on top of the day's reports and B-Cal's, three hundred Libyan Dinar float money, and closed the lid.

He picked up the case and was turning to leave when the door flew open and in strode what looked like half the Libyan army.

"You can't come in here! This is B-Cal property! Get out! What the hell do you think you're doing?" he demanded.

"Ledingham?" asked an NCO.

Doug's eyes narrowed. He was expecting trouble, but not like this.

"Batentis!" barked the NCO.

Doug produced his identity card. The NCO unfolded the pink card and turned to the soldiers.

" 'Ere! Give me back my briefie!" bellowed Doug. "You can't do that!" The soldiers dragged him, fighting for his case, his balance and his breath, out of the office. The door rocked quietly to a halt.

Over the next few days, the Metropolitan Police wanted to arrest the occupants of the Libyan High Commission.

The Libyans claimed diplomatic immunity.

The Foreign Office protested.

The Libyans claimed diplomatic immunity.

Sooner or later the food was going to run out.

The Libyans claimed diplomatic immunity.

The Foreign and Commonwealth Office broke off diplomatic relations with Libya.

Over the same few days, Robin called his Main Office in Tripoli. The only person in any authority was the Financial Officer. Robin suppressed a groan.

"The FCO is advising Brits who do not have to be in Libya to get out, and those who do not absolutely have to return to stay out," Robin told the Financial Officer. "All the indicators are that we should not return to Libya, at least not until this mess has died down. I have tickets for the 28th April. What is your view?"

"Don't come back for a day or two, until the situation is clearer," replied the Financial Officer.

"What do you mean clearer? Do we have to come back or not?" said Robin.

"If you've got tickets for the 28th, call us when you get to Malta and we will see what the situation is from there," said the Financial Officer.

"Why can't we just wait 'til the dust has settled and then get a later flight?" said Robin.

"There's no guarantee that you'd get on a later flight," said he.

"Why?" said Robin.

"Libyan Arab probably wouldn't let you on, and B-Cal has suspended all flights to Tripoli for the moment," said he.

If for any reason, Robin had asked more in hope than expectation, he flew his family to Malta and it proved impossible to carry on to Libya, what provision would be made to fly them home again?

"There'll be some monies available," was the response that Robin finally managed to bleed out of the Financial Officer.

A few minutes later Robin got off the phone, having been told, "It would not go down well on your records if you refused to come back."

Robin was annoyed by the threat. He had already decided to go back anyway. He had a job to do. It was just a question of when. But, there was nothing to be done immediately so he decided to just watch the diplomatic deadlock and see where things were going.

Colonel Gaddafi could see exactly where things were going.

One of his closest aides, probably a Lt. Col., had been responsible for placing the precise persons in the diplomatic mission in St James's Sq. in the first place.

"Sort it out," had said Col Gaddafi. And, in the Arabic pronunciation, "Find The One Who Killed The Bolice Woman. Either he dies or you die. Go to London. Tell me the result when you get back."

A single minded aide flew to England.

What followed next is not altogether clear.

What is certain, however, is that within seconds of the aide's arrival at the Libyan High Commission in London, one voice was heard to do a great deal of shouting.

The story has it that the aide took an automatic pistol out of the Diplomatic Bag, and threatened to blow out the brains of anyone who did not quickly contribute to the solution of The One Who Killed The Bolice Woman. Shots were heard within the first minute.

To the amazement of the watching public, the entire Libyan Diplomatic Mission was seen on the Six O'Clock News, in Indian File, expensive suits, bare feet, and silence, to exit from the Libyan Diplomatic Mission, without a gun or a gesture in sight.

The ten day standoff was over.

The Libyans were allowed to board a Libyan Arab Airlines flight back to Tripoli.

Everyone breathed a momentary and mournful sigh of relief, including the Libyan Diplomats. Among these, of course, was the standard bearer of the revolution, whose task it had been to scare off the Stray Dogs demonstrating against Col Gaddafi outside the Libyan Embassy in London, and whose efforts had resulted in the death of WPC Yvonne Fletcher.

According to contemporary accounts, the flight back to Tripoli can't have been a joyous one, and any joy upon arrival at Tripoli would have been short lived as, upon disembarking from the aircraft, The One Who Killed The Bolice Woman was immediately driven to a distant corner of the airfield and shot dead.

Some time later, a machine gun was found buried deep in the confines of the Libyan High Commission, in St James's Sq., London, whose ballistic finger print matched that of the bullet that killed WPC Fletcher.

Robin, Pat and the three children took their scheduled, Air Malta flight from Gatwick to Valetta the following day, Saturday, 28th April and, not even bothering to call the British Post Office Consultancy Office, BPOCO Main Office, from Malta, stepped directly onto the Libyan Arab Airlines flight for the final, hour long sector to Tripoli.

The in-flight service was up to its usual standard - warm 7-Up, and passengers No-Smoking anywhere they wanted.

The flight approached the North African coast and with it, Libyan airspace. As it did so, the jollity and humour, born of two or more weeks of vacation and fuelled by alcohol from at least one previous flight, disappeared from the faces of the expatriates aboard. It was replaced with inscrutability and finally with tension as they prepared themselves for entry into SPLAJ - the Socialist People's Libyan Arab Jamahiriyah.

Upon landing, Robin gently carried the sleeping, one and a half year old Christopher in one arm and a number of bags in the other. Katy and Ross each carried their own over night bags as usual, and Mummy gamely brought up the rear with the remaining suitcases on a broken baggage trolley.

Following currency check, surrounded by soldiers carrying the Kalashnikov, the tension that had started upon re-entering Libyan airspace now became heightened at the familiar sight of the white boards, suspended from the immigration hall ceiling, upon which appeared in English and Arabic, revolutionary slogans in Green.

"Committees Everywhere," observed one.

"Partners - not wage workers," exhorted another.

"In Need Freedom Is Latent," proclaimed a third.

Robin and his family cleared customs without a hitch, seventeen inch salami notwithstanding, and they stepped into the main arrivals hall.

Tripoli Airport was exactly as they remembered it - a large, open toilet with a lot of officials, guns and taxi drivers, but no facilities. It is for the absence of facilities that the airport had never been granted "International" status. The Libyans had attempted to cover their embarrassment by christening the toilet "Tripoli Universal Airport". The international, three letter abbreviation for Tripoli airport is TIP.

Entry into the SPLAJ successfully completed, Robin and his family made their way to their first floor villa in GP, a western suburb of Tripoli.

And so the grind began. Robin only had to complete four more months and he would have finished his contract. Then he would be out of this dreadful country for good, with any luck. It had been an experience, but he had hated every minute of it. He might even be able to take a two week leave after his on-cycle of 11 weeks, although his boss in Libya, Roger Kimpton, the Project Manager, might take some persuading with only the short time that would be left upon his return. That would be hard to bear, given that the two weeks in England just now had provided no real relaxation.

Then Pat's sister committed suicide.

Robin got a phone call from Roger, at work early on the Monday morning.

"There's a message here for you - something about Pat's sister committing suicide. I don't know anything about it," said Roger, looking away.

Margaret had tried it a couple of times before in a half hearted way, but she had only been playing - seeking attention, one suspects.

Robin said, "Oh, she's killed herself," part in anger at Margaret for her suicide and part in exasperation at Roger for his manner of delivering the bad news.

Roger repeated hesitantly, "I don't know anything about it."

Robin knew that he was going to get no help from Roger, but asked, more in hope than expectation, if there was anything more.

Roger told him that there was a phone number and read it out. Robin recognized it.

Roger finished with, "I think you'd better tell Pat."

Robin put the phone down. Before he told anybody, he was going to have to check the facts. He drove to the Main Office, where Roger was covering for his boss, Ian Ridout, the senior BT manager in Libya, who was on leave. The scrappy note from Roger with the phone number on it told Robin nothing new.

An hour or so later, after England had wakened up, Robin was calling his father-in-law from the privacy of the Main Office. Ten minutes after that, the news was confirmed. Barbiturates and a quantity of alcohol.

By eleven o'clock, Robin was in his apartment. Katy was at the British School, Ross was at his new play school, and Christopher was playing quietly in the sitting room.

Robin asked Pat into the bedroom.

"Sit down," said Robin compassionately. She sat on the bed.

Then he told her.

Pat cried inconsolably. The anguish and grief were genuine even though it was more or less predictable that sooner or later Margaret would succeed. Margaret had, after all, been Pat's safe haven for half of Pat's life whenever she'd needed a bolt hole.

Robin made the tea.

An hour later, as the tears were subsiding, it was time for school. Robin scooped up Christopher, changed his nappy, and the three of them went in the car to pick up the other two. From there they would go to the Main Office.

They decided not to tell the children anything until they were in full possession of the facts and any necessary arrangements had been made.

On the way in the car, Robin brooded about how, quite unfairly, he had found Pat's tears hard to take. But it wasn't really surprising since Pat had never shown him that much emotion in all of the almost ten years that they had been married.

Once at the Main Office, Pat spent a long time on the phone to her father. After she'd finished, Robin asked two of the administrators if they would look after the three children for a few minutes while Pat and he talked. It would not be a problem. All the children would need was some things to play with. Then Katy would take charge and they would all play together happily for hours.

Pat told Robin that Margaret never, never expected her husband to leave her.

The funeral was to be in a week, which would give Pat time to get an exit re-entry visa and a ticket home to the UK.

Pat and Robin took the children back to the apartment and told them that night over tea.

Pat spent all the following week arranging her trip to the UK. A telex was required from the UK, to state that a domestic tragedy had occurred, in order to expedite an exit re-entry visa and ticket. Laundry needed doing and all the bags had to be packed.

As the mound of bags on top of the trunk grew on a daily basis, Robin questioned the importance of so much baggage for a trip home for the funeral.

"I'm not coming back," said Pat flatly, and looked away. The excuse that she gave was the need to organize her two year, Health Visitor Training Course, starting in September. In reality, she was fearful for her own safety and that of the children. Robin tried to persuade her that her fears were over the top; that she had spent most of her adult life being terrified of one thing or another. Look at how badly she had needed Margaret as a bolt hole in case life proved too difficult for her at home. Libya was a dangerous place. But you didn't deal with risks by running away from them.

The tickets were for the 9th of May. For her ten or so remaining days in Libya, Pat was increasingly fixated with her safe departure and that of the children, and Robin was increasingly of the feeling of being dumped. The side of his neck began to hurt.

But they worked together to pack everything that Robin wouldn't need, including the photographs and the guitar, but not the saxophone. He was definitely going to need the saxophone.

Over the days before the ninth, Robin tried to console himself that he had just under four months to go and, with some luck, would see Pat and the children in mid July in Malta, perhaps, before going home at the end of August.

Robin also phoned the flute player, Simon Edwards, to see if he wanted to come around for a bite to eat on the Monday evening before going to diving club. But Simon was about to go to Jefren, and so suggested the weekend. Robin said that it would be coming up for full moon at the weekend so there would be no beach party. But with his wife leaving and now, a burgeoning earache, Robin could do with getting out of Tripoli for a couple of days. They arranged to meet on Thursday at the sewage works at Jefren, on the jebel, where Simon was the civil engineer, and they could spend a couple of days playing music.

Then someone tried to assassinate Col Gaddafi.

Assassinations had been attempted before. In fact, there were about two attempts a year on average. Only, this time they got a lot closer than ever.

Early on the morning of the 8th of May, the guards checked the papers of the crew of the dustbin waggon that sat in the entrance to the Azizia Barracks, Col Gaddafi's Tripoli Headquarters.

The crew of the Russian tank, set in its concrete pit in front of the entrance to the barracks, sat disinterestedly with headsets half on and half off their heads.

The gunners manning the anti-aircraft guns on the gantry above the entrance scanned the skies for enemy aircraft.

The fourteen foot high concrete wall, the three strands of electrified, barbed wire, and the closed circuit television cameras that scanned the perimeter were the only examples of effective maintenance in the whole of Libya - with the possible exception of the airport road.

Any pedestrians and all the early morning drivers kept their eyes very much to themselves as they passed the barracks.

The guards let the dustbin waggon in, and turned to check the next vehicle.

Years later of course, Katy would tell her father, "Suddenly... You know that bombs were always going off - they could be heard near the British School - well, one day, suddenly there were twice as many bombs going off as usual! And you and Mum decided that it was the safest thing to leave me at school. All the other parents had come and got their children from school, but not mine! I sat there after all the other children had been collected, and wondered, in confusion, why my parents hadn't come and got me. The teachers decided that it was time to call up my parents because I was the last one left. You left Ross at his playschool as well.

"I was very settled at the school, and I didn't have any qualms about staying with my teacher who incidentally, was the wife of our GP, Dr. Carroll." It had been the safest thing to do.

The dustbin waggon negotiated the maze of defensive walls inside the barracks, and entered the inner courtyard where stood the dustbins and Col Gaddafi's tent. The crew got out.

But instead of emptying dustbins, they drew a barrage of foreign made rocket launchers from the back of the waggon and were only seconds away from firing them at Col Gaddafi's tent where Gaddafi was actually sitting at the time, when the immense firepower of the barracks' internal defences poured down and cut to pieces those who did not surrender.

The Libyan border with Tunisia is an iron curtain of barbed wire and mines except for places where natural features prevent or impede crossing, and for border check points such as Nalut, deep in the desert, and Ras Ajdir, on the Mediterranean coast.

Three counter revolutionaries, Stray Dogs, were caught by a Libyan border patrol, trying to cross the wire into Libya about three kilometres South of the check point at Ras Ajdir. And the leader of the assassination attempt was captured.

A photograph of the three dead bodies appeared in the Libyan daily newspaper the following day.

A fourteen year old girl had drawn a cartoon in the margin of her newspaper, depicting Col Gaddafi with a noose around his neck. Her friend had giggled. A classmate had reported the prank. A long video was shown on both of the Libyan television channels simultaneously, compulsory viewing for everyone in the country, of the slow death by hanging of the two fourteen year old girls when, as Col. Gaddafi described it, "Revolution came to The Great Al Fatah University."

Pat left it as late as she dared before picking up Katy and Ross. The children had been fed at their schools, which saved one problem, and Pat had phoned Robin to pick them up on his way home from work, at five o'clock. Robin did so and took them home without incident.

The streets were mostly deserted on the Wednesday, the 9th of May.
 The Deputy Project Manager, John Palmer, had loaded up the two Peugeots with the luggage of Robin's family.
 Off they went to the airport, hoping that it had not been closed following the excitement of the previous day.
 Instead, the airport was a zoo with half the world trying to get out of Libya.
 But the crowd parted like the Red Sea at the approach of a woman and her young children - especially a beautiful, white woman, with her pretty daughter and her beautiful, platinum blonde boys.
 John and Robin each carried a number of bags in one hand, and shared the trunk in the other. They had to suppress a smile at simply walking to the head of the queue. The clerk checked that all Pat's papers were in order and weighed the luggage. It was all within weight, but the trunk was of dimensions that exceeded international flight rules.
 Robin observed that they had brought the trunk in by Libyan Arab Airlines.
 The clerk said that he would get into trouble if he were to accept an oversized trunk.
 Robin offered to pay the excess, but at three hundred Libyan Dinars, about nine hundred pounds, it was nonsense.
 "You will have to repack."
 There was nothing for it. The good news was that the trunk contained two packed suitcases, in addition to some loose clothing. The trunk had served its purpose and owed them nothing - forty five quid from Robert Sayle in Cambridge - and at a stretch they would get everything repacked into the remaining suit cases.
 John and Robin carted the trunk to the back of the check-in queue, and applied themselves to repacking it in the thirty minutes left before departure, while Pat held the fort at the check-in desk.
 The job done, they ran the suitcases the twenty yards to the desk and Robin pushed Pat through departures with barely enough time to kiss her and all the children.
 John and Robin stood around until it was clear that Pat and the children had got airborne, and turned to leave.
 "Are you taking the trunk?" solicited John.

"Sod it!" said Robin. "If I can't board it now, I can't board it when I come to leave."

"Well, you can't just leave it here," said John.

"Just bloody well watch me," said Robin.

And they walked past the empty trunk on their way to the cars, without a backward glance.

On the way home, they dropped Robin's car off at the BPOCO garage for routine maintenance. John would be going on leave and Robin would be using John's car until his own had been serviced.

Robin went home exhausted, popped three aspirin for his earache, and went to bed.

Robin was a bit happier now that his weekend was accounted for. He had folk club tonight, to blow a few tunes with Simon on Thursday and Friday, and the diving club party at the Daewoo camp on Saturday night. Maybe it wasn't going to be so bad without Pat after all.

At Folk Club that night, Robin borrowed a guitar.

Each person did his prepared piece and, after drinks, the communal, four chord wonders sounded about as dreadful as ever. Upon leaving, the usual cries of "See you at Dead Cow" were replaced by "See you at Daewoo". But the responses this time included, "You can go if you want", "Too dangerous after what's been going on this week" and "Oh, yeah! The party's still on", "Take your Korean dictionary" and "Just make sure you turn into the Daewoo camp and not the university".

Robin knocked off as early as he dared on Thursday, even though he was supposed to be in charge. Ian Ridout had returned from leave. But Roger Kimpton had gone to the UK to conduct some interviews, and John had gone on leave with his family, which left Robin as the senior manager on the ground.

"I am sorry that you can't draw pay as acting level three for this week even though you're in charge," he told Robin. "Because even though I am in London, I am still active on the project."

It didn't make a scrap of difference to Robin. He hadn't expected any such largesse, and he had got to the point where he felt that nothing he did was either truly welcome, or in any way influential on the project anyway.

So, shortly after one o'clock on Thursday, Robin drove John's Peugeot home, threw his overnight bag into the back on top of the saxophone, put his handbag in the glove box in front of the gear lever, and started the one hundred and ten kilometre drive to see Simon at Jefren.

As he drove he counted the electricity pylons, as ever, to see how many you could see at one time - thirty three at max but, in today's dust storm, only about twenty.

Robin mused about the project.

Roger's contract entitled him to unaccompanied status, wherein his wife was eligible to fly to Tripoli for their vacations together. Robin had met Roger's wife once. She looked as though she had been married to Roger for a long time.

Robin's contract entitled him to accompanied status. But BT hadn't let Robin take his wife for the first four months. They didn't want Robin to have the additional burden of having to take care of his family while he himself got settled into the job and the way of life in an unhealthy country. Didn't these idiots in London know how much better Robin functioned with his wife and children close by him? And if they thought that his family needed taking care of then they didn't know who they were dealing with. Pat and the children had been with Robin in Libya for nine months.

John's contract, like Robin's, entitled him to accompanied status with his wife and family.

And then there was John's wife.

Her passport described her as a writer.

Foreign Office jargon would describe her as undesirable.

She wasn't the former, and she certainly wasn't the latter.

She was a brunette - an immensely pretty brunette.

Though short in stature, she deported herself beautifully, her full breasts always thrust forward. Full - she continued to breast feed her son of two and half years in order to keep them that way. Thrust forward - she supported the big, round, beautiful things with pretty bras.

But she wore no undies.

"There's no point in putting them on just to have to take them off again," she once confided to Robin.

By these devices, she could bring to attention the pricked imaginations of red blooded men.

"After John has gone to work and I've taken the children to school, I just stay home all day and wait for someone to come round and fuck me."

Her benighted husband - she was already pregnant when she joined him at the altar at the age of seventeen - was sometimes constrained to go off on a tour of the cable project for three days at a time. His suspicions were such, however, that he always cut short such tours so that he was never away from home for more than one night at a time.

On every occasion that he went away, he contrived to have a least one friend or contact whom he judged trustworthy, to visit his wife during the evening on which he was away, to make sure that she was alright.

One day at the office, upon Robin inviting Roger to his house that evening for a few drinks, Roger politely declined, declaring (something he rarely did) that he had been asked by John to visit the wife to make sure that she was alright.

"You too?" Robin ventured.

"What? Is everybody going around to check on her then?" Roger said, surprised.

"Not everybody," Robin replied. "Only half of Tripoli."

On one occasion John tried warning her that he thought Robin had designs on her.

"Don't worry, John," she'd replied. "I know what to do with men."

Robin approached Azizia, the first town to the South of Tripoli, as the trip indicator showed fifty kilometres. The usual roadblock at Azizia was slightly more officious than usual. Robin stopped at the barrier. The hinge had been freshly oiled.

"Batentis inte, batentis sair," said the soldier.

Robin reached for his papers and the car's papers. He took his pink card and driving licence from his handbag in front of the gear lever, then the car's papers from the sun visor, and handed the lot to the soldier. Then he placed both hands on the steering wheel where they were plainly visible and sat motionless.

A militiaman stepped out of the shade of the sentry box and up to the car door. Robin could see only a field of blue serge from his groin to his open collar - and the machine gun pointing half through the open window at his chest.

Robin didn't want any accidents, so he raised the index finger of his left hand, and the militiaman directed his attention from the soldier with the papers back to Robin. Robin lifted his left hand from the steering wheel and, putting his fingertips on the gun's muzzle, edged it away.

The militiaman withdrew the gun, muttered an apologetic "Malleish, malleish", and stood back a couple of feet.

Robin was let through the checkpoint with barely a second look at his papers. They knew BPOCO's company cars.

About two kilometres later, at the fork for Gharian - the first town up in the two thousand foot high jebel, the Nafusa Mountains, and the last town going South before you leave the Mediterranean coastal belt and enter the desert - all vehicles we being stopped even though there was no formal road block.

Robin indicated and started to bear right onto the Jefren road in order to melt into the dust storm and just disappear, but he was shouted to a halt. He sat with his hands on the steering wheel and his body motionless. His impassive eyes carefully scanned all around him.

The fork was a pathetic little junction, bolstered by a breeze block shack situated in the middle of the cleft, and about thirty yards from its apex. The crumbling, Italian blacktop, skirted in places by telephone and power lines on crumbling, Italian telegraph poles, merged with the drifting dust. Through the dust, Robin could only sense people milling around. But as the dust settled, he saw what he was looking for.

The gunman stood three quarters of the way from the car to the shack and was backdropped by a bush covered in dust. The gun was normal but the gun man was not. He was older than the usual militiaman. He wore not a uniform, but desert garb - and an unusual garb for this region. And he aimed the gun with both eyes. But something more singled him out from most other gunmen. The relaxed, unemotional eyes were not looking at Robin as a person - to form a relationship - to terrorise. The eyes were looking at Robin as a target - to shoot - to kill.

After a few seconds, another man appeared beside the car's open window, yet leaving Robin in full view of the gunman.

"Gharian?" he asked.

"Jefren," said Robin, motionless.

17

Robin raised the index finger of his left hand. Then slowly, lifting his hand and turning his head, he looked, frowned and flicked his hand downward a couple of times at the gunman. The rifle didn't move.

Upon scanning the car and catching Robin's eye, the other man gave a single point of his left arm.

Robin looked up into his eyes and placed a hand on the ignition key. The man nodded. Robin turned the key and drove the few feet onto the rocky desert.

"Batentis."

Robin raised the index finger again, slowly reached for his handbag and then for the car's papers.

The car's papers were handed back within a second.

Upon examining Robin's papers, the man told Robin to get out of the car and started questioning him. When Robin clearly could not answer the Arabic, the man re-read the pink identity card and walked off. A gathering crowd watched the tall, white man in the white, seersucker shirt, with the gun pointing at him.

Robin didn't want any accidents, but waving the gun barrel down hadn't worked. So he widened his eyes, looked straight at the gunman, and started to raise his hands. Very, very slowly.

By the time his hands were beside his head the crowd had started talking.

By the time his hands were above his head the gunman had shaken the Kalashnikov.

By the time his arms were fully extended the crowd had stopped talking and the gunman was getting cross.

When Robin's arms started to shake, the crowd started talking again and the gunman became furious with embarrassment.

Then a younger man came and told Robin in English to put his arms down. When Robin continued to shake, the young man told the gunman to lower his weapon. Which he did. Robin lowered his arms and suppressed a smile.

"Would you please open the back of your car?" the young man said.

Robin raised his eyebrows and raised the rear door. The immense tail board of Peugeot 504 Estate dwarfed his overnight bag and saxophone box.

The young man reached for the overnight bag, examined the contents with a swagger stick and set the bag aside.

Then he reached for the saxophone box.

"No!" jumped in Robin. "I'll do that."

But the young man just looked at Robin without removing his hand from the closed lid. "What is in there?" he enquired.

"Saxophone. Shwear!" cautioned Robin, with the hand gesture. The young man smiled at Robin's attempt at Arabic.

When the box was open and it was indeed a saxophone, the young man invited Robin to pick it up. But, not wanting desert sand all over the precious instrument, Robin declined, drawing the box closer to the young man instead.

"You are fond of music?" the young man asked.

Robin smiled at the young man's attempt at English, and proceeded to close the box.

"Ah! One moment," said the young man, proffering the swagger stick.

Robin lifted the neck of the saxophone, removed the wooden plug, and offered it for the young man to insert the swagger stick.

With all closed again, the young man said, "Enjoy your weekend in Jefren."

Robin took off slowly in a cloud of dust.

Forty minutes and sixty kilometres later, Robin was at Jefren. Two minutes after that he was in Simon's billet.

Simon was shaking more than usual. He was the only English speaker in Jefren, among dozens of incompetent, immigrant labourers and uncommunicative locals who, inattentive to his instructions, poured the concrete for the sewage treatment plant and the two water filtering beds. There was nothing to do in Jefren, less to drink, and Simon had been there for fifteen months without a break, a replacement, or any contact in English save when he went to the monthly diving club beach parties in Tripoli during the summer, or the rare occasion when he could get to the folk club, which was where he and Robin had first met a year previously.

"How is Pat?" he asked.

"She is fine, thank you."

"And how are Katy and Ross?" he preferred.

"They are both at school, now."

"Oh? And how is little Gak-Gak?"

"Gak-Gak is Gak-Gak."

"Ah, yes. Isn't it?" he said.

His black, wavy hair, oily skin, and tense, muscular frame, permanently on the edge of terror, gave no lie to his proud Welsh origins. His good looks were made macabre by the lacerations on his face, gained at the expense of three, drunken Nigerians on a motorcycle who had catapulted themselves out of the bush and onto the coast road directly in front of his Toyota Land Cruiser, which he promptly rolled in an unsuccessful attempt to avoid killing them. Simon had later escaped from a Lagos hospital, after lying to the police who'd wanted to charge him with murder, about the whereabouts of his passport, and fled the country on the first 'plane out.

Simon was self taught on guitar and flute, as was Robin on guitar and saxophone. The smooth, unpainted concrete walls of Simon's spacious but soulless apartment were lined with flute exercises and tunes which he practised every waking hour - until it was time to eat, sleep, defecate or pour concrete - and, along with the Canadian music teacher at the American School, in Tripoli, who played piano, they had formed a trio and were really getting somewhere following only a few practice sessions.

And now Simon was blowing his silver flute to the scripts plastered to his walls, before Robin even had the door shut.

"This one's crap," he said, moving onto the next. Simon's impressive ability to read music at sight was as daunting to Robin as was Robin's knowledge of jazz chord progressions to Simon.

They blew a few tunes together. They sounded terrible. And it soon became clear that both of them needed something other than this.

"Oh, fuck it!" despaired Simon.

"Yeah, I know," said Robin, slowly lowering the sax until it hung by the neck strap.

"Let's go to the Bilfinger camp," said Simon. "It's about twenty five klicks down the road. Maybe we can get a beer."

"Have you got nothing here?" asked Robin.

"Yer, I've got one bottle of cheap, crap, Cypriot wine - if you want it," he replied.

Twenty five kilometres later, the entrance to the Bilfinger camp was down a byroad and hidden in the bush that tops the jebel. Once into the driveway, even in the bright daylight, one still couldn't be sure that it led anywhere. Then the track opened up into a parking space with a low green building by one side. The inside of the building was like a Tardis. The Germans had done a superb job of disguising the existence, as well as the size and layout of the camp.

Once inside, Robin started to feel less tense, and Simon visibly shook less. Within seconds they were confronted by a great, big bear of man - a caricature of a wisp-bearded Aryan - only, three times the size. His corduroys and his white, roll-necked, Aran sweater did nothing to minimize the manifestation. Simon shook a prolonged but indifferent handshake with him, and introduced him to Robin. Robin's German was better than his Arabic and it was met with gentle and smiling approval from the immense Kraut who, Robin was sure, could have crushed him on a whim.

"There is plenty of beer," he directed with his left paw. "And help yourselves to some fillet steak in the refrigerator if you would like to take advantage of it," he articulated, smiling, with his right.

"Oh, thank you very much," lilted Simon with restraint, and visibly relaxed some more. Unaccustomed to such hospitality in a contractor's camp, Robin kept his peace. The Teutonic Bear loped off to more important things, presumably. Doors shut along corridors, and there was silence.

"Fuck it!" announced Simon. "Where's the fucking beer?"

Simon shuffled into and out of a couple of side rooms.

Robin felt anxious at being out of sight and earshot of his friend. But then, "Fucking Hell, Robin!" exploded, the valley baritone. "We've struck gold!"

Robin followed the Welsh Warble into a fluorescent lit, white walled room that was dominated by a head height, timber frame that supported three, one thousand litre, white, food grade, polythene tubs. An orderly, Germanic, plumber's nightmare crested the barrels. One look told Simon and Robin which barrel of the production line was ripe. They drew and drew. Appreciative nods for the alcohol if not the flavour, which ran a close second, were followed by pints of similar, and they sat down, delighting in each other's company and the opportunity to jaw.

Robin cut thick slices from the long fillet and fried them in butter and garlic. And what, with the diving stories, the music stories, and the sex stories, merciful oblivion soon took hold.

Around midnight, The Teutonic Bear came back to see how things were progressing. He of the daily bottle of breakfast vodka was not likely to criticise. Robin and Simon, however, felt it incumbent upon themselves to entertain their gracious, Prussian Host and, retrieving musical instruments from Robin's car, placed moistened mouth pieces to over-moistened lips. They gave up at the first attempt.

So, cuddling replenished glasses of beer and further plates of garlic steak, they sang choruses of the Jamahiriyah Calypso:

> 'Here in the Jamahiriyah,
> Life could never be freer.
> So drink up your wine and your beer.
> Drink a health to the Jamahiriyah.'

And to this day they have no idea where they slept that night.

Fillet steak and fried eggs for breakfast went an inadequate way to soak up the wreckage of the night before.

They drifted their way towards rehydration by about mid-day, when they decided to leave a note of thanks, and departed.

Robin drove Simon back to the sewage works. They dreaded to think how bad the place would smell during late July and throughout August. They shook hands and kissed. Robin left. He never saw Simon again. Within an hour and a half, Robin could smell Tripoli.

With the unusual road block at Aizizzia now gone, Robin arrived at his empty apartment without incident in a little under two hours, took two aspirin, changed the cotton wool in his ear, and went to bed.

Ten rewarding hours of sleep later, Robin went to the office. Ten unrewarding hours of work later still he went home again. But it didn't matter. There was the Daewoo party that evening. The good news was that he had got his car back from the garage. Robin sat in front of the expatriate television channel, took two aspirin, changed the cotton wool in his ear and dozed.

He awoke to the televised, sundown call to prayer. It meant the end of BBC television programmes for the day. He turned off the television to no avail. The wail from the local mosque just replaced it. He mooched around the apartment trying to find something to do.

He even went into Ross and Christopher's old bedroom, curious to find out what it looked like. There had never been enough light to see it. Nobody ever opened the ghiblis - the heavy roller blinds that could be raised and lowered over the outside of the window by use of a built in tape and pulley mechanism inside the house, and made of interlocking wooden slats that protect the house against sandstorms driven off the desert by the hot, South Wind - The Ghibli - either because they didn't work, or because the curtains were broken and it would be indiscreet among the locals.

Ross had, on one occasion, fallen out of bed and split open the back of his head upon hitting the marble floor. There had been blood everywhere. Robin had thrown everyone into the car and roared off to the Oil Clinic in the middle of the night to get Ross treated. At the entrance to the clinic, the old Hajji on guard duty had refused to raise the barrier to allow the car pass. Robin had threatened to smash the barrier down with the car if the Hajji didn't open it.

They saw the doctor.

Robin went into Katy's old room, but that was even more impenetrable because the light simply didn't work. That had never bothered Katy. She liked it like that, so there had been no call to fix it.

Robin couldn't make his mind up about the Daewoo party. It was a bit risky, but you don't deal with risks by walking away from them.

He looked in the wardrobe for some home brew. But it had all gone.

His car responded to the key as it always had since the new engine had been put in. And he was off. At least this way he could get a drink.

There was one roadblock on the way to the Eastern suburbs that was always manned, and closed after dark. A routine check made no impact on Robin's journey. Nor did the gigantic potholes in the road or the manholes, whose conical covers that never seated properly because of the sand, had been flipped out by the massive driving wheels of the Calabrese trucks. Most such holes in the road had been marked by some civically minded citizen by use of a disused refrigerator or oven. You had to know the locations of such holes that had not been so marked.

Robin was able to look further than just ten feet in front of the bonnet, now, as he turned onto the highway that led to Daewoo.

But care was still needed as the highway had no street lighting. Any buildings to left or right were similarly in darkness. The old well, which presaged the coast road and all points East – Sirte, Benghazi, Tobruk, Egypt - could just about be picked out a good half mile ahead. But Robin didn't want to go that far if he could avoid it, because that would mean coming back on the opposite side of the highway, only to have to do the same run again and he would start to look conspicuous. Then, there was light just down a side turning, and light activity at a barrier. Then he saw a large wooden sign on which he could just make out the Korean script. Robin turned right into the entrance. He stopped behind a waiting car and beside a tree in a large brick tub.

There was the usual barrier, flooded with a sharp pyramid of white light. One end of the barrier was lost in the darkness. The other end, the one that raised and lowered, fell a body's-width short of the guard house.

Shielding his eyes, Robin could make out two cars between him and the barrier. Wisps of water vapour issued from their exhausts. At each driver's door bent a young man. But the white, Daewoo boiler suits had changed to brown uniforms.

Robin frowned. Craning to the right and ducking to see out of the right hand windows of his car, Robin caught sight of the large wooden sign again. The Korean script had changed into Arabic. His heart started to race.

He looked frontwards again and now picked out blue uniformed militiamen with Kalashnikovs slung over their shoulders. He couldn't swallow. Upon looking to the left, he could now see the outline of the mature tree. But the large brick tub had changed into a small roundabout.

Robin threw the wheel across to the left and lurched forward, too close to the car in front.

He threw the car into reverse, saw nothing over his shoulder and started to creep back the few feet to be able to make the U-turn around the roundabout and the safety of the highway.

Robin looked to the left to judge the turn. But his rearward motion was shunted to a premature halt by a Peugeot truck pulling up behind him.

Robin's neck burned. He lifted his arm to wave the driver back a few feet but instead, his head was jerked aside as he was thumped in the jaw by the muzzle of an automatic pistol.

By the time Robin had blinked, someone had opened the door and dragged him by the hair out of the car. Before he could stand up, a hand on the back of his neck had Robin clean off balance. As he tried again to stand up, he received the flat side of the automatic full across the side of his face and was thrown face first against the side of the car. Only momentarily stable, he was again whisked off balance to the back of the car where he was finally forced to assume the position, with the flat side of the automatic striking him full across the side of his head.

Someone screamed at him, and instantly started a loveless frisking.

"In the Peugeot! In the Peugeot! Batentis! In the Peugeot, you fucking idiot!" cried Robin. And the mauling stopped.

But with nothing visible to him, the brown uniform screamed again. Robin found himself flying down the length of the car and head first through the driver's doorway. The only advantage to getting a mouth full of the gear lever was that he could quickly grab his hand bag and proffer his identity card. Then this nonsense would be over and he would be able to go to the party.

The brown uniform tore the pink card out, and hurled the handbag to the ground. In the silent few seconds that it took to read the card, Robin realised that the brown uniform had been screaming non-stop since first ramming the pistol into his face.

Robin avoided direct eye contact. But he could see that the uniform bore no badges or insignia, and that the face of the wearer was younger than the usual soldier.

The screaming resumed as Robin was ordered to open the back passenger door. The young man pushed Robin in the chest with the barrel of the Browning to make him stand back a pace, and looked at him as an order to stand still. Then he knelt on the back seat and rummaged through the few items that lay on the floor, swapping the automatic from one hand to the other as he did so. Robin thanked God that he had nothing illegal in the car.

The brief search over, the screaming started again and the youth grabbed Robin by the arm. As he tried to march Robin off, Robin dug his heels in. The youth grabbed Robin's hair, stepped across in front of him and, as Robin straightened up, thumped

Robin on the side of the head again with the automatic. Robin was dragged by the hair into the guard house.

A soldier turned slowly as they entered the door and the youth respectfully snapped out a couple of words of Arabic. With a final scream at Robin, the youth returned to the car and the soldier immediately looked at Robin.

Robin shook hands and greeted, "Kef halik?" From under the black moustache and the stubble, Robin heard, "Sit down," and did so, grateful for the English and the physical respite.

But the respite lasted only seconds. A stream of barking Arabic had him back on his feet again.

And so the first interrogation began. But it was quickly interrupted by a loud racket from outside.

Robin looked past the soldier. He could hear the heart being torn out of his beloved Peugeot as the idiot thrashed the engine and crashed the gearbox in a vain attempt to drive the car off. When he found a gear of sorts, the car bucked about like a kangaroo for a few feet, until he gave up and let someone with a little less revolutionary zeal drive it peacefully away.

Robin's muscles went weak.

Robin gestured over his shoulder. "Daewoo?"

"Daewoo?" the interrogator queried. "La. Al Fatah University."

The Great Al Fatah University.

Robin's stomach turned to water.

Over the next hour, Robin was asked questions in broken English about who he was, what he was doing in Libya, what he was doing at the university, where he lived, who his friends were, where did he get his car, who his contacts were in the UK, who he worked for, what his job involved, who he reported to, what were the maps in his bag, why was the GP Post Office marked on the map, what was he planning to do at GP Post Office, why was he spying, who was he spying for, what previous information had he reported, where were his weapons hidden, where he lived, where was his camera, how did he get the film out of Libya.

Once it had very quickly become clear were the interrogation was heading, it became paramount to Robin to lie even where the truth was perfectly innocent, for fear that the truth would invite false accusations and provide evidence and be taken as proof in what was now an increasingly difficult and dangerous situation. Straight away, Robin needed a cover story, which he did not immediately have. Fortunately, the cotton wool in his ear provided necessary evidence that he had just been out for a drive, for some fresh air and, on choosing to do a U-turn to go home, he had unintentionally turned into the university drive way. It was limp, but it was all he had. Any talk of Daewoo might have started he knew not what, but was desperate to avoid.

Robin put on his best BBC English, and looked the soldier straight in the eye as he answered the questions. The soldier was professional and thorough and, in spite of himself, gave Robin the impression that there was nothing here of any consequence. But Robin was not home yet.

A car pulled up. The revolutionary entered the gate house and immediately grabbed Robin by the upper arm and started to pull. The soldier spoke curtly and the pulling stopped. Instead, the soldier made a sharp motion with his finger, that Robin was to follow. The revolutionary was not to be outdone and made a last attempt at holding Robin's upper arm and pushing him thereby. Robin violently shrugged him off. Robin received a severe clout in the middle of the back from the automatic for his trouble, but there was no more pulling.

Forced into the back of a waiting car, with a driver, and an armed young man in the back seat next to him, Robin considered the possibilities of dumping the contents of his handbag out of the lowered, rear door window. There was nothing genuinely incriminating in his bag, but that didn't appear to matter given the content of his first interrogation. Robin thought better of it, on the grounds that while he still carried his stuff with him, he felt that he had some measure of control over who would see it.

Fifteen heart pounding minutes later, the car arrived in the inner suburbs of Tripoli. Robin was escorted out and taken quickly into a small office, where a careful and dutiful NCO had a desk in a tiny and cramped office.

Then the interrogating began again. The same saga as before was repeated only in finer detail. But, the NCO's English was not up to the task, so he called in a translator. The translator's English was not up to the task and the interrogation dragged on interminably, with the inevitable misunderstandings. Right now, whether or not Robin got out of here tonight or indeed at all might depend on accuracy and precision. Robin taxed the interpreter and found that he spoke French. Now Robin was under way. The downside of course is that they now knew he spoke French. A minor detail given the number of polyglots around.

Unfortunately, in Robin's handbag there were indeed two maps. One was carefully hand drawn, with landmarks, such as the GP Post Office, and major routes highlighted in yellow marker pen. The other was a rough sketch of local roads, and handwritten details of at least one set of directions to a friend's house. There was also an invitation to a friend's leaving party. Finally, there was travel brochure.

Some of the interrogation revolved around the maps, with no apparent consequence. The reverse was true when attention was turned to the travel brochure.

The brochure advertised holidays from "Cyprus by boat to Alexandria, Egypt and on to the pyramids, but also to Tyre, Sidon, and Haifa, Israel."

"What does this say," barked the NCO, underlining THE WORD with an index finger.

"Oh, God!" thought Robin. "They hate the place so much that they can't even bear to say the name Isra'el. Robin shrivelled as he pronounced the word."

The NCO and the Frenchman stopped dead, mouths open.

Robin let out a breath between barely parted lips, dropped his shoulders, spat out a stream of French and shook his head from side to side. He stated that the plan had been to go to the pyramids with his family at his next scheduled leave, which was true. He finished with an exhortation to look at his passport and see that he had never been to Israel, which would not have proven a thing, and he knew it, but he hoped that the performance was convincing. It appeared to be, because Israel was quietly dropped.

Once the NCO had repeated the interrogation of earlier, and completed a transcript, Robin was offered tea. The Frenchman picked up two whisky glasses of tea and offered them both to Robin. Robin took one and rested, claiming that it was too hot. The Frenchman promptly drank the other himself. Then Robin drank his.

Robin was taken out. The Frenchman looked him in the eye and indicated that it was a straight drive home now. But before they got half way out of the building, the small party was stopped by a couple of noisy, younger men in civvies, who told them to wait. Robin recommenced walking and was promptly told by them to stand still. The Frenchman and the NCO looked wary. Then the NCO bellowed his best, parade ground bawl and got some attention from the younger men. There followed a heated exchange of views and the laying on of hands by the NCO on the two who increasingly appeared to be revolutionaries as the NCO attempted to push them up the corridor and away from Robin. Established authority versus young zealotry. But young zealotry won. And the NCO looked down and sideways under Robin's gaze. Right at that moment, Robin could have kissed the NCO for what he had attempted to do. Instead, apprehension reigned all round as Robin was whisked off, and the revolutionaries ensured that they had the maps. The car contained a driver, and bore a piece of white paper with a hand written number on it, stuck to the driver's side window. Robin was alone in the back.

After a few hundred yards, over the roundabout by the People's Palace - what, in pre-revolution days, had been the Royal Palace of King Idris the First - and down past the cinema in the direction of the harbour, Robin levelled his trembling voice to the extent that he could, and said, "Where are we going?"

"Where?" smirked the driver. "There." And they drove down a narrow street that was guarded by a No Entry Sign. Robin felt sick.

The car stopped in front of two, huge, green, steel framed and plated gates. A toot on the horn had the gates opening.

A crowd of young men clamoured to get at the car and the doors open. Better standing than sitting in the car if going to be attacked, Robin moved swiftly, despite some difficulty getting his right leg out past the door pillar, to get out of the car. But the young men were upon him and half dragged, half carried him through the car door, some by the shoulders, some by the arms and some by the shirt. At a yelp of alarm from Robin, only some of them let go.

The gates were fully open by this time, and Robin was presented on the opposite side of a courtyard the size of a cricket table, with the facade of a large colonial building on several floors, dimly illuminated at ground level, and through some of the doors and windows where the ghiblis were not lowered. Robin smiled inwardly at the thought that some of the ghilblis almost certainly hadn't worked for years. The rooms behind them would be banked up with sand.

Robin was dragged into the spacious courtyard, far enough to allow the gates behind him to be closed. As the gates were being closed, he saw to his right a guard house illuminated from within, and big enough to seat four men, one of whom was already on his feet making notes. For the rest, it required a sweep of Robin's eye to take in the height, weight, size and number of most of the men either milling around or, what appeared to be, playing football, and to see that the whole courtyard was surrounded by a wall as high as the gates.

But the survey was cut short, by a shorter, young man coming out of the gloom in the shadow of the gates to deal Robin a series of severe smacks around the sides of his head and face with the flat of the hand to deter Robin from looking. Robin was cowed but unbowed by the initial assault, until it became clear that the assault was only going to stop when he either looked down or turned away. The former was not sufficient. The latter was accompanied by a barely controlled, "Alright, alright," until he found himself face and arms to the inside of the gates to make the point, and the rain of blows ceased. Robin had got the layout of the place, but it was now time to be more circumspect.

After a few minutes, the party moved off in the direction of the building. A couple of revolutionaries stepped forward to grab Robin, but this time he was having none of it, and he stepped forward, looking them straight in the eye. Their advance ceased.

The subsequent interrogation covered much the same ground as the previous two had done, only much more swiftly. The emphasis this time was more on the maps, which the interrogators produced from nowhere. And many of the questions that were asked by the older and more mature revolutionaries were answered from among themselves. Little sense of protocol or order was manifest, in sharp distinction to the relative professionalism of the last two interrogations, conducted by soldiers. On a few of the occasions when Robin tried to intervene to establish the facts of the matter, he was screamed at and harangued to silence.

Following an hour of intimidating chaos, he was allowed to leave.

After much practice at picking up his passport from Libyan officials, he knew not to indicate any degree of hurry when gathering up even one's own legitimate possessions in front of any Libyan authority. So even after having been told that he could go, and thus leave this dreadful situation and these vile, young idiots, he vacillated until almost all of the hotheads had left the room, before attempting to pick up his pink ID card, dark glasses, bits and pieces, one at a time, slowly, seamlessly - until he got to the maps.

Holding out his left hand, he asked, "Can I have my keys please?" in genuine anticipation of getting his car back, and palmed the maps with his right hand as he did so.

"Where do you live?" someone asked.

"I don't know," Robin replied.

"Oh, come. You must know where you live," was the rebuke.

"I don't know where I live," he re-affirmed.

"You must know where you live. You go home there every night," he thickened up.

"I do go home there every night," Robin agreed politely.

"Then you must know where you live," increasingly impatiently.

"I know where I live but I do not know the address," said Robin in level tones.

"Why not?" enquired the voice.

"Because I do not speak Arabic and I cannot read the road signs," replied Robin reasonably.

They sat back.

"But you must know where you live or you could not get back there each evening," they stated logically.

"I know where I live sufficient to get back there each evening. But I do not know where I live sufficient to tell you where I live," Robin replied.

"Do you live in east Tripoli?"

"No. West," said Robin.

"Which road do you go on to get to West Tripoli?" they enquired calmly.

"The GP road," said Robin.

They looked at each other. "So you live in GP?" they concluded.

"Yes." Their shoulders dropped.

"Why didn't you tell us that when we asked?"

"Because I didn't know that that was the name of the area," said Robin.

One more request for his keys was met by a signal to leave. Robin felt that he had pushed his luck as far as he could and that it really was time to get out, even without his car

As Robin turned at their signal and went up the corridor in the direction of the now fresh, May evening, a revolutionary halted the party and spoke to the one in charge

"Wait a minute," he said, and they proceeded to ask for – to demand the maps

"No," Robin preferred. "We've been through all that." And started to walk off.

But met with revolutionary fervour in the next exchange, Robin had to give the maps up.

When Robin asked what they wanted now, the more mature revolutionaries said that they wanted to photocopy the maps for their records.

While the copying was under way, Robin was made to stand outside, facing the wall of the building. He stood at ease with his hands in front of him, holding his handbag. After what he estimated to be an hour during which he assumed they were field stripping the photocopier to try to get it to work, someone brought a chair and said slowly, "Would you like to sit down, Sir?" Robin construed the use of the honorific as a positive sign, but shook his head from side to side. After this kind of treatment he was not going to be swayed by gestures of kindness, no matter how tired he was getting. "Sit down," said the voice quietly, and pulled him by the arm into the chair.

Another half hour or more followed. Now the soaring silence of the air of midnight was beginning to tell as the interminable photocopying went on.

Finally, they gave Robin his maps back and put him in a truck.

As four of them clambered in and around Robin, the Frenchman walked up. Instinctively, Robin had learnt to trust him.

"Qu'est-ce qui se passe?" Robin said.

The Frenchman walked up to the passenger side front door at which Robin was sitting, and told him what was happening.

"Il n'y a pas de," he raised his eyes to look at Robin, "problème pour vous en Libie."
"Vous êtes bien sûr, monsieur?" stalled Robin.
"Il n'y a pas de ..... problême pour vous en Libie," he repeated and turned and went.
Robin's car had been confiscated. They drove him home in a white minibus.

Robin tried to get them to drop him off a block away, but they insisted that he show them the precise house, and it was too risky to assume that they would leave before they had seen him enter.

As he picked out his apartment block, the occupants calmly and professionally observed its location and juxtaposition to other landmarks

Robin went in shaking. Only this time it was with hunger and tiredness. He ate a slice of bread, set his alarm clock for the usual seven in the morning, took two aspirin and got into bed. After five hours in the hands of the Libyan security service, he was dead asleep in ten seconds.

The tension was too great to lie in bed for even a second after the alarm went off. Besides, Robin had to catch Ian before Ian went to the office, to tell him the events of the night before.

Robin washed and dressed quickly, and took the steps downstairs two by quiet two to Ian Ridout's apartment on the ground floor.

As Ian prepared his breakfast standing in the kitchen, Robin attempted to gain his attention.

The quick, jerky movements of Ian's head to side and side, interspersed with equally jerky nods and noises of understanding or agreement of incompletely spelt out points, demonstrated the authority of the man.

Within two days of arriving in Tripoli to take up the post of senior manager on the ground, Ian Ridout had made the pronouncement that "We'll have this project running like any project in England within three weeks." Robin and a number of those present who had been in Libya for any length of time raised their gazes for just long enough to see that Ian was indeed serious and that he actually believed himself. Then they let their countenances and shoulders fall to the silent tune of long exhalation of breath.

Robin sat opposite Ian and watched him as he smashed in the cranium of his first boiled egg with a tea spoon.

The quick jerky movements of the head continued throughout the recounting of the night's events - Daewoo, the university, the interrogations, the "U-turn", the maps of suburban Tripoli - and the management speak suggestions of what Robin might do now. The dialogue lasted only as long as it took to finish the second, rudely decapitated egg. And Ian showed Robin to the door. As he left to the sound of Ian's "Toodle-oo", Robin felt that it was with less than when he'd arrived.

From the day that Robin had arrived in Libya thirteen months previously in April, 1983, he had been anxious during every waking hour.

And after only three weeks in Libya, he received the news that his mother had died. Pat had called one Sunday evening, late in April, 1983, to say that his mother had had a heart attack while in hospital for tests for an unrelated complaint. Upon return from work the following day, the Monday, there was a message by the phone in the apartment that Robin shared with Leroy, for Robin to call home.

When Robin had finally got hold of Pat, she'd interrupted his greeting.

"Robin," she said. "Robin! Your mother had another heart attack."

"When?" said Robin.

"Early this morning," she said, "only a few hours after the first one."

"How is she?" asked Robin.

"Robin," stated Pat flatly and professionally. "You mother died at about four o'clock this morning."

Robin had said nothing. In fact, he'd paused to see what he was feeling before he said anything.

He said nothing. Because he felt nothing.

He hadn't spoken to his mother for two years.

In fact, one Sunday morning, early in April 1983, the day before Robin first went to Libya, Pat had said to him, "I think you ought to go and see your mother, today."

Robin had asked why.

Pat said that if he went to Libya, she didn't think that he would see his mother again.

Robin had said that he didn't want to go to see her.

Pat said that she thought he ought to. She was his mother. "I think she's got cancer," said Pat.

Robin had picked up the phone and called his Dad at Orchard Way. "Could we come and see you today? I've got to go to Libya tomorrow, and we'd like to know if we could come down for lunch."

Following a muffled conversation from his father's end of the phone, his father came back and said, with barely concealed scathing in his voice, "Your mother's not feeling well enough to receive anyone at the moment, so I'm afraid the answer is no."

Robin suggested a cup of tea, and was similarly rebuffed.

Robin concluded the call with a desultory valediction. Over the next thirty minutes, Robin silently squared himself to never seeing his mother again. It would be disappointing, but no more of an end to the relationship, he rued, than he might have expected. "What a waste," he said, and started to get up to find something to do.

Then the phone rang. His father was bright and cheery. His mother felt a little better and would it be alright if they popped up for a couple of hours.

"Yes," said Robin. And offered, no more than proprietously, "Would you like to come for lunch?"

A muffled exchange elicited a response that thanked Robin for the offer but, no, they would not stay for lunch on this occasion. "We'll see you in about thirty minutes, then," said Robin's Dad brightly.

They hung up.

Robin raised his eyebrows and let out a sigh. Pat looked faintly pleased.

When Robin's parents arrived, Pat was all public school manners. Robin greeted them smilingly, but with lips drawn back only by unfamiliar muscles.

Mother slowly progressed to being seated at one end of the Chesterfield. The mid morning sun of early April picked out the sharp relief of the now age lines on her face. Robin sat at the other end of the Chesterfield with his arms by his sides. He faced the centre of the room.

Dad made a cheery effort at conversation.

Mother asked a few questions, about Libya.

Robin carefully ducked any answer by claiming to know nothing of the place yet. The exchanges were few, and Robin avoided the dangers of committed or intelligent answers, following too many years of being scorched by his mother for making such.

Pat carried the hour impeccably, however, asking Anne how she was. Robin felt prompted to join that particular enquiry, and honour at least was satisfied all round.

Then Anne said to Geoffrey that she thought she would like to go. The most diplomatically that Robin ever remembered her saying such a thing.

They rose. Robin would swear that he saw the beginnings of tears in her eyes. But it was too late. She should have thought about that when she'd had the chance - fifteen and twenty years previously when she'd called Robin a liar to his face, without a shred of evidence to justify the baseless remarks.

Pat conducted Anne and Geoffrey to the door. Robin remained standing in the sitting room.

"Was Dad at the hospital with her?" Robin enquired.

"No," said Pat.

"Why not?" Robin followed.

"He didn't know," said Pat.

"Why didn't he know?" said Robin. "It was her second heart attack."

"He wasn't there for the first one," she said.

"Well, didn't the hospital call him in after the first one?" Robin said.

"They couldn't get hold of him. He was," she paused, "out at the opera with Janet."

"Who's Janet?" Robin asked.

"Someone in your Dad's music group," explained Pat. "Your Dad had got tickets for your mum and himself for the opera, but Anne felt ill and went to hospital for tests. So your Dad went to the opera with Janet instead."

Robin started to interrupt.

"Anne said it was OK for him to go with Janet," continued Pat. "Then she had the second heart attack very early in the morning while she was under observation. There was no response from the phone when they tried ringing Geoffrey at home."

Then Robin's mother appeared to him.

On the Thursday evening, Robin was standing in apartment in Tripoli, having just put the phone down after discussing with Pat his return to England for the funeral. He was vaguely aware of movement at the other end of the room and looked up. It was his mother – a grey wraith, but with more hair and fewer lines - as he remembered her.

31

She looked directly at him and he heard her say, "Will you be alright, son?" Disengaging his eyes and turning away, as he had done for years, he said out loud, "Aye. We'll be alright." And she melted away as she turned to go.

At the funeral, Robin and his older brother, Barry, failed to restrain the levity which they brought to all suitable occasions. Their father and their younger brother, Andrew, failed to restrain the dolour which they could bring to any such occasion. Geoffrey let out a hideous sob at a suitable point in the proceedings. Janet sat discreetly at the back of the crematorium.

As the coffin lay on the bier, Barry said to Robin that he hadn't realised she was so short. Robin pointed out that they are all the same length when they're lying down. Pat told the two of them to shut up. Barry looked at the coffin, shook his head and uttered, "What a waste."

Robin took charge in the car park afterwards when the mourners appeared at a loss as to know what to do. He got them all into cars, and back to the house where a wake was fuelled by the limited quantity of alcohol that Barry had succeeded in wringing out of Dad.

All of a sudden, the three brothers and their father found themselves alone in the kitchen with the door shut.

Robin announced that everything that Dad had ever said about the Arabs from his time in Egypt and Libya during the war was absolutely true. "They're the biggest bunch of wankers on earth," he proclaimed. The boys laughed and were joined, quite uncharacteristically at that kind of language, by their father. They imbibed. Dad relaxed.

But upon return to Libya, the honeymoon period was over. The normally wearing grind of anxiety was heightened by the prospect of no further relief from the reality of Libya for fifteen weeks to come.

And now, almost thirteen months later, Robin went into work in the sound knowledge that on top of all of this, he was also now a marked man.

Then the tanks started firing.

Throughout the Sunday morning, the 13th of May, a pounding noise could be heard. To start with, most people ignored it and got on with their work. But as the late morning wore on, the intensity of gunfire increased and a pall of dust and smoke could be seen hanging over one of Tripoli's suburbs.

The failed attempt on the life of Col Gaddafi the previous Tuesday had been unusually well planned and organised; so much so that it was difficult to believe that it had not been organised by some agency outside of Libya - the CIA, the DGSE or, God forbid, MI6. Just about the last thing that anybody wanted in a place like Libya was to be thought of as involved in anything such as an assassination attempt. And absolutely the last thing anybody wanted was to be accused of spying.

Any number of Stray Dogs had been involved in the attempt. Three had already been killed trying to cross from Tunisia into Libya. Others involved suffered other fates.

Just outside the Azizia Barracks, Dorothy was on her way to work at Robin's office. She drew up behind two cars waiting at the Azizia Barracks intersection, for the traffic lights to turn green.

An army vehicle screeched to a halt alongside the car directly in front of Dorothy and, before it had settled on its suspension, an occupant had emptied a magazine of machine gun fire into the side of the car directly in front of Dorothy's.

Someone in the car had returned small arms fire - to no avail.

The occupants of the army vehicle rushed around and opened the doors of the car, and were greeted by dead bodies slumping into the road.

They pushed the bodies back into the car, jumped in and drove off towards the barracks, accompanied by the army vehicle.

Dorothy went on the office.

A friend of Robin's said that she had just turned down a street near her house on her way home from a night shift, when she noticed a load of soldiers on either side of the road. Thinking nothing unusual of it, she kept proceeding until she was within thirty yards of them doing thirty miles per hour. Then she realised that they were shooting at and killing each other. Without touching the brakes, she banged the car into reverse and hit the throttle.

And then there was the tank fire.

Another group of Stray Dogs had been found, holed up in an apartment block in the suburbs. The building was then surrounded by soldiers, and the "authorities" gave the occupants the opportunity to give themselves up. Some surrendered. The building was cleared of all residents. The remaining occupants were given a further opportunity to give themselves up. Small arms fire emanated from the apartment block. The soldiers returned fire. The gun fight went on for some time. Then an army tank was brought in and started to open fire. Then another was brought in. Then another. The apartment building was systematically reduced to rubble.

The Stray Dogs who had surrendered were given a simple choice. To go along to their respective Basic People's Congresses and account for their actions, or be summarily shot. If their respective Basic People's Congresses accepted their accounts, they would go free. If they didn't, they would be shot.

A number of them chose to be summarily shot. The others went to account for their actions. Some were shot. Some were actually set free.

Others, captured in the battle in and around the Azizia Barracks, were tried on TV, and publicly hanged.

By mid afternoon, it was clear that something serious was amiss.

Robin went to see Mr Abugheila, the Libyan Project Manager, whose office was on the floor below Robin's. Mr Abugheila was responsible and accountable to a revolutionary committee for the project on which Robin was engaged as the senior engineer. Mr Abugheila understood the revolutionary nonsense of the committees. You could almost do business with Mr Abugheila.

Robin knocked on Mr Abugheila's open door and was bid to enter. Mr Abugheila was not at his desk but seated in an easy chair at a low coffee table. In another easy chair around the coffee table sat a smirking man. At most he was in his middle thirties and at best he was casually dressed. Robin had never seen him before.

Mr Abugheila looked back and forth between the smirking man and Robin with a faint look of discomfort, presumably at the minor interruption. The smirking man broke away from his conversation with Mr Abugheila every few seconds to look half up at Robin and chortle faintly.

Robin waited. When Mr Abugheila turned to him, Robin greeted him and indicated that the BPOCO office was concerned to know what was going on and how it might impact the project. The casually dressed man uttered a word, which Mr Abugheila repeated. "Balestine. Balestine," the second time a little louder. Robin left, little wiser, but more anxious.

Robin telephoned Ian Ridout to inform him of what little he knew. Ian, in the company office on the North side of the city and in the lee of a down that rolled towards Tripoli harbour and the sea, was unaware of the commotion. Nevertheless, Ian instructed those in Robin's office to go home as soon as possible. Robin relayed the instruction to his office. Dorothy made her usual noise and stated that she wasn't going to be told when and where to work. She would go when she was finished. Robin insisted, and asked Graham, the very capable office factotum, to lock up when everybody else had left.

"Right you are," said Graham.

On the way home Robin was driving at an inconspicuous pace along largely deserted roads. With only a mile or two to go along the GP road home, he was aware of a column of Peugeot pick up trucks coming towards him, occupying most of the width of the road. As the only vehicle abroad apart from the trucks, Robin kept his course, only to be repeatedly flashed by the leading truck. Robin put his foot down with a view to out running them before they could turn around. He needn't have worried. The column flew past him, with unkempt men in their thirties hanging out of the back and sides of each truck, Kalashnikovs and revolutionary fervour firing into the air.

Robin went home, took three aspirin and slept badly. For the first time in his life he understood how Damocles had felt.

The office phone rang early the following morning. It was Mike Peace calling from London. London based, Mike was one of the senior management team on the Libyan Coaxial Cable Project. Roger and John were both out of the country, so Robin raised his eyebrows and took the call. A few taciturn exchanges later, and Robin was none the wiser why Mike had called. Robin believed it important, however, to let Mike know of developments in Libya – that, after all, is how effective teams function. Robin said, "Some gentlemen from Palestine are involved in a situation."

The phone call fizzled out. Robin got into a car and drove himself to the BPOCO Main Office in central Tripoli, directly across the road from both the Italian Embassy and the central police station.

He solicited the help of one of the administrators to go and look for the confiscated car of the night before, took a spare set of keys and departed.

Cruising around the area where he had been interrogated on the Saturday night, all Robin achieved was being stopped by a policeman and asked for his pink ID card.

Now that this had become a risky waste of time, Robin drove the mere 400 yards back to the Main Office, and went in to talk the situation through with Ian.

*** *** ***

PART TWO

14th May to the 3rd Week of Ramadan, 1984

I was arrested on the Monday. Monday the 14th May 1984. I had had all the indicators that trouble was brewing for me. But I was also fed up. Fed up with Libya, fed up with idiotic Libyan drivers in the lunchtime rush hour, fed up with company management and their needless games, fed up with Pat going back to England - so fed up that I was not watching the ball. Naively, I overrode an all pervading sense of impending doom and, blindly, just pushed forward with what I believed was my job.

About the middle of Monday morning, I had gone to look for the confiscated car, and on to the company Main Office just on the North side of the city centre. It was, as I expected it would be, another pointless exercise in trying to get something done. Following a fruitless interview with Ian, I sat, a little more productively, having coffee and nice-time, with a couple of the administrators at the office.

After the hour or two of time, more or less wasted, I left the office and drove uneventfully through the brilliant, lunchtime sunlight.

Uneventfully, that is, until I turned off the main drag through Tripoli and onto the boulevard that led to the "centrale", where my office was.

The lunch time traffic was unusually dense at this point, exacerbated by a tail back that seemed to originate from the direction of my office building.

My sense of foreboding was heightening all the time, as I dealt mentally both with the events of the last two days and with the traffic jam in front of me. The deadline that I had set for myself to return to the office was rapidly evaporating before my eyes and I was getting irritated.

I inched my way down the boulevard. I passed slowly by the cake shop that had been closed down in January, 1984, by Colonel Gaddafi. I thought how much I could do with their nice, thick, rich Madeira cake for my lunch. The cake shop slipped by.

The road narrowed as older buildings on the right caused a chicane. The traffic normally popped out of the chicane like peas from a pod, as the road widened slightly, leaving room for the left turn into the entrance way of my office building.

On leaving the chicane, I indicated left and moved to the white line in the middle of the road. To my surprise the gates where shut. The bevy of indolent Libyans that loaf listlessly around the normally open gates, somehow were more alert and circumspect than usual. I flicked my left hand off the steering wheel with the recognized gesture that meant, "Shuney?" "What?" In reply, one imperceptibly shook his head and they turned away with more than their usual indifference. I wound down the window to try to attract their attention. They ignored me with more than their usual ignorance. This was too much. But any expostulations from me were cut short at the sound of prolonged screeching of tyres only yards behind me. I checked my mirror, getting ready to hold my head in case someone shunted me. I saw nothing in the mirror except traffic waiting for me to turn. The screeching culminated in a heavy metallic clump. Horns stated to blare. A voice began to roar with authority. A pitiful squeal emanated in reply. The gate showed no sign of opening. A police car siren started to wail. A car started to pick its way through the gaps in the traffic. I was blocking the road. Seeking to force the gate keepers to open the gates, and to clear the road, I proceeded to make the left hand turn towards the gates. The gates didn't open, but I did nearly have an accident. The car that had been picking its way through the traffic had accelerated up my off side, and only narrowly avoided colliding with me as I commenced my left turn. We both banged on our brakes, and regarded each other, I with faint exasperation, he with desperate disbelief. Simultaneously, we motioned each other to get out of the way. Then, as the amber light of the police car hove into view, I understood. I threw the steering wheel to the right, dropped the clutch and gunned the engine up to full revs to get away. I had had all I wanted of involvement with the police for quite a while. As I roared off up the 400 yards of empty incline to where a single turn would lose the police, I saw in my rear mirror the young man being apprehended. For the only time in my life, I felt sorry for a Libyan.

After a right turn at the top of the incline, I brought the car back along a side road and parked out of sight of the centrale. I waited until the activity had died down and then walked the few hundred yards back to the gates.

I took out my ID card and PTT pass and stepped up to the gates. As I approached, several heads, which now lined the gate, repeated the imperceptible shaking which was denying me access. One gateman met my eye, which was unusual. I showed my papers. He ignored them and just looked at me as they all did. I gesticulated further, and they relented. The gate was opened. "At last!" I thought. "The message is getting across."

I walked to the bottom of the half dozen or so steps that rose before the double doors of the PTT building. To the left of the doors, and seated half way up the steps, was a group of men. In spite of the afternoon heat, they were attentive to one man amongst them, less roughly suited than usual, though not smart. With sparse movement of his head, and little of his hands, he was reluctantly obliging them with an intermittent discourse. I stepped past them with a small turn of my head. No-one offered me an acknowledgement, except the red-headed stranger who turned and saw me without looking. I stepped inside, glad of the air conditioning and to be away from the odd little group. I took the lift to my floor, went to my office, closed the door and sat down at my desk. My mind would not focus. I could think of nothing to do at my desk that mattered. In fact, I was deeply unsettled.

I realised that I had not informed anybody of my return. I phoned Graham in the general office.

"Er, er, er! City Desk!" said he.

"I'm back."

"Er, er, er! From where?"

Oh, God! Doesn't anyone know what's going on around here?

"From seeing Ian."

"Oh! We didn't know you'd gone."

"Yes, I have just spent two hours over there trying to get up to date."

"There were two men to see you. Something about the police."

"Hang on," I said. "I'm coming in."

I hung up, got up, opened my office door, walked the ten or so paces to the door to the general office, and went in.

"City Desk," said Graham as he answered the phone.

A light hearted phone call followed between Graham and one of my men in the field. Graham was good at his job, but I was rattled at the exchange from within my office, and I wanted to scotch the flippancy.

"What's going on?" I asked of no-one in particular.

Dorothy made her usual noise that accompanied secrets abroad that no-one is supposed to tell.

"What's going on?" I repeated.

Graham told his caller to hang on, and that the boss had just walked in. He turned to me and asked me to wait for just a minute. He obligingly finished his call and turned back to me.

"Well, I-I-I-I I don't know."

Oh, brilliant!

"You said there were two men," I stated. "Would you start at the beginning?"

"Well, two men just came in and said that the police were outside and that-that-that they wanted to see you."

"Who wanted to see me? The two men or the police?"

"Well, er-er-er, the two men."

"Right. I have had enough of police to last me a life time. If they come back, would you just carry on as if I am not here? Perhaps they'll go away."

"Er, er, er, right you are."

I turned on my heel. As I closed the office door behind me, I started to feel alone.

I went into my office and sat down.

"What a week," I thought to myself.

First somebody in the Libyan embassy in London shoots a police woman. Then the Foreign Office advises Brits. in Libya to get out, and others not to go back there. Then the company tells us that it would not go down well on our records if we refused to go back. Then I have to wring out of the financial manager a concession that there would be "monies" available if I had to fly my family back out of Libya at short notice. Then I discover that British Caledonian has turned around in mid-flight a scheduled airliner actually on its way to Libya as the news of WPC Fletcher's death is breaking. Then the Libyans arrest the British Caledonian airport manager at Tripoli. Then Pat's sister commits suicide. Then Pat flies back to the UK to attend her sister's funeral. Then she decides that she will not be returning to Libya, but will be organizing her course for the autumn. Then someone tries and fails to assassinate Colonel Gaddafi. Then the news emerges of counter revolutionaries being picked up or shot dead at the Tunisian border. Then, like a lunatic, I go out to a party on Saturday night, take a wrong turning into the university, and get arrested and interrogated for five hours. Then all day on Sunday we hear the sound of army tanks shelling something in the city. And now I have an office manager who cannot divert obvious trouble away from me. Why the Fucking Hell did I come to Libya?

The phone rang. Graham told me that there were two men to see me.

"Can't you tell them I'm not here?"

"Well, I-I-I sent them to your, your office."

Thanks, Graham.

There was a tentative knock at the door. I started to rise, in order to take the initiative by opening the door personally. As I rose the knock was repeated. I got not half a pace as whoever it was that had knocked opened the door, shut it and opened it again.

Lamely I squeezed out, "Who's there?"

First one head and then another appeared. Two, slightly ingratiating men tried hard not to enter. They failed. As they ineluctably crept in, I took what I thought was control. I offered them my hand, a chair each and some coffee. They were reluctant to sit, narrowly succeeded in shaking my hand, and missed the coffee bit completely.

They sat irresolutely while I asked them their names and how I could help.

Half way through my pleasantries, the man on the left rose half out of his chair and started to speak.

He spoke a very few words. I did not understand one of them. I smiled and inclined my head, inviting him to try again. He did. His chin was upturned, his face was solicitous, but not a flicker of a smile in response to mine entered his face. He was deadly serious and very frightened. Some uncontrollable force caused my smiling muscles to stop working. I could no longer hold my geniality. I caught a name I didn't recognise. I persisted in holding his gaze. Suddenly, the Babel Fish started working. I recognised my own name. I heard him say that the police were downstairs to see someone. I told him that the police had no business being here, that this was a restricted establishment. "No, no," they both said, the police were downstairs to see someone. I told them that the police should come to my office. "No, no," they both said.

"Are you Mr Blummen?" they said together.

"No," I replied, my neck burning. "There is no-one of that name here."

They half turned to each other. The senior man took out a piece of paper.

"Mr Plummer." The 'P' came out only with effort.

I ignored my name.

"The police are downstairs and they want to see you."

"No," I said, beginning to shake.

"You have to go. You have no choice."

"What have I done? Is this a traffic offence?"

They looked up in incomprehension.

I resorted to Arabic. "Batentis sair." The car's papers.

"No," they both said shaking their heads in unison. "You have to go and see them."

"Where are they, then?"

40

"Down at the door." And they slid out of their chairs, out of my office, and out of their role as heralds.

There was no escape. The front door to the building was the only way in and out, and it was blocked.

I emptied my handbag of everything but my ID card, my cash, my cigarettes, my ball point, and my sun glasses. After Saturday night's episode I was not going to be caught dead with anything incriminating.

I palmed my handbag and strode into the general office, somehow expecting someone to do something to make all this go away. To my dismay, the two men were standing in the middle of the office. They looked uncomfortable, but they turned and their mouths opened. The familiar message started to be repeated. I dismissed them and they fell silent, looking both hapless and down at the floor.

"Graham," I ordered, while feverishly trying to fasten my handbag to a belt loop. "Phone Ian, now, and tell him what is happening."

"W, w,w,w, well, wh, wh, wh, what is happening?" he offered, genuinely disconcerted.

"I'm being arrested."

Dorothy was on her feet, lower jaw on her ample chest. Graham was frozen with telephone midway to his ear. The heralds looked left and right in their discomfort.

"What for?" squeezed out Graham.

"I don't know." I hammered back.

"Have you done anything wrong?" he added helpfully.

"I don't think so. Maybe it's because of where I parked the car just now."

"What?"

"Oh, never mind. I'm being arrested. Get on the phone, now, and tell Ian."

I don't know what I thought I was expecting to achieve by letting Ian know. But my boss was in England, and Ian, his boss, was the only person who might have any sway with the Libs.

"Tell Ian to inform Mr Abugheila and see if he can get this nonsense stopped."

"Er-er, er-er, right you are. But I-Ian's line is engaged."

"Try someone else at the office," I hammered out.

"I-I already have."

"Try again."

As Graham lifted the receiver in one more futile attempt, the two men started moving towards me.

I started to back away, hands at the ready, as I had now finished hooking my handbag to my belt loop.

"You must come now."

I attempted to stall. "I thought you said that you weren't the police."

"We aren't, but they are waiting below. If you do not come now, we will be in trouble."

My heart bled for them.

"Mr Plummer!" barked the senior man.

Dorothy spoke. "I'll come too. They're usually better when there's a woman present." This broke the tension to some extent because what she said was generally true. I relaxed a bit. If I had to go and see the police, right now a woman's presence could make a lot of difference - certainly more than Ian could probably do.

I sighed. I breathed out, "OK. Forget it Graham." But he continued feverishly to punch numbers into the telephone.

"No, no. It's quite alright old chap. I-I'll keep trying 'til I get him."

"Thanks."

I spun on my heel. The room spun around my head. The world spun on its axis. And, as I walked out the door, nothing was ever going to be the same again.

Eschewing the lift, I strode down the two flights of stairs that led to the mezzanine, my strides determined but measured. I started down the long stair case that led to the entrance hall; my footfalls rang as my leather soles struck the marble steps. The vastness of the hall was revealed as I descended below the level of the ceiling. But so too was a figure that stood between two others. The man's motionlessness conveyed its own authority. My beating heart quickened. Rather than falter, I sort of changed gear as I came to the foot of the staircase. I rounded the curve in the last three or four stairs, and brought myself to a walking pace. A pace which I hoped looked unafraid. The barrage of sunlight that illuminated the hall left the eye devoid of detail. Notwithstanding, I could see that the figure was taller and older than me, and his eyes refused to alight on anything. He had seen me nevertheless. Hell, he had heard me from three floors away. My approach towards him was obvious. But just in case he thought that I was going to walk straight past him and out of his life, he disengaged himself from the other two, and opened himself up to leave me no way past. He looked, however improbably, like a rugby player waiting to garner a breakaway.

As my eyes adjusted to light, I recognized the two, who had by now started moving out of the building, as the heralds from upstairs of just few minutes ago.

Now my gaze was locked onto the tall visitor. As I covered the few remaining yards between us, I identified him as the storyteller in the strange group that had been seated at the entrance way not half an hour ago as I had entered. He had red hair.

"Kef halik?" I led, while thinking that the red hair must be a bad joke.

He dismissed my "How do you do?" with a line of Arabic.

"Shuney?" I tried again. "Inte, Bolice?" said I, stating the obvious.

His reply was a dismissive wave of the head and of the left arm in the direction of the doors.

I ignored his invocation and stood about four feet off.

"Batentis!" I ordered.

And just as he pulled out an identity card, the doors to the lift hissed open, and out walked Dorothy and Charlie, who I did not even know was back.

And as I swept my gaze passed Red Head towards the approaching Dorothy, I saw a young revolutionary holding at waist height, and pointed at me, a machine gun.

Dorothy and Charlie saw it too.

I was not about to have any accidents. With the usual wave of my hand, I brusquely ordered the revolutionary to point his gun anywhere but at me. It worked. He was only in his twenties, and scarcely old enough to shave.

As for Charlie, any thoughts on his elderly part of disarming the situation, quickly subordinated themselves to thoughts of healthy retirement. He froze. His usual smugness quite converted to fear.

Dorothy, however, was as good as her word. While advancing, she opened up in a spirited attempt to shoo Red Head out of the building as having no right to be in a restricted place. And, for just a moment, I thought she was getting somewhere. Then Red Head turned his head. While not ceasing to watch me, he issued a word in Arabic and the revolutionary bean pole snapped the gun up and towards Dorothy. Dorothy shuddered to a halt. All colour drained from her face.

I tried to recover the initiative.

"Batentis!" I barked again.

Red Head once again drew forth his identity card. His back to Dorothy, and his left shoulder to me, he offered me his card with his left hand. I reached forward with my right hand to take it, or at least to hold it steady while I attempted to read it. But as I did so he transferred the card from his left to his right hand away from me. "Ah! Games," thought I, and smiled. As I reached further, I put myself on the point of balance. His free left hand closed around my right, and he intertwined his fingers with mine, as lovers do when strolling along the beach. He turned away from me. My loss of balance was complete, and he dragged me without effort through the door, down the steps and out into the car park. Charlie stuttered. Dorothy protested. Neither followed.

I could not breathe properly. I swallowed and gasped my way across the car park trying my best to shake free. I forced Red Head to drag me mostly off balance to see if his grip would slacken. But he had me in a practiced grip, the fingers of his left hand intertwined in mine, his left elbow clamping my right forearm against his body, and his right hand firmly locked around my right wrist. His rock like posture was immune to attempts at release. After about thirty yards of being dragged off balance and every avenue for release being explored, I decided to fall in the hope that while trying to pick me up he might also let go of me. He just dragged me along. Somehow I recovered my feet. Then I heard myself uttering, "Alright, alright." Resistance was useless. I stopped resisting. Perhaps now he would ease up. And after a few seconds he did ease up. The grip did not slacken, but now at least I could walk only half off balance. I felt myself start to go tight in the throat. Towards the gate I was dragged, which was odd. I expected to be taken to a car in the car park. But the gate! As I passed each familiar item - the sentry box, the gatekeepers' seats - I sought a reason why we might stop there, instead of parading off into the unknown. My mind was reeling. On passing the gatekeepers' seats, I tried in vain to catch the eyes of the men who, only so recently had tried to warn me not to come in. My gaze rested on the head gatekeeper with whom, in earlier days, I had passed some pleasant moments. He sat with his body neutral but eyes raised to the heavens. The gate was opened for us without word or signal from Red Head. Where now? I had never walked this street except once when I'd had a puncture. Nobody walks anywhere in this part of the city. By now I was consciously inhaling and exhaling deeply to try to control my sense of panic. I was going weak in the limbs. Through a break in the rush hour traffic, I was dragged across the road, now trying to read Red Head's body so to comply and conserve energy. Then, relief, I was herded through the gate on the opposite side of the road into the main PTT building. At least I was going to be brought up before a senior member of the Posts, Telephones and Telegraphs department of the government, which would afford me an opportunity to account for myself. Account for what? I had no idea what I was supposed to have done wrong. And I had to have done something wrong to be dragged around like this. But I was damned if I could figure out what. We approached an unoccupied car. My misgivings were added to at the sight of this wreck with a large paper sticker on the driver's side window. Who the hell was this guy? His pass seemed official, but then everybody in Libya has a pass. It had a stamp mark, but then everything in Libya has a stamp mark. We stopped at the car. The intertwined fingers did not slacken. The right hand let go and he reached with it into his right hand pocket and extracted the car keys. This was too easy. I hadn't encountered such formidable technique since I was up against black belts at university. I tried to remember my own technique. "If you offer no resistance, they have nothing to fight against." Yes well a fat lot of bloody good philosophy was now. Why the hell didn't I remember all that a few minutes ago instead of offering my hand and then my balance. Plummer you're a prat. What the fucking hell have you got yourself into now? Well at least don't get in any deeper. Don't offer any resistance. So I didn't. I just stood there letting Red Head hold my hand. It was incredible. This guy was good. As soon as he felt my relaxation, he softened. Alright, let's see. So I hinted at a turn and sure enough, without opposing me, he just immobilised me. OK, so I'm not going to get hurt. I just have to cooperate. That was welcome news.

The car door opened. I was made to sit in the passenger seat. Red Head closed my door and almost casually walked around to the driver's side. He knew I wasn't going to get out of the car, and so did I. My experiences of Saturday night told me that the child proof locks would be on. And, anyway, there was no point in declaring my hand by testing out the car door. So I sat there. Red Head got in. From somewhere he produced a small sheaf of papers.

"Blummen," said he.

I ignored him.

He raised his head slightly, the nearest thing I had seen so far to a human reaction. Then with the care of a studious clerk, he scrutinised his notes and carefully repeated, "Mr Blummen." The head and eyebrows went up, and so did the temperature. In spite of the mispronunciation, they knew exactly who I was. Well, the definition of "strategy" is, "Keep firing, even when you've run out of bullets." So I kept firing.

I ignored him.

In a minute he would start to speak English and we could have a civilised discussion.

"Inte. Batentis." It was a statement, not a threat or a command.

I rolled both hands over, to no avail. I felt no pain as he merely took my handbag off my waist. But I erupted as he opened the zipper. This was a violation even in Libyan terms. I was cross not because he had opened my bag, about which there was nothing I could do, but because my personal space had been violated. So he gave me back the bag while dipping into it to announce the importance of my pink identity card. No contest. If asked, you have to produce it. Produce it I did.

Of course, resistance <u>was</u> useless. I was merely stalling for time, of which there was a lot. Trying to figure out what was going on, which I couldn't. Seeing how far I could push the system, which wasn't very far. Looking for weaknesses, of which none were evident, unless you count stupidity. But we keep trying.

Red Head finished reading my card, made a pencilled note on a piece of paper, and handed the card back to me with calm efficiency. Momentarily, I felt that a transaction completed meant that I would be allowed out of the car and returned to work. Instead, Red Head started the car.

We drove across the largely vacant car park and around the big guard house. The barrier lifted after a brief exchange between Red Head and the Gate Keeper, who was careful to ignore me.

Red Head turned left out of the gate and into the last of the lunchtime traffic. The Centrale disappeared to my right. I never saw the Centrale again.

The once familiar street whirled with unfamiliarity as we approached the main drag.

We turned right onto the main drag, Sharah Jamahiriya. In light traffic, the faintly yellow whiteness of the city could be seen quaint, illuminated by the late spring sun now off its zenith. We drove the few hundred yards to the Garden City roundabout, and made the familiar turn towards the harbour wall road, in the direction of BPOCO Head Office. The prospect of remaining on familiar turf warmed me slightly. And then only a few yards before the left hand turning which would have taken us past the head office, we turned left into back streets my heart sank. I was faintly surprised that we emerged into the broad avenue at the opposite end of the back streets, and then depressed again as we turned down the very street with the No Entry signs that had heralded my interrogation on Saturday night. Well, at least here they knew me and knew that I was sound. They would vouch for me. Red Head negotiated the last couple of twists and turns and we halted in front of a building, adjacent to the building in which Saturday's interrogation had taken place.

Three or four indolent Libyans paid passing regard to me after noticing the square of paper stuck to the car's window. Red Head paid no regard to anyone, as he pulled on the hand brake which, to my surprise, worked, and got out of the car.

He quickly rounded the bonnet, smartly opened my door, and gave the indifferent beckon that I was learning to fear. I pulled myself out of the car, turned, and shut the door. Red Head intertwined his fingers in my free hand, and ignored the Libyans who watched. Off balance again, I was dragged into the building.

We started to mount the stairs. Against expectation, we ascended at least two floors, after which I started having difficulty keeping my balance. I motioned that I needed to use the bannister rail. Red Head let go of my hand. I took the rail. I was panting, and had to swallow hard with every other breath. Yes, I smoked, but I was also as fit as I had been since university. What was wrong? Oh, God! Please don't let me have a heart attack. I took deep breaths to calm my breathing, with only scant effect.

We paused on the next landing where we were joined by two young goons. They fell in behind me to escort me at Red Head's silent bidding. We mounted two more flights of stairs and then left the stairwell for the fourth floor. One on either side, the goons pretended to ignore me. This helped. I drew myself up to my full height, ignored them, gave the appearance of looking ahead only, and proceeded to walk properly again. Red Head slipped away, silently and unseen. Within feet I was motioned into an office on the right hand side.

Just inside the door was an office desk which faced to the right. The chair sat with its back to a suite of bookcases that sported a few unread books. On the desk was a portable stereo radio cassette, and some non descript bits and pieces. Behind the far end of the desk, and slightly to the right of it was a large window.

One of the goons spoke almost silently to the other. The other sat at the desk, and toyed listlessly with the paraphernalia. The first goon left. Unhindered, I took stock. The large window did not have bars which heartened me. But the distance to the ground outside precluded notions of jumping. It was a standard Libyan office. Everything was the normal dusty brownish yellow colour. A central area in the dust showed the limits of people's movements. Colonel Gaddafi less than dominated the room from his portrait.

The first goon reappeared and spoke silently to the other at the desk. The other barely responded, but waited until the first goon had left again. Then he faintly motioned me to sit. I regarded the chair which faced him across the desk, and pull down the corners of my lips and faintly shook my head. He exploded at me in Arabic. I shrugged and sat down. The tirade of admonishing Arabic continued. I closed my hands with interlocked fingers and, with arms on the desk, leaned forward attentively. I did not however catch his eye.

"What do you want with me?" I asked slowly. He ignored me. And as if to prove the point, he turned his attention to the small ghetto blaster.

When he finally found the "on" switch, the room became alive with static. Then he found the tuner knob. The radio squealed and squeaked its way down the short wave band. I heard diverse dialects of Arabic, and eastern European English, and then - joy - the inimitable strains of Lilliburlero. My whole body surged. I had to fight to suppress my reaction. I sat there clinging to the vain hope that the first item on the news would be the arrest of a British engineer in Libya. Then Pat would know, I would be out by nightfall, and this day - this silly aberration - would be over.

The second and a half of silence that followed Lilliburlero dragged on. Then, in those beautiful BBC tones, the announcer said, "This is the BBC World Service. The time is fourteen hundred hours Greenwich Mean Time. There now follows the news, in the World Service of the BBC, with Mel Oxley ......". But the radio squealed and squeaked again as the goon rolled on down the short wave band to find something more interesting. And he found it. The sober and punctilious tones of the BBC gave way to Westminster chimes. The odd sounding peal introduced a syrupy, American trained voice, which greasily intoned, "Moscow Radio calls upon all the peace loving peoples of the world to ......"

The rest was lost as a red mist descended over me. My thoughts and feelings raced as I grappled to understand how anyone could believe this rubbish. "...calls upon all the peace loving peoples of the world"? Stalin had 20 million people murdered. The Soviet empire is arming and funding barbaric regimes like yours, you ignorant moron. Radio Moscow? And you deliberately listen to that rubbish in preference to the BBC?

At first I thought that he had skipped over the BBC because he understood no English. Then I thought that he had realized what he was listening to and moved on knowingly. Then I realized that my view of life was simply very different from his. It was probably an offence to listen to the Beeb, anyway.

One thing was clear, however. It was exactly four o'clock in the afternoon.

The minutes dragged on with not a wit of communication between the goon and me. I was at one and the same time worried sick and in someway calm that nothing was happening. The idiot retuned the radio every time he got bored, which didn't take long, so I was unable to hear anything of any benefit for long enough to find out what was going on in the world, and I stopped concentrating on the radio. Inevitably, I started trying to figure out what the hell was going on. I ran back over the events of the day, but could not concentrate for long enough to piece anything together.

"Should I get up and just walk out?" I thought, out of nowhere. And promptly dropped the idea.

My mind was simply meandering.

Then the door opened. The first goon came in, said something in Arabic, indicated to me to get up, waved me to sit down, ignored my attempts to understand, spoke to the idiot, and turned to leave. A new face prevented him from leaving. Middle aged and with a fixating stare, the new man said one line of Arabic to the first goon and simultaneously transferred his stare to me. The stare evolved a degree of loathing. The wave said follow. I had no choice. I followed with the goons in tow. The goons fell away I knew not when. The slapping around that I had received on Saturday night was enough to make me circumspect now. We descended the four floors of stairs and went out into the hot afternoon sun, turned left and started walking along the street.

Where were they taking me? It wasn't to a car. My escort walked with the determination of one who has a simple task to do which will be accomplished shortly. We stepped off the pavement into the road. We crossed a small intersection on two corners of which sat sullen, sunken faced young men, who watched without appearing to look. We passed by a low wall or wire fence behind which was an unkempt front garden and then a modern building, set back ten or fifteen metres from the road.

We continued to walk in the road, a few feet from the kerb. The pavement was an obstacle course of cracked and unlevel paving stones, delaid by the roots of trees that lined the boulevard. Debris and sleeping animals lay on the pavement in the shade of a high wall. The wall's white coating was faded and peeling. Though scruffy, this was a mature part of town, a fact which gave me hope. My unease was getting worse however, and white expatriates walked by and ignored me as I tried to catch their eyes. Couldn't they see what was going on? Couldn't they tell by my looks that I needed somebody to get a message to someone, even to Ian Ridout? But the more I looked at them the more they ignored me. Damned expatriates! I'm alright Jack! I resolved never to rely on an expatriate again. Then, mid way along the wall, there was a gateway. Two gates, ill fitting but closed, were as high as the wall and as wide as car garage doors. The simple, Italian, wrought iron work of each gate was supplemented by a sheet of steel, welded in place to prevent onlookers from seeing through, and painted green. As my escort turned towards the gates I started to feel very uneasy.

Barely a word was spoken and one gate opened. I hesitated. There was no-one exactly telling me to go in. I could run. Where to? Away from this lot. The only place I knew from here was the Grand Hotel. To run in that direction was to leave behind these dreadful buildings. But on the very next street corner less than thirty yards away, sat another sullen faced goon with a machine gun.

Through the open gate I expected to see something very forbidding, with more lacklustre revolutionary lackeys loafing lazily in the late afternoon heat. Instead, there was a straight, white pathway with masses of tall greenery on either side. The pathway lead to the large, staired porch of a house. Over the windows of the house the ghiblis were pulled firmly shut. They had not been opened for a long time. I walked through the gate with a deliberate and measured stride, and was immediately and unexpectedly surrounded by a small group of people. They were of different ages and intelligences, all with very alert eyes, rigidly fixed upon mine. As the gate closed behind me, the group advanced towards me, mainly from the sides and rear. Was I to be seized, or beaten up? Was this the end? I measured my strides in a straight line towards the door, and time seemed to slow down. I looked about me to my right, with a slow and measured gaze. I took in each pair of eyes in turn. I hinted at a pause and a redirection of my stride towards my right. They must have seen real danger, for, to my surprise, but no more than I'd planned, the entire advance faltered and then ceased. I had made a mark. Their demeanour now switched from threat to watchful and distant respectfulness, and I was almost ushered up the stairs and into the porch.

Stepping through the open door, I was relieved by the air-conditioning and then alarmed by a low and controlled, business-like buzz emanating from a room nearby. By now my senses were reeling and I was finding it difficult to rationalize much of what I was seeing. Directly in front of me, against a wall a few paces from the door, was a worn out settee. Framed and hanging on the wall above the settee was the ubiquitous photograph of Colonel Gaddafi in revolutionary pose. The walls of the entrance hall were painted a sickly green. I was ordered in Arabic to stand still. I was then told to stand in a certain place and, in spite of the Arabic, it was clear that I was to stop looking around me.

I stood motionless with my eyelids lowered, and was forced to learn how to observe with eyes turned down.

The floor was tiled or marbled in pink and green and white. A shaft of bright light came up from somewhere to my left as I stood with my back to the settee, the front door to my right, and not quite facing the room with the buzz - an office. My escorts were silently milling around a few feet in front of me, exchanging glances with each other. One of them had gone into the office. Moments later, the office door opened and out came a man of about thirty years old. He wore the Arafat head dress. He was extremely economical with his movements, and my escorts fell instantly silent. He spoke a few, quiet words to no-one in particular. The most intelligent looking of the men looked at the rag head with the large, watchful eyes that had regarded me in the garden minutes before, and replied briefly. A hint of a nod from the raghead and the intelligent one, who looked like a young Col Gaddafi, departed.

Seconds later, a gaggle of children appeared at the head of a staircase which funnelled the shaft of brilliant sun light up from an open door in the side of the building. In the manner of school children, chattering excitedly on a day trip to a museum, one by one they cannoned into the person in front and then fell silent as they stumbled onto what was obviously the main attraction. The chatter of the foremost changed into an anxious mutter. A terse word brought silence. They peered around each other not daring to get too close. A calm announcement was made by one of the men. The children's eyes widened, and hatred, fear and awe appeared across different faces. One child spat invective at me, and advanced from the centre of the crowd, arm pointing. Others smiled and caught each others eyes at the prospect of doing damage to this curiosity with his eyes turned down. One man stepped forward with his arm horizontal. But it didn't still the crowd. Now it was my turn. These weren't children. These were trainee revolutionaries, victims of propaganda - The Munchkins - who, dressed in police uniforms during their summer holidays, had the power to stop motorists many times their own age. I turned my head the few degrees to face the children, took half a pace straight in their direction and stamped my foot on the floor. The children leapt back like scalded cats. Some could even be heard clattering down the stone staircase behind them. The braver among them recovered a little of their lost ground but now they too kept a very respectful distance. Bravado returned, but there was no more invective after that.

The children were shushed away by a kindly older man. I would have pegged him at about 60. He was quite used to shushing children away. When the children had disappeared, the rag head spoke again. All but about two of the men lead off down the staircase whither the children had vanished. The raghead stood motionless, his eyes down turned and fixed on some unseen point a few feet in front of him. Any attempt at movement by me - the merest shifting of my weight from one foot to the other - brought disapproving looks from the other men. What followed made me feel as though someone had grabbed my ribcage and shaken it violently.

A tremendous, metallic banging started and persisted for what seemed like an eternity. It just didn't stop. What on earth were they doing? Bang, bang, bang! The most incredible din. More banging was punctuated by what sounded like helpful comments. There was a bright metallic ring as whatever hammer they were using hit the ground. An indeterminate rattle ensued, followed by more comments. A dull metallic scrape of the hammer being picked up heralded more banging. What on earth were they doing? Then all was relief as the opening of a flimsy metal lid produced a wobbling sound. The kindly old man re-appeared at the side door, and uttered two or three words. The raghead gave his imperceptible nod, followed by the merest turn towards the two remaining guards. They, mindless striplings of about 20, advanced towards me without warning. I turned towards them. They were used to this by now, for, once again, they faltered. The raghead saw the potential and spoke quietly. Instead of trying to seize me, the striplings positioned themselves so that there was only one direction I could go. Rag Head gestured to me. I had no choice. The old man ahead of me beckoning me down the stairs, the rag head and the striplings behind me, I walked through the door way that gave onto the stairwell. The downward staircase was slightly to the right. I turned to negotiate the bend and was struck by another sight that spelt even more despondency. In the corner of the stairwell was a collection of sticks. Not firewood. These were the size and thickness of Boy Scout staves. And they all had a curve to them. I wanted to believe that they were used for something other than beating people. Now I was scared. Why should we be going outside? Surely it was far more natural to hold me inside a building. Was this some exquisite humiliation been planned? Had they been opening the lid to a metal coal bunker that I was to be thrown into? I stepped out into the sunlight, to be confronted by a high perimeter wall, in front of which stood a profusion of storeroom junk. There were old boxes, a broken refrigerator, old enamelled basins, dented buckets. The men had arrayed themselves amidst the junk to allow me only one direction to go. To where? Around the front of the building that I had just left? To what purpose? Walking down three high steps from the side door, I surveyed the array of faces. The old man. The intelligent one. A black kid. A tall, slim, handsome, resolute, moustachioed man. The gaggle of would be revolutionaries.

The old man conducted me. The intelligent one regarded me. The black kid menaced me. The moustachioed man ignored me. He could afford to. He carried a machine gun. The gaggle of children walked backwards, retreating with each of my advancing steps. This was some reception committee. Whoever they thought I was, and whatever they thought I had done, these people were very, very scared of me. Then the children gave the game away. As I advanced upon their retreat, some of them looked anxiously back and forth between me and a point mid way along the wall of the building. There was no coal bunker as I had feared. Instead there were two doors situated halfway along the outside wall of the building, open and swung outwards. So this was it. A basement room that held I knew not what. Was I to be tortured? Beaten with the sticks? From behind me, the rag head spoke. Everybody stopped. A hand, thrust into my back, had me off balance for long enough to see me through the doors. The room was pitch dark. I stepped aside to pre-empt an assault from within. It was a good, instinctive move but an unnecessary one. I was alone in a dry, musty basement storeroom. I turned to face the entrance, to be met by the rag head. He stood several feet back, almost as far as the perimeter wall, but neatly framed by the brightly shining doorway. The black kid was receding. Children peered around one side of the doorframe. Rag head's mouth moved and the children disappeared. They were replaced on the opposite side of the doorframe by the moustachioed one and the intelligent one. The moustachioed one stood erect and alert, with the machine gun slung over his shoulder and his thumb through the strap. He would have a clear shot at me if he wanted one. Not, I suspect, that he could see me, because I was deliberately standing well into the gloom of the room. The intelligent one approached me. His fixed eyes tried to hold mine although I wouldn't play. He hesitated and then walked up to me resolutely and spoke. I ignored the Arabic and looked dissolutely at a point around his navel. My heart was pounding and I could barely breathe. He resorted to dumb show to tell me to hand over my hand bag. I was thankful that I had removed anything potentially incriminating. I permitted myself a moment of inner congratulation. He motioned at me to remove my neck tie. I declined. He looked me straight in the eyes. I had no choice. Next was my watch. Damn! The one aspect of my environment that I was hoping to rely upon. Damn, damn, damn! Sensory deprivation. I wondered how I'd deal with it. These people were well trained. He indicated my pockets. I shook my head. He flicked his head up at me just to be sure. Again I shook my head. Only this time, it was with pursed lips as I realized how easy I was making it for them. But what was I to have done? Nothing, of course, except to remain as dignified as possible, give them nothing to get hold of, remain as outwardly calm as possible and not give them an inkling of the runaway terror inside that was reducing me to jelly. I just had to keep thinking what to do next, and to put up as much passive opposition as possible to let them know that I was not in fact a push over.

Rag head stood there, outside the open door. His rag was around his shoulders and his arms were folded, like an old woman pulling a shawl around her. I studied raghead's motionless authority, while the intelligent one was leaving the room.

As he walked away, and started to close the door behind him, I felt as helpless as at any time in my life. My mind was reeling, my innards were churning, and my blood pressure was choking me. I worked to appear calm, and remained motionless with my head up and eyes lowered. I had to suppress a desire to go after them and try to explain. There was nothing to do but let them go, knowing that shortly I would at least be alone and have time to think. The closing of the door was followed by another eternity of clanging and banging as they hammered home the bolt on the door. The banging once again left my rib cage vibrating. I was relieved when it stopped. Now at least I knew what the racket had been. I wondered what could possibly require that much effort.

I had never felt so alone and helpless in my life. Everything that I had ever been able to depend on had just been taken away from me. My body shook. My breath was coming in rasps, my exhalations loud in my ears. The room seemed to be swirling around me. My eyes could not hold a fixed point. Then, as the guards' footfalls receded into silence, and my entire support system evaporated before my eyes, my head turned involuntarily to my left, I started to cry silently, and - my mouth opened trying to find my mother's breast.

I let out an involuntary sob.

No! No! Get a grip! Think! Think! Don't cry! You can't allow yourself to cry! The lump in my throat was restricting my breathing. Think, Robin! Think! Get control! Control of what? I don't know! Just get control! Think, Robin! Think! My name is Robin Plummer! My name is Robin Plummer! Don't forget your name! There's no-one here to give me a name! All the more important that you remember it yourself! OK, I remember it. Yes, you're Robin Plummer. Don't forget it! Now, get a grip on yourself! No, don't sit down in the corner and cower! Get control! Get control! I can't! I'm afraid! Be your age! Think! Don't feel! Think! Of course you're afraid! Get a grip! Get a grip! On what? Get a grip on your breathing! That's right! Breathe regularly! Focus! Focus on what? I don't know. The room is bare! There's nothing to focus on! Well, damn it, find something! Focus on the slit of light! Good! Now get control of your environment! How? I don't know! Well find something! What? I don't know! Make a sundial! Of course! What time is it? You know what time you were arrested - you heard 'Lilliburlero' on the BBC World Service. You know roughly how long you've been held. So it's about four twenty in the afternoon. Come on! Make a mark on the ground - start a sundial! Good!

As the afternoon sun shone through the narrow slit above the door, it cast a shadow of the top of the door onto the floor. I strode towards the edge of the shadow, stooped and made a mark in the dirt on the floor. And began counting seconds.

And so it started.

Regular breathing produced relative calm. The fixing of my attention on the narrow slit of sunlight above the door reduced disorientation, even though my eyes still would not focus on a fixed point. And the dreadful insecurity, only a fraction below the surface, was constantly but a hair's breadth away from breaking out. At last I had a grip on myself. I started to relax. But the moment I did so, the insecurity boiled over into near panic. I realized that self control was going to be a full time occupation for the foreseeable future. I was going to have to keep my mind from wandering if I was to stay sane.

Think, Robin! Think! What can I do? There is nothing but four walls and a door. Well, those are the facts. I wonder what is going on outside? No! Don't think about that. This is your world for now. Nothing outside can exist for you, or you will go mad. This is your world. Forget the door. But my children? Beautiful Katy, little Rossy, and Gak-Gak. I nearly died. No! You can't allow yourself to think about them. They're OK. You're the one in a jam. I turned to the right to disregard the door as any means of access to a world to which I was not admitted. In turning, I noticed for the first time that there was a window. The almost total blackness of my cell was in stark contrast to the brilliant sunlight of the outdoors. Even the narrow slit of sunlight from above the door had prevented my eyes from becoming accustomed to the gloom. So it had taken several minutes and a turn away from the door for me to realize that another slit gave into the room. The second slit was the same width as the one above the door, about four inches. But it was much longer, about seven feet. As I approached the slit, the bottom of which was far enough off the ground that I had to stand on tip toe to see out, I noticed a window sill about twelve or fifteen inches deep. A quick look revealed that the "window" was in fact a wrought iron grid, about seven feet wide and about four and a half feet high. To this had been attached a plate of quarter inch thick steel that covered the entirety of the grid, except for the four inch high slit at the top.

Now that I could see more clearly, I started to cast about the room to see what else there might be. There was nothing, except for a mattress, a thick layer of fine dust all over the floor, and a white coating, peeling from the walls and ceiling.

So this was it. Locked up in a basement room, with no artefacts, and a lot of dust on the floor. Bastards!

My survey was interrupted by a loud metallic click followed by an electronic howl. "My God!" I thought. "Propaganda time." But this wasn't the Gulag. It was a Muezzin, who burst forth with a painfully tuneless "Allah-u-Akbar!" "My God!" I thought. "They're not piping that dreadful incantation into the prison are they? And at that level of decibels I'll go deaf - if I don't go mad first!" Then I kicked myself. Partly for the realization that the call to prayer was telling me what the time was - very useful for my sundial, and partly because I had stopped counting seconds which was supposed to help me calibrate my sundial. All in all it didn't matter. Sensory deprivation wasn't going to work. I was now able to put another mark in the dirt on the floor where the shadow of the top of the door now fell. The shadow had migrated only about two or three inches in the forty or so minutes since the first mark, but I now had visible evidence of control of my environment. Somehow I felt heartened. I made a mental note to avoid walking through the marks in the dust.

I relaxed. A big mistake. The insecurity burst into panic again. The lump in my throat returned to choke me. I verged on tears once more. No! No! You can't cry! You mustn't give way to tears! Therein lies your ruin! Get a grip on yourself! I can't! You must! Get a grip! I can't! You must! How? I don't know! Just get a grip! Focus! What on? Try the slit of light! OK! No! It isn't enough! It isn't enough! I need something more! What? I don't know! Find something! There isn't anything! Just four walls and a stupid mattress! So pick up the mattress! It's just a moulded rubber mattress! Oh, Christ, Robin, get a grip! How? I don't know! Understand your environment! What? Yes! Pace the place out! Brilliant! I walked to the outer wall that abutted the door, and placed my back against it. I paced my way along the length of the room in strides that I took to be a yard in length. Five yards. Well, five and a bit. OK, five yards and one foot. Ah! Five metres. Of course! This place was built by the Italians. That took six seconds. Now what? But there are three dimensions to a room. Good. Now I have something to concentrate on for at least another two or three minutes. Then what? I was beginning to learn that to relax and lose focus was going to be disastrous. So even as I was doing the next thing to keep focussed, I now saw that I had also to try to figure out what I was going to do to retain focus after that. This was going to be hard work.

And hard work it proved to be. Over the next couple of hours I constantly had the twin challenges of concentrating on the current job and of trying to figure out what to concentrate on next, so that there would never be a break during which the insecurity could come rushing back. By the time I had paced out the room and calculated the area of the floor and of each wall, and the volume of the room, all in square or cubic feet, and then measured and recalculated the whole lot in square or cubic metres, it dawned on me that I was rapidly running out of things to do, and that I was going to need a great deal more than this if I was to stay sane. What else was there? I was going to have to find something from inside me. What? Well let's start with the precise predicament. No, Robin! No! You have just spent the last two hours trying to take your mind off that. That's true, but right now, you've run out of things to occupy your mind - and sooner or later you're going to have to try to figure out just what the hell is going on.

OK. Let's start at the beginning. What did I do that got me into this mess? I don't know! And in not knowing, and having nothing to focus on, the insecurity came screaming back.

My thoughts were interrupted by the Muezzin's last call of the day. It was dusk. In a few minutes it would be dark. I was plainly here for the night. So I said to myself that I had better make the best of it and get some sleep.

The mattress was about four feet from the wall opposite the door. I lay down on the mattress. It smelt musty. It had not been lain upon in the recent past. I lay on my right side with my back to the wall, trying to interpret the mattress's lack of use. I could not decide whether it was a good or a bad thing that no other person had been here recently. In the end I could only see bad whatever I thought. So, still choking, I got as comfortable as possible not having a pillow, focussed on deep, regular breathing and resolved to go to sleep.

I can't say that I was sinking into sleep, but I was calmer and my mind was emptier when, after what seemed like only a few minutes, shuffling feet halted outside the steel sheeted window. Unintelligible grunts were accompanied by a soft, fluffy sound. I opened my eyes but remained motionless. The grunt was repeated, and then again with a note of imperative. I lifted my head. There was no need for too much caution because the room was impenetrably dark. The only shaft of light in the room, from a sodium street lamp nearby, impinged upon an inner wall of the room, far above my head.

I stood up and put my shoes on. Was this release? No, they would have come to the door. Was it someone coming to tell me that I would be released tomorrow? Let's see. I walked to the window and craned my neck to look out of the four inch slit above the steel plate. The soft, fluffy sound had been that of a blanket being pushed through the wrought iron grille. As I approached close enough to take the blanket, I saw the whites of two wide eyes. It was the Black Kid. All hope of communication was dashed.

I lay down again. I was glad for the blanket. The night was not cold - it was the 14th of May in North Africa - but the blanket meant that I would not be feeling the gentle breeze that wafted through the room. I started to pray. I fell asleep.

Click - howl. The atrocious wail broke forth from the mosque. I was wide awake. Jesus Christ! Did they deliberately build the mosque this close with the intention of torturing their prisoners? At the shock of my abrupt waking, I instinctively started to curl up into a ball. The security at curling up gave way to an absence of solace at being curled up. I turned rapidly away and straightened out, my breath coming in rasps. My lips were dry and caked, but my shirt from the chest to the collar was sodden with sweat.

I must be going home to-day. Yet I knew I wasn't. I opened my eyes. It was dark. I seemed to have been asleep for only minutes. Then I became aware of hearing cars driving. It was a new day. I listened to the tuneless dirge from the mosque, and as the reality of my situation overtook the euphoria of the twilight zone, the insecurity returned to choke me. I fought to suppress an inward desire to scream out loud.

I started, chill in my sodden shirt. I rolled the blanket a little closer to me and relaxed. My heart started to beat faster and faster. I started to squirm.

Get a grip Robin! It's OK, go back to sleep. I got into my familiar sleeping position, pulled the blanket up over my ear, closed my eyes, and waited for sleep to return. But my heart was banging faster and faster and louder and louder, and no amount of pretending was going to put me back to sleep. And then I was screaming inwardly and the full horror of my predicament consumed me.

I threw off my blanket, leapt to my feet and started to throw myself around the room to dissipate the insecurity. But there was no solace there either, and I quickly went through all the arguments of the previous day to get a grip on myself. But this time there was no light to see by, only the shaft of street light on the wall which wasn't enough.

Now I was in a jam. The transition from peaceful sleep to roaring insecurity with no warning had left me unarmed. And then there was the Muezzin with his agonized wail. I hoped he was dying of cancer. This was difficult. I started to concentrate on breathing. I paced out my room again to check yesterday's calculations. I berated life, the universe and everything for getting me into this mess.

In a few minutes, the muezzin's ghastly acapella ceased and I was able to concentrate.

Do something! Pull the other one. Do what? Do the movements. Brilliant! Just be careful not to bang into a wall; it is dark after all.

I crossed my hands above my face, and, as I lowered them with a steady exhalation of breath, I closed my fists and slowly swept the front of my body. I did the first kata entirely. I did as much of the second kata as I could remember. When my concentration broke, I resorted to familiar fighting moves and parts of higher katas that I could remember. It was working. I was absorbed in the flow.

My breathing was calmer now, but it was to be fully twenty minutes before I had pulled myself back from the brief excursion into panic.

And after those twenty minutes I had exhausted all the moves I knew. So I did the first kata again. I now needed something to do next, because I was soon going to drop out of this hard, dissipative exercise into a void. I had to slow down gradually. I resorted to breathing exercises. Slowly, throughout many minutes and many repetitions of the breathing cycle, I came to a much more peaceful state. I knew however that the peaceful state would only continue while I had something to occupy my mind, and I was running out of things to do.

I sat down on the mattress and tried to think. Yes, well, if you had just taken things a little bit slower and looked around you a bit more, you might not be here now. Your father-in-law did say that you need to develop a bit of humility. You didn't listen at the time, did you? Well, no. But then why should I have done? He never understood the first thing about me anyway. Well maybe, but for once he might just have been right. But.... No, don't argue, he might just have been right. OK. "Lord, grant me humility and circumspection," I started. I repeated it over and over again until it became a mantra. Slowly, slowly, I calmed even more. When the mantra ceased to have any further calming effect, I turned to the Lord's Prayer, which helped some more. "...And deliver us from evil..." I afforded myself a silent snigger, which I promptly considered irreverent, and solemnly finished the Prayer - about six times. I was much calmer now. "...Give us this day ..." Christ! I thought. I haven't eaten for nearly twenty four hours. Well, I'll be out soon and I can have a big nosh. No. Have another go.

I went through all the proceedings of the previous day and tried to piece together what had happened, what had gone wrong, and what I should have done. What I should have done? Forget what you should have done. Concentrate on where you are and what the implications are. No, just stick to the facts. Not easy, laddie, you're not a man of facts. You are a man of possibilities. Well, don't torture yourself with what might be, just concentrate on the facts. OK.

Many times my mind wandered from the precise facts into what the Libyans were going to do with me. Many times I wound up in my mind being shot - God alone knew what for. So this is how it ends. What a way to go. Thirty three years old, my whole life still before me, three beautiful little children. Bastards! What the fucking hell were you doing all the time, Ian, you're so fucking clever. Why didn't you see this coming instead of playing stupid management games with your staff?

However true it may have been, I should not have allowed myself to think like this, for floods of black anger washed over me, and all the insecurity came rushing back. I got up and paced out the length and width of the floor again, re-ran the calculations in my head and got the same answers as before. I needed something more. OK, so you've measured it in yards, and calculated areas and volumes. Now try converting the imperial values into metric values. Wow! That's a good one.

Seating myself on the mattress, I started to write the arithmetic in the dirt on the floor - and abruptly stopped. I quickly reasoned that I did not want the Libyans to see me in ownership of any support system - they had only yesterday stripped me of every important artefact that I owned - and for good reason. Then, if I did the arithmetic in my head, it would be more difficult, more time consuming, and the task would absorb me, yet I would be able to make progress at it. So I did. And that was the beginning of a road to salvation.

Getting comfortable on my mattress, I closed my eyes and set about the task with a will. When I had finished the conversions, which took a satisfyingly long time, I started on other calculations. As I did so, it dawned on me that here was a whole raft of things that could occupy my mind, not only because I understood the problems that

I was trying to solve, but also because I knew the techniques to solve them. Soon, I was doing integral calculus in my head. The volume of the solid of revolution generated by the curve "y equals ..." That's a good one. Remember that one, Robin. It was wonderful! I had a routine! Hold on a minute ... start a calendar. I made a mark in the dirt on the floor between the mattress and the wall. I would take a chance that the Libs would not suspect such a thing. Hold on, update your sundial. I couldn't. It was past sunrise but the sun wasn't far enough up. Yes it was, but the sun was out of sight on the other side of the building. Damn! OK.

The area bounded by the function A, equals the double integral of a function of x between the limits of.... This was great!

I did every puzzle I could think of. I started developing interactive game software in my head. I even got into multi dimensional objects in multi dimensional space. I got up to the seventh order before I ran out of brain power. And as the sun rose, I took a look out of the crack above the plated window to see what I could see.

The walls of the buildings on the opposite side of the road showed contours. Windows recessed in the walls were in umber. Air conditioning units that projected through walls cast long, rectangular shadows along the wall, and parallel to the ground. The road plainly ran East-West.

But hang on. If the shadows were parallel to the ground at sunrise, I had a new dimension to my sundial. I didn't need to wait for the sun to come around to my side of the building. Isn't life exciting! I stood and looked at the opposite wall for a while. The minor imperfections in the craftsmanship were thrown into sharp relief by the angle of the sunlight. The buildings looked mature. It reminded me of the South of France. I began to think of the holidays in France that I had enjoyed so much. I thought of my children playing on the Provençale beaches, all my pretty chickens and their dam, so occupied. I thought of Katy, already showing Ross and Gak-Gak how to dress themselves and how to conduct themselves at table - and she was only five already. I became awash with the warm feelings. And then - Crash! Down went my defences, up screamed the insecurity! Oh, God! Think, Robin, think! Oh, God! The area bounded by the function A equals the double integral of a function of x between the limits of ... This was useless. Try again! The area ... No! Too complicated. Try something else! I paced out the floor. No! Not enough. My children! Their beautiful mother looking on! OK. But the children! Worse! My children! Oh, God! No pain was worse than this! Bastards! Deprive me of my children, will you? We'll see! Bastards! Just try me! Alright, you are trying me. We'll see! Just watch me! Just bloody well watch me!

So I tried to take stock.

I had been incarcerated. That was bad.

I didn't know what for. That was bad.

I was in solitary confinement. That was bad.

Solitary was already proving to be taxing beyond my present capability to cope. That was very bad.

So don't cope Robin, manage the situation. You're always going on about people at work who cope with problems instead of managing them, so get on and manage. OK. Don't problem solve, Robin, just establish the facts. OK.

I haven't eaten for twenty four hours. That's not too bad.

I don't know when I'm going to eat next. That's bad.

The company knows I have been arrested. That's good.

Nobody knows where I am. That's bad.

Roger is in England, so he can't do anything to help. That's bad.

Ian is the only person in Libya who has any clout. That's bad.

Pat has gone back to England, so can't hustle to get me out. That's bad.

Pat has gone back to England, so won't be involved. That's good.

On the whole, I would prefer her to be here, she can at least hustle effectively.

And the anger at the ineptitude of my managers bubbled over again. This time I could not hold it, and I quickly found myself in a serious lather of emotion which I was unable to assuage. Ian, with his "Toodle-oo," whenever he left, and his bag dangling by its strap from his hand, and the way he twirled it when ever he walked - I mean, for God's sake, we all carried handbags, it was too darned hot to carry anything in your pockets, but for Christ's sake - he was the company manager. What a bloke!

The anger was beginning to takes its toll. Get a grip Robin, get a grip! Well, that's all very well for you to say, but you haven't had to work for idiots like these for the last three years. Not a single, sodding one of them ever had the faintest idea what you were capable of. So you pushed yourself harder and harder, doing what you thought was your job, trying to get some recognition, and now you've fucked it up, good and proper. And even while you were fucking it up, they either weren't there to counsel you or they had no more idea of what was happening than you had. Well, fuck the lot of them. I can't depend on any of them to get me out.

So where does that leave me?

It leaves Pat - the only person on whom I can utterly depend to get me out of here, and upon whom I can totally rely - who probably doesn't know yet and probably won't know for - who knows how long.

Which means that I am on my own. Well, that makes a change - you've been on your own all your life. No, shut up and listen. You're on your own. Everything that you would normally be able to rely upon, everything that supports you when you go home at night, every familiar thing - gone. You're on your own. It's you. There isn't anybody else. Well, this is the moment every Samurai spends his life training for. No it isn't. That is the moment of death. Well, what the Hell do you think this is? You're not dead yet. That's true. And if I have anything to do with it I am not going to be dead for quite some time.

All well and good. But you don't know why they've got you. You don't know what they intend to do with you. This is true. The possibilities are endless. You could go home tomorrow. You could be here for weeks, months, years. They could take you out and shoot you tomorrow. This isn't England after all.

Shit. So this is how it ends. What a way to go. Thirty three years old, my whole life still before me, three beautiful little children. Bastards!

Stop speculating. And stop swearing. Grow up. You're in a jam. Think!

I went over the whole thing, every minute detail of the last twenty four hours to see if I could extract one shred of good out of it. I couldn't.

My drive for acceptance, coupled with my managers' incapability of recognizing real ability when they saw it, who thereby failed to accept me, produced a vicious circle. I was running blind trying to do what I thought was my job. And in being blind I had landed myself in this. I had been arrogant, and I had certainly lacked circumspection.

I was dizzy and exhausted with the emotion. I recalled my father-in-law again. "You need to learn a little humility," he had counselled. I had disregarded him at the time, as I had done over the bulk of the years that I had known him. With justification, I thought, because his way was to come up the hard way. If you haven't come up the hard way you haven't come up at all. I, of course, had been to university. But that didn't count. I hadn't come up the hard way - I wasn't humble enough.

Then on the other hand where had my way got me? Here! So maybe he was right. I started to pray.

'O Lord. Grant me humility and circumspection.'

It was a good start. Maybe I also had God on my side. Right now I probably only had God on my side. Better not cross God. I prayed again.

What do we know of humility?

First learn correct technique. Then power comes with speed. OK.

So I started to practice the movements again. I repeated the exercises of earlier in the day, and was surprised to find that I could remember more than I thought. I was careful to practice slowly as an exercise in humility. But soon the fighting movements took on a life of their own and I was laying about me left and right with all the power that comes with speed. Opponents fell before me at every turn. I could walk on rice paper and leave no mark. But I <u>was</u> leaving marks. And I froze as I heard a footstep outside. No more fighting technique, I thought, lest they see you and misconstrue. Stick to simple exercise. But what exercise? I can't do press ups. Well, I can - but only twenty. How long does that take?

I began to remember the Samurai who sat down to take his own life. He considered himself a failure. He felt that he had let down his wife and children. In not knowing what to do to recover the situation, he had decided to end it all. As he sat and tried to summon up the courage to make the first cut, he found himself hearing his own breathing, and he started to listen. Listening brought wonderment. Soon he was transfixed at the regularity of his breath - and remained so for the next four days, by which time he had forgotten all about suicide. At the end of four days he got up, got on with his life, and made a success of it.

Standing, I began to inhale. With each slow inhalation of breath, I made a gentle but expansive circular movement of the arms to open up the chest. At maximum expansion I rose onto tip toes to complete the expansion of the body, hold the breath, then come down off the toes and contract with slow exhalation. Each breath cycle took forty or so seconds to complete.

Three or four cycles later I thought that I had done enough. But I hadn't. The moment

I stopped the insecurity came rushing back. So I started again. As the breaths rolled slowly by, I became calmer. Twenty palliative minutes later, the constant buzz of anxiety had subsided to mere tension. I was calmer than I had been since being kidnapped. Now, I had to capitalize on my newly acquired self control.

Now practice humility. Walk without leaving a trace.

So I started to walk. Up and down the length of the cell. Sixteen feet one way, sixteen feet back. Seven paces one way, seven paces back. But you're not using the full length of the cell. I know. Somehow I feel uncomfortable being too close to the wall - enclosed on one side. Try going closer to the wall, become at one with your surroundings. OK. So I did. And off I went, feeling better. You set a cracking pace, Robin. Yeah. Slow down. This is supposed to be an exercise in humility. Besides you're getting dizzy with all the going about at each end. True. Slow down. Yeah, I am sweating. With fear? Well, it's not hot in here, is it? Mm. I wish the cell were longer. Walk the diagonal. Of course. Oh! And wrap the blanket around your shoulders. OK.

So I started to walk with a blanket around my shoulders. Up and down the length of the diagonal. Nine paces one way, nine paces back. All the way into the corners, Robin. OK. Easier this time. Nine paces along the diagonal against seven along the length. Let's think. The cell is sixteen feet long and twelve feet wide. Sixteen feet is four fours, twelve feet is three fours. OK. Three, four, five - the diagonal is twenty feet in length. Aren't the Italians brilliant.

My feet pounded the floor. They could have heard me in Benghazi. The falls of my left and right feet sounded different as they hit the floor, and beat out an arrhythmia as they did so. I concentrated on making my gait symmetrical. To do this, I had to watch my feet and gauge equal strides. Then I tried to walk symmetrically without looking at my feet, on walking slowly and without anger, and then on walking silently.

The click and howl took me by surprise. I had been walking all morning. The midday call and its painful local variant had me looking at the air-conditioners again. The shadows were at their shortest. Good, but I realised that I needed to go to the toilet. I looked at the door. There was a halo of light around it, now that the sun, at its highest, was bathing the outside courtyard. After a few more minutes of walking, I heard a door open, followed by footsteps – footsteps of several people. Voices muttered, accompanied by a sound like the clinking of a cheap tubular bell. A second later the world exploded.

The din of repeated blows of metal pounding on obstinate metal filled the basement room. My ears were in pain, even with my fingers in them. My rib cage vibrated at each blow. Even my eyes hurt. I catapulted myself the farthest I could from the racket. But it made no difference within the rectangular, concrete floored room. After half an eternity, the banging stopped and the door was pulled open. A cascade of reflected sunlight flooded into the basement storeroom, and I had to raise a hand to shield my eyes, rather than turn away. I could not afford to miss an attack if that was what was intended. I stood waiting. Men outside stood motionless.

In the fierce glare, the Moustachioed One stood dignified, erect and indifferent to me, with the Kalashnikov slung over his left shoulder. After a few seconds, the old man appeared just outside the doorway, and waved the back of his hand at me. Reassured, I stepped a few paces backwards, deeper into the gloom. I knew I could take him.

After a brief pause, he entered, bearing a meal on a tray. He uttered a couple of words and placed the tray on the concrete floor a few feet inside the door, while never for a second taking his unblinking eyes off me. He walked backwards out of the door.

After another brief pause, the rag head who had inducted me the previous day, stepped into the sun bathed door way, uttered a couple of words, and slid sideways into the gloom in one smooth movement. Still clutching his hatta, he regarded me impassively and motionlessly. I looked straight back at him. The Moustachioed One took the opportunity to sneak a look at me.

After yet another brief pause, the First Day Guard nodded in the direction of the tray. I did not move. First Day uttered a few inaudible words. The old man stepped in, picked up and moved the tray closer to me, and stood up to leave. First Day looked up at me for an acknowledgement. Instead I said, "Toilet. Toilet." First Day raised his head a little higher, uncomprehending. I repeated, "Toilet, toilet." And made a gesture with my right hand vertically downwards between my legs in an imitation of urination.

Upon a few words from First Day, the old man flicked one hand at me in bidding. As I advanced, the old man and the Moustachioed One backed in off in unison to maintain a healthy distance.

Surrounded on three sides, with the wall to my left, they tracked me as I measured my way along the wall to the steps, never allowing themselves to get closer than a respectful distance.

The entourage walked up the stairs to the side door, along to the turn in the staircase, then down the stair case into the main basement. After the stark midday light of outside, the gloom at the bottom of the stairs required a guard to guide me hard right to the door of the Hole in the Floor toilet. I pushed the toilet door open and clenched my teeth and swallowed hard to resist the gag reflex as I pushed my way in, carefully avoiding falling into the porcelain hole, still soiled from the previous visitor. I knew the drill from holidays in rural France. I stood on the porcelain "bricks" - the raised parts of the porcelain moulding designed to take the feet. I dropped my trousers and underpants as far as I could to ensure that I did not accidentally soil them myself. But then found to my horror that I could not squat to the extent necessary owing to the old injury to my right leg. What was I going to hold onto to enable a suitable posture? Fortunately, there was a grab handle on the inside of the door, which I took, and thereby supported my weight. I prayed that the door would not come off its hinges. I completed my toilet amidst the smell and the flies and reached for the toilet paper. There was none. Neither was there any water when I turned on the wash hose. As I fought back the gag reflex once again, I turned and saw a piece of green kitchen paper on the side of the filthy sink. I finished, using my left hand. While dressing, I saw in the sink a large quantity of second hand toothpaste, visible in the gloom only because it was bright pink against the greyed white of the porcelain sink, and because my eyes had now adjusted to the gloom.

Stepping out through the toilet door, I could now make out a blank piece of wall a good pace ahead of me, and the wide wooden planks of a second door, immediately to my right. The wooden planks were interrupted at head height by a barred, glassless window of about a handspan wide and again high. This gave onto a large room whose detail was lost in gloom, and which I was given no time to study before I was marshalled back up the stair case and back to my basement cell. Before I made the turn to go, however, I gave a firm push against the locked door, as if guiding myself in the gloom.

Under machine gun escort, I was returned to my, now evidently, basement store room. I sat on my mattress until the interminable banging home of the bolt on my door had ceased, and proceeded to eat my lunch of "Libyan Soup" using the spoon provided, and the bread, using my right hand.

Throughout the afternoon, I strained to interpret tiny sounds within the building that gave hope of release. Agonized and confused by the quiet of the afternoon, I went over and over again the events of the last 48 hours - I even asked myself who I would be prepared to shop to the Libyans in exchange for my own freedom - until the third call to prayer, and movement. Then another call to prayer, and food, and dark and near tears, and a second blanket, and more marks in the dirt, and darkness and the fifth call, and praying and sleep.

I had to watch my feet and gauge equal strides. Then I tried to walk symmetrically without looking at my feet, as one plays an instrument without looking at it. Ha! Just like playing the sax. That's odd. I haven't played the sax for three days. And I haven't really had a good blow since the session with Simon on Thursday, not that that was a good blow. Well there's a thing. My sax. I wonder if it's still there. Or have the bastards nicked it? Well, there's not a lot I can do about it, I don't have it here. I made a mark in the dirt. I kept walking.

"You must take the 'A' Train,
To go to Sugar Hill way up in Harlem
If you miss the 'A'..."

D Major, E Major sharp five, E minor seventh, A seventh, D Major. I ran it through my mind. Middle eight. 'A' section again. And around the head again until I got fed up with it. The dark of a New York subway at night was replaced by the limited light of a prison cell. As my concentration broke, I realised that my gait had become uneven again. I tightened up and recovered my rhythm. But the 'A' Train kept running through my head.

I stopped walking.

Two fingers of the left hand.

Three fingers of the left hand, left thumb, middle finger of the right hand.

Two fingers of the left hand.

Six fingers, left thumb.

Three fingers of the left hand, left thumb, middle finger of the right hand.

Two fingers of the left hand, edge of right index finger.

I'd got it. I could play the damned saxophone in my head. Salvation! How many songs did I know by heart? 10? 15? This could keep me going for days. And scales! Arpeggios!

I started playing scales. First off, something simple - C Major. OK. Then F. B flat. I started to run into trouble with E flat, and foundered with A flat. But it was enough to be getting on with. I had something I could do. Something taxing, but something I could do.

Having foundered I took up walking again. The degree of control over my surroundings elated me. Now I felt confident to start thinking again. So I did. I went through the whole thing again from start to finish to see what I could conclude. However much I hated it, however painful the reflection, I must do it sooner or later - and preferably sooner if I was to be prepared for anything that might happen.

The old man and the usual military escort brought lunch. I asked if I could have a knife to go with the spoon and fork. I was refused, on the grounds that I could then use it as a weapon. I asked if I could have some water to drink. Nobody understood.

"Aqua, aqua," I said, and mimicked the act of drinking from a large vessel.

Nobody knew what I was talking about.

But the old man knew. "Ana araf. Ana araf," he said with animated nods of the head, and disappeared.

Three minutes later he was back with a large, bright orange, plastic jug full of fresh tap water. As with all Tripoli tap water, it smelt of swimming pools. But that boded well for my general health.

As the escort turned and left, I stepped towards the old man and took his left wrist with my right hand, gently turning the wrist to read his chrome coloured, Casio, digital watch. He chortled. I smiled. He left. I made a mark in the dirt.

As the day wore on, I sank to a depth. Yes, there was the possibility that they were going to kill me. Under the circumstances, such an outcome was improbable or they would have killed me by now. The only way I was going to be killed, I reasoned, as much in hope as expectation, was by accident, overweening zeal on the part of a revolutionary, or if I made a move one shade too fast. There was the possibility of a show trial and a show execution, pour encourager les autres. That would happen on Revolution Day in Green Square, in front of the assembled State of the Masses. How would I behave? With dignity. Hang me would you? We'll see. But if they were holding me for Revolution Day, I was going to be here at least until September. My heart sank.

An accident they would be careful to avoid. A fast move I would be careful to avoid. An overzealous revolutionary was a chance I would have to take.

"You don't have anything to fear being around people with guns," I was later told.

"Let me hear you say that when you've been around a few people who carry guns," I later replied.

A show trial? I had read the history of the Gulag.

By the end of the third day I had resolved that if they were going to kill me, they probably would have done it by now. Also, that if I was going to put up a fight, it was only going to be if they were going to kill me - and then there would be one hell of a fight. Those things resolved, I began to calm down. And lastly if I wasn't going to cause any trouble, I might as well be as innocuous as possible, put the Goons to sleep, and just disappear - until it was time to disappear.

On the fourth morning, I had my breakfast, and was allowed out for ablutions. Following the early morning checks, the "officers" had left and things had subsided to their usual, daily quiet.

After about twenty minutes, I heard movement outside the front window of my cell. Someone was shuffling around outside the window, and was interested in looking in through the narrow gap above the steel plate. I sat motionless on my mattress and ignored whoever it was, eyes cast down, heart pounding. I also ignored whispered words of Arabic, intended to attract my attention.

The words were repeated a little more loudly and with more insistence. Heart pounding more loudly, I ignored the words all the more. Metallic clinking, followed by the thrust of a projection through the steel grate galvanized me. As I rolled away from any bead drawn up on me, I saw that it wasn't the Kalashnikov. It was a hand bearing a steaming whisky glass. I came out of the roll and rose to my feet, careful to recover an aloof and inoffensive bearing. The whispered Arabic became conciliatory, and was accompanied by inviting gestures of the hand which bore the glass.

I slowly raised my head, then my eyes, which ran from the glass, up the outstretched arm, until they met the eyes of the old man. His face was warm and smiling, his demeanour alert. He cocked his head and continued in soothing Arabic. I walked up to his now motionless hand, and sniffed the glass. Hot, delicious coffee. Black nectar! But it was too easy. I shook my head minutely. The old man offered the glass again. I looked him in the eyes, shook my head, pursed my lips and started to turn away. Again he offered, and then he understood. He flicked his head up slightly and back down again, lowering his eyelids and opening and closing his lips as he did so. "Shouf, shouf, shouf!" he instructed. I looked as he sipped from the glass. It wasn't drugged. I nodded my head. I took the glass and drained the coffee into my throat. Ah! Bliss. "Shukran," I said. Further conciliatory Arabic offered me another coffee even before he had put the first glass back on the tray. He raised the second glass of coffee towards me. I declined. It would be too easy to become dependent on our jailers. He returned the glass to the tray and picked up another. Tea! "Maleish! Maleish!" he said, as he sipped it. I took it, drained it, and returned it. He stood there.

Now I felt safe to approach closer to the window that was in the direct daylight, and saw for the first time the tray he was holding. On it sat three groups of whisky glasses, each group filled with a differently coloured, dark liquid. Coffee, tea, and what? What was this? "Shouney?" I asked. Who was all this for? He spoke lightly, made circular motions with his free hand and, with a flick of his head, indicated all the other prisoners. Well, there couldn't be that many prisoners - the place wasn't big enough -

certainly not if they were all in solitary confinement.

"OK," I thought. "They can't drug all of us." I motioned towards the tray. He raised his eyebrows and animatedly offered me another tea. I indicated my interest in the third group of glasses. He selected one and I took it through the grate. Chocolate! Hot, sweet, chocolate! And still hot enough to scald my throat as it went down. Oh, bliss! Hot drinks! And joy! Humanity in the midst of barbarity! I let a hint of a smile creep momentarily into my eyes. He regarded me. He had children. He had been to Mecca. I Christened him "The Hajji". He quietly pad-padded his way off to refresh the other prisoners.

The heat rose.

The guards opened the door shortly before noon. As the dreadful clanging was reverberating away, I was registering surprise, because they did not usually open the door between meals, and it was too early for lunch. But I was buoyed up because here at last was activity.

The usual escort could be seen just outside, in the shadow of the house. To my continued surprise and buoyancy, I was summoned. The usual wave of an arm was by a guard I couldn't recall seeing before.

Without a backward glance, I stepped out of the gloom of the cell and into the relative light of the building's shadow.

There they were. The Moustachioed One with the Kalashnikov, the First Day Guard, and the Black Kid, a heavy set man, who stooped a little, looked at you slightly sideways, and hinted at guarding his face with an eyebrow and his left shoulder. With raised, clenched fists, the boxer's defence would have been complete.

I was escorted to the hole in the floor. I didn't need to go, but I took the opportunity and relieved myself anyway, to try and acquire information. When I came out of the toilet, the Black Kid stepped out of the group of guards that was just standing around, and mimicked the washing of the face to the accompaniment of an elongated, low pitched vowel. I'd already washed my face that morning. But this was better than solitary, so I left the door open, and washed my face in the filthy sink. I noticed once again, lumps of pink tooth paste lying in the sink and felt that someone could have cleaned up better than that after they had finished.

As I was drying on a piece of green kitchen paper, that lay conveniently by, the Black Kid started hurrying me with a scary, basso, "Fisa! Fisa!"

Self preservation made me hurry, determination made me procrastinate. I took my time drying until the "Fisa! Fisa!" was eventually shouted at me.

I left the toilet, and started up the first flight of stairs, heading back to my cell. As I waited for the side door to be opened, the bass voice herded me up the next flight of stairs, and not to the outside.

Ah, good, real activity! My emotions raced. I felt buoyancy at the prospect of action, trepidation at the unknown.

We progressed to the entrance hall and stopped. The Intelligent One looked me up and down appraisingly. He saw that I was as smartly dressed as possible, but mimicked the act of smarming down the hair. Pointlessly, I obliged.

The office door opened, someone came out, brief words were spoken, and we were off. The inevitable hope that it was all over was contradicted by the lack of finality in the body language of the guards.

Out the front door, down the steps, along the garden path, we stopped for the gate to be opened, and went out into the street.

The street was in a restricted area, every access to which was marked with a "NO ENTRY" sign. Pedestrians walked freely in the street however, as the street was a main thoroughfare. Behind me, a good quarter of a mile off, was the Grand Hotel. Going east, in the direction that we now walked, was a main street on which resided the BPOCO main office, and the Italian Embassy. Restricted or not, an odd feeling of relief swept over me at being out in the open. And even though there was no traffic in the restricted area, the sound of traffic elsewhere was to be heard, now undamped by the walls of the prison building and by its high garden wall.

At a fast pace, we covered the fifty or so yards, over a side turning, to the last building on the block - the one in which my Saturday night interrogation had taken place.

The gate opened without request and I started choking. I was out of breath from the walk, anxious, and now frightened. The last time I had been here, they had slapped me around. I didn't actually hurt that much.

I kept my head down, and thus don't know how we got to the next office. But once into it, things continued to move at a fast pace.

Working my way past a man seated between the half open door and a desk, I was immediately offered a curt hand shake which I took and was told to sit. As I eased myself into an upright chair facing the desk, I took in three people. One occupied the seat behind the desk. He had black hair, and was well groomed, dark suited, and business like, with a continuous flow of quick, busy, almost nervous movements. He had yet to make eye contact with me, handshake notwithstanding.

To my right sat a suited, older man with salt and pepper hair, and a moustache, big nose, glasses, and an absurdly long finger nail on the little finger of his left hand. I knew without guessing that he used the nail for disgorging diverse waste matter from various orifices of his body.

To the left of the desk, and blocking the door of the office, sat a smirking man. He broke away from his conversation with the man at the desk every few seconds to look half up at me and chortle faintly. At most he was in his middle thirties and at best he was casually dressed. I had seen those eyes before.

Upon ascertaining my name with the inevitable, Arabic hardening of the letter P to a B, Black Hair asked me why I had been arrested. I told him that I did not know.

More truthfully, I had no idea initially of where this interview was going, and I wasn't going to give them anything to steer the interview until I had found out what they wanted. So I mentally weighed up what I knew already.

There was nothing to indicate who Black Hair was. Lawyer or interrogator, prosecution or defence?

Whoever or whatever they thought I was, this was now completely out of proportion to anything that I had actually done.

All I knew was that I was now in deep trouble. But not why. I had been only limply able to account for my presence at the university. I was damned if I was going to tell them that I was on my way to the Daewoo party, because then a whole lot more expats would find themselves in my position.

So far the only thing they had on me was the maps.

But if I could just persuade them that I had simply been out driving to get some fresh air because of my earache, and that I had taken a wrong turn into the university entrance, they might just shrug their shoulders and let me go. It was a limp story, but I had to make it stick. The good news about telling lies is that the more often and the louder you tell them, the more people tend to believe them.

Black Hair ordered coffee and cigarettes. The coffee smelt good and tasted wonderful - rocket fuel. The Rothmans cigarette was no more than a prop to me, to use as a distraction while being questioned. But it did make a change to have a decent cigarette after American brands or, worse, Libyan camel dung.

As I drank the coffee and smoked, the questioning over the details of my interrogations on Saturday night became ever closer and I picked my way around the answers ever more uncheckably. But if I faltered, I was very quickly upbraided for trying to duck a question. Over only a very few minutes, I slowed down the rate of delivery of my answers so that I would have time to think out answers where necessary, and mimic that same slow delivery in order to disguise it where it was not necessary to think. But after twenty minutes and a second cup of coffee, I was struggling to articulate myself and breathe properly at the same time. My heart was pounding at a phenomenal rate. So fast, that I was afraid of having a heart attack. In fact I resorted to deliberate long breaths to control my breathing and heart rate with almost no effect. All the while the casually dressed man held my gaze and smirked. Then I remembered where I had seen those eyes before. Back at the centrale, in Mr Abugheila's office on Sunday. My heart rate went through the roof, and I spluttered for nearly half a minute to draw breath.

The calm, persistent questioning, the painstakingly neutral answers, and the pounding heart went on for an eternity. Then it just stopped. Black Hair gave every impression of being satisfied that there was nothing more to come than that which I had already stated on Saturday night.

The switching simply changed into requests for personal details, such as who I worked for, passport number, height, weight, and any distinguishing marks. I deliberately dissembled at some of the questions to which I could argue that I did not know the answers. But I raised my right hand and showed them the permanent damage to the wrist, resulting from the road accident of a number of years previously, rather than show them the catalogue of grief that was my leg injuries.

Then Black Hair offered a hand shake. This time he caught my eye - if only for a split second. It was impossible to know how to interpret the look. I would like to think it was respect. Much more likely it was knowledge of what was going to follow.

Escorted back, I had no more than a few seconds to consolidate the geography of the street. Futility soared in me as we crossed the side turning. I nearly missed the dark blue plate. But the street sign registered in my scan even though it was marked uselessly in Arabic – but with Roman lettering underneath! An untouched relic from Italian colonial days. "Sharah Türkiye". Turkey Street. Now I knew exactly where I was!

I was returned to my basement storeroom, and spent much of the rest of the day trying to second guess what the Hell was going on. Only now, two things were clear.
I was still here.
And things had now got completely and utterly out of hand.

Then it was time for saxophone exercises. This time I made a lot of mistakes in things I thought I knew. Concentration was becoming more difficult. Each time that my concentration broke, it brought another inrush of screaming insecurity.
Once, all I could do was to start counting. It was the only effective thing I could find to concentrate on. I got to about six before I had got a grip again.
Then, I realised that I couldn't remember whether or not I had made my daily mark in the dirt on the floor beside my mattress. My mouth opened. My breathing grew raspy. My eyes bulged. I went dizzy. I recalculated. I made a mark in the dirt. I got up and walked around.

I looked at the section of wall that ran from the doors to the corner of the building. That is my exit. I can break a hole through the wall. I can't get out through the doors - they are bolted. But I can get through the wall. I will persist, I will kick. I will break the wall. I will be outside the cell. And I will walk away.

I ignored the door. I ignored outside. The rest of the world did not exist and could not exist for me while I was in solitary. The inside of the four walls of my filthy, unilluminated, basement storeroom, prison cell was home. This is where I must build a life.
"I cannot walk in freedom outside the cell. But within the cell I am free."
"Freedom is a state of mind?"
"Yes. I can come and go in my cell as I please."
"But you will only actually be free within this cell."
"Yes. But, within this cell, I will be free," said I.
And, so, I set out to become free."

I was developing a routine. Twenty minutes of breath power techniques each morning would get my breathing under control and, to a certain extent, my heart rate. I used prayer as a means of calming my spirit. The prayer that I used as a mantra was getting longer by the day, as I saw more and more about my life and situation about which to ask God for help. When repetition of the prayer had on any occasion brought about a measure of calm, I would turn to the Lord's Prayer and say that increasingly slowly, about six times to calm my spirit further.

I set out to review my life, to see if I could divine a single thread that would help me figure out how I got into this mess, and at the same time give me something to concentrate on, I went over everything I had ever done in my life. But by the end of about two hours I had only a catalogue of disaster – a seemingly endless litany of virtually everything bad that had happened. The left hand side of my nose started to twitch.

Thoughts of ending it all by smashing my head against the wall were at best defeatist and, at worst, unlikely to be successful. But I was staring into a bottomless abyss – a void.

But the Way is in The Void. And by looking into The Void, I realised that if I could produce a catalogue of disaster by thinking about all the bad things in my life, why not think about all the good things. So I did. And by the end of about another two hours I had a catalogue of success – a seemingly endless litany of virtually everything good that had happened. The education I had got, the career I had made, the number of skills I had acquired, the languages I could speak, the number of musical instruments I could play, the number of girlfriends I had had, the wonderful wife I had got, my lovely children ...

And, crash! The whole edifice came tumbling down.

The pain of being deprived of my children was too much. I could think of my wife, but, Oh! the pain of my children was too much to bear. Thenceforth, I resolved, I would not think of my children again, until I was out.

On the seventh day, I resolved to go diving. I lay on my mattress and went through the whole process from start to finish. Kitting up, diving, stripping off. Two hours. I checked my sundial. I played the saxophone.

I was now up to 15 songs note perfect.

It then took me a week to get Take Five right. The fourth bar of the middle eight was the killer. But it finally clicked at one o'clock one day just as the sun came over the edge of the building. Suddenly, the concrete outside my cell door was illuminated, and the sunlight broke its radiant way through the gap above my door and into my cell. It was the sort of thing that only happens in films. I wondered if it was an omen.

I walked.

The following morning the door opened. A man walked in. He was a little shorter than me, even allowing for the big shock of naturally frizzy, black, Motown hair. He was vaguely handsome, in a Libyan sort of way. His buttoned up, sleeveless, red shirt sat in perfect contrast to the ironed, buttock fitting, black slacks and black leather, slip on shoes. The whole ensemble was completed by a gold coloured Rolex on his wrist.

He insinuated his way into the storeroom. I reached out from under my blanket and shook his hand.

"You have?" he started, and looked around him.

Nothing. Don't ask stupid questions.

He looked up and down at my blanketed appearance.

"You cold?" he continued.

"I sweat," I started. I didn't bother to tell him why.

"Cigarette?" he offered.

"No thank you," I said. "I don't smoke."

He took the packet out and jostled them in my direction. I took one. We smoked.

"What you do?" he asked.

I told him I didn't know.

"For work. For work," he clarified.

"Engineer," I said, and pulling myself up to my full height. "British Telecom."

That should sound prestigious enough to get me out of here.

He ignored me.

I asked him what he did. He told me that he worked at the embassy. This sounded hopeful. I asked him which embassy.

"All embassies," he told me.

That didn't make sense.

"What do you do at all the embassies?" I pressed.

"Make sure things doing alright," he vaguely waved his hand to indicate interlocution, and looked at me out of the sides of his eyes to see if I believed him.

"Make sure everybody do right...for revolution," he said. Now I was worried. Not only was he a liar, but he was a revolutionary as well.

I stamped out my half finished cigarette right there. My career as a smoker was over. So was the conversation.

"You want?" he asked.

Cigarettes? No. If I don't smoke, then it is one thing less over which they have control of me.

"British Consul," said I, taking advantage of my full height.

"Tomorrow, God willing," he said. "Maybe the day after."

I was in for a long wait.

"I get you magazine," he said.

"I don't want a magazine," I lied.

"I get you magazine," he said. "I come back."

I thanked him. We shook hands and he left.

The bolt was slammed home.

I walked.

By now I was doing two kilometres a day. But all that practice meant that I was getting quieter and quieter as I walked. This was going to be important when it came time to escape.

I opened my mouth to reduce the rasping noise of my breathing, and to hear better, and just kept putting one foot down in front of the other.

But something was wrong that I couldn't put my finger on. My right shoe didn't feel right. In fact it was very uncomfortable. Much more of this I would be unable to walk. That would be a blow indeed.

My big toe was hurting. It took me a while to figure it out. The toe nail on my right big toe was catching on the inside of my shoe.

I need a pair of nail clippers - or at least a knife.

What were the chances of finding a pair of nail clippers or a knife in a cell that had evidently been meticulously cleared?

I scoured the floor.

Nothing.

I scoured the window sill.

Nothing.

Then I found it. At the end of the window sill, neatly lodged in the angle between the horizontal sill and the vertical wall that made the end of the window frame, was the serrated blade of dinner knife with the bone handle missing.

I listen for movement outside before picking up the knife blade. When all was quiet, I peeled off my shoe and sock, grabbed the knife, trimmed the nail with great difficulty, and returned the knife.

Then it occurred to me that I hadn't washed my socks or indeed my underpants for a whole week, and that things were in fact getting a little uncomfortable.

The next time I went to ablutions, I carried my socks and pants in my pocket. After my personal functions, I ran my socks and pants under the running tap to "wash" them to the best of my ability. I wrang them out and went back to the cell where I hung them all up to dry on a small nail protruding from the brick work, found, just as improbably as the knife blade.

Back to my routine, I walked my usual two kilometres or so with no socks on inside my shoes, ate dinner and went to sleep.

When I woke the following morning it was to a foot that was even more sore. But this time it was the fourth toe of my right foot, upon which the skin had simply blistered and come away through rubbing unprotected on the inside of my leather shoe while I had been walking. Now I was in a fix.

An open sore on my foot, with all the potential for a runaway infection and no potential for antibiotics. This was going to require careful management.

The plan was simple but dire. Lie on my mattress, bare footed, until the blister healed. No socks. No walking. When I do walk, it must be with a sock on. When I next come to washing clothes, it must be only one sock at a time, so that my right foot is always protected to prevent repetition.

I lay on my mattress for seven days with the blister exposed to the air before the skin cover was sufficient to risk a sock and shoe for any distance other than to the lavatory.

Every day, Red Shirt came in. He brought the promised magazine. A copy of Time. Over the course of the week that I was laid up, I read it from cover to cover. Twenty two times.

I read two feature length articles. One about Bill Gates and his business partner. One about Richard Branson and his. Now those are two people I could work for, I thought. I read a review of Emil Kunderer's recent book, 'The Unbearable Lightness of Being'. The magazine quoted the hero from the book as saying to his woman, after he had been deprived of his high flown and serious profession, and forced by the socialist state into the relatively menial task of driving a tractor on a collective farm from which there was no escape, "Can't you see? I am happy here." Not in this man's army, Emil. Not in this man's army.

So on Red Shirt's daily visits, my conversation became increasingly laconic, until it became clear to Red Shirt that, whatever his purpose in coming to visit me, he was wasting his time. And after three weeks he stopped coming.

I was taken to the Hole in the Floor toilet. I pushed the door to the toilet to no avail. I stood there with the door to my right, my gaze lowered and waited for the toilet to be vacated. I ignored the guard to my left, but watched him out of the corner of my eye. In front of me, the wooden door with the barred window that gave on the large room was slightly ajar. The guards made me step away from the toilet door, but to my surprise eased me into the now opened doorway in front of me.

Into the large room that opened up, only a small amount of light entered from the distant back. Upon the floor, I thought I identified about four berths - mattresses like my own with perhaps a single blanket on each. Very obviously, however, about a body's length in front of me sat an older man, motionless upon a mattress whose blanket was untidy and which was covered in what looked like unfolded clothes. He looked Caucasian.

Another guard from within the room approached me from my right. I kept my eyelids lowered and my gaze in the direction of the Caucasian who had not yet moved. My first reactions were to ask myself how many people were being held in this building, and secondly, did these bastards really make war on men of the age of this fellow right in front of me. But as I considered this, I studied the new guard standing close enough that I could have touched him. He was darker, with a more hooked nose, than the average Libyan, but that was nothing new, when one considered the Black Kid, with his flat, boxer's nose. He also wore a style of turban different from most Libyans, but that was nothing new when I considered the Touaregs and their blue cheesecloth veil.

Without moving any part of my body, I said in firm and clear baritones, "Would somebody please introduce us."

The Caucasian's shoulders went up and then down.

"Do you think we'll ever get out of here?" he said in refined English tones, but with labouring emphasis on the word "ever".

"Yes," I replied, not having any idea whether I was telling the truth or not.

The new guard said, "Oh, yes! Your government will get you out. You receive best treatment because you are British. When you have Empire, you treat your colonials well. It is well known. Therefore you will be treated better than us - better than the Americans, the French, the Germans."

The generosity and erudition of this comment came as a welcome relief from a guard.

He wasn't then a common guard at all.

Then it hit me. "Who is "us"?"

The refined English tones said, "He's not a Libyan. He's a Sudanese."

There had been antipathy between the Arab, Muslim elite, who ran the Sudan from Khartoum in the North, and the black, nomadic, Christian tribesmen who occupied the centre and West of the country.

The Sudanese man in front of me was an educated Christian in his middle 30s. A lawyer. He could see exactly where things were going in the Sudan during 1984 and, because of his profession, realised that he had to get out, or be arrested, detained and possibly tried, but almost certainly murdered.

"He escaped from Sudan because he is a Christian, and came to Libya seeking political asylum. The Libyans put him in here with us because he's a Christian," said the refined English tones.

He changed tack, which did not surprise me. "What do you do all day?" he said with pathos.

"Mathematical puzzles, play my saxophone in my head," I answered. "What do you do?"

"Well, I...," he petered out. "I..., I..., I don't know," he anguished.

"You need to find something to occupy your mind," I said. "Do you know any poetry?"

"Well, I .... No!" he replied plaintively.

"Do you know the Lord's Prayer?" I went on.

"Not really," he said.

I tried a different tack. "What do you do?"

"What do you mean?"

"What do you do? For a living," said I.

"Oh! I teach English at the university," he said, which did surprise me.

First, because if it were true, the Libyans were now making war on older university lecturers.

But secondly, and more surprisingly, here we had a university lecturer in English, of a certain age, plainly British himself and very English, who claimed to know no poetry and not even the Lord's Prayer.

"Robin Plummer," I said, offering my hand.

"I'm sorry!" he exploded.

"What for?" I asked.

"Oh!" he said disdainfully, starting to offer a hand, and then withdrawing. Finally, he shook my hand limply and uttered, "Michael Berdinner."

"OK, Michael," I said, as I heard the toilet door being unbolted behind me. "I'm busting for a pee. I've got to go. Just remember that I'm up there," I said pointing my thumb over my shoulder, "and I will be thinking of you. Try to find something to occupy your mind, such as poetry. We are going to get out of here."

"Well, I, I...," he fizzled out. And then, "I want to see the Mudir," he announced. "I want to see the Mudir!"

73

And my guard cast nervous eyes about him and silently shifted his weight from one foot to the other.

"What's the Mudir?" I asked.

The Sudanese turned faintly in my direction. Michael raised his hands and shoulders, uttered "He's…. Oh!" and dropped his hands and shoulders again.

"Who's the Mudir," I asked.

The Sudanese translated, "Mudir - manager."

"He's the only one who can get us out of here," sighed Michael, with the same heavy emphasis on the word "only".

"Right. Let's see if we can get to see the Mudir," I concluded.

I turned on my toes towards the Hole in the Floor, took a deep breath and entered.

A few minutes later, I was returned to my cell, and started thinking about how we could get to see The Mudir.

On about the tenth day, I was taken for morning ablutions. After passing through the side door, I turned to go down the staircase to the Hole In The Floor. This time I was told to go up. More activity? Forced to turn right upon entering the entrance hall, I took two or three more paces before being halted and I stopped a few feet in front of the door which was in the corner of the entrance hallway. The Intelligent One glanced across the eyes of the other two, and ordered me to remain stationary. The other guards watched me, while the Intelligent One opened the door a crack and peered inside. Satisfied, he opened the door enough to get through, swung himself in and closed the door behind him in one movement. A few seconds later he re-opened the door fully and beckoned me into a small, dim anteroom. His left arm was outstretched and indicating the direction that I was to go.

The door closed behind me and I was alone. I stepped to the right through a second door into a fully tiled bathroom. On the right, past the opened door, lay a bathtub, complete with taps and a hand held shower head. Farther down sat a matching bidet and a lavatory pan, still with the protective tape around the rim but with no seat. On the left was a large hand basin. To the right of the basin was a cream coloured, wall mounted, immersion heater. On the far, outside wall, the ghibli had been lowered over the window. Above the sink appeared to be another ghiblied window. The urge to urinate had now taken over. I relieved myself. Now, I could concentrate. Enough light to see by was filtering through the open slats of the ghibli and also under the gap of eight to ten inches that had been deliberately left below its bottom. The lightness and airiness of the bathroom were almost romantic after the gloom and squalor of the basement. I shut the door, and inhaled an unfamiliar smell. Then I turned to wash. There was no plug. I ran water and rubbed my bare hands together, then scrubbed my face with my bare hands. Next, I cleaned my teeth with the index finger of my right hand, hurrying all the while. As I scrubbed, I raised my eyes to look at the wall above the sink, and saw that what appeared to be another window was in fact a mirror.

It reflected a face tanned and drawn, with dirt in the lines of the forehead. The tanned face was surrounded by hair - top, sides and bottom - now black, now brown, now flecked with red. There were no ears – only hair – a continuous mat of thick, greasy hair that surrounded the face. A pointed finger scrubbed at two rows of bright, white teeth.

But there were two discs of white. Two enormous discs of white with hazel brown circles in the middle and black centres, where eyes are normally to be found. The discs of white with the coloured circles danced a jerky dance around in a continuous figure of eight.

Below the tanned and hirsute parody of a face, sat more tanned skin, adorned by a swathe of seersucker white, now greying from the filth of captivity. The dancing white discs had by now seen enough in the mirror to know that the tanned animal in greying white posed no threat, and they danced further afield for other predators.

Ablutions finished, I urinated once more, stepped towards and tapped on the door. As I stepped out and was escorted, mob handed, back to my cell, the faint draft through the door carried the whiff of disinfectant.

Later that morning, I asked the First Day Guard if I could hang my blanket out to air. Each morning, my mattress was soaked with sweat, and it was slowly rotting. My blankets were always damp as well. I think mosquitoes and other bugs were using the moist blanket as home. I was sure that I could see them. I was certainly getting mosquito bites in ever increasing numbers.

Although it would be nice to air my blankets, my prime reason in making this request was of course to see by slow degrees how far I could push the guards. I had made a conscious policy of never attempting to push them any further than I was reasonably sure would succeed. I never took the view that if they said, "No," it didn't matter. Success against the guards was going to come in slow, careful steps, and to invite a refusal might set me back many steps in the psychological battle. Today, I was more likely to get a positive answer to a reasonable request because the First Day Guard and, senior to him, White Shirt, were in charge. If I could get something done by White Shirt and the First Day Guard, it might set a precedent for the future, especially in front of the Black Kid.

The First Day Guard gave an order to open the door of my cell. One could always tell when he was about because of the calm authority and peace that he radiated, and because nobody even moved without him saying so. He was different from White Shirt in whose presence people discreetly got on about their business. With the First Day Guard there was no business in his presence except that which he ordered. The orders came with delectable calm and very few decibels, and were always instantly obeyed.

Still he wore the keffiyah, familiar from 70s' and 80s' media coverage of Middle East affairs, and as worn by Yassir Arafat. First Day always stood up straight, with his head slightly forward and slightly bowed in a posture of deferential humility.

Then he turned away from facing me directly, so that his left side was towards me. His style was indifferent, that of a man to whom it was of no importance to stand idly by in unspoken conversation, waiting for the next matter of no importance to come up.

I read the mood and brought up the next matter of no importance. By prefacing my words with the ubiquitous face saver, "Malleish," I both attracted his attention and told him that what I was about to say was of no importance. I asked if I might hang my blanket over a length of clothes line that I knew to be attached from the corner of the mansion just outside my cell door, to a shackle mounted on the perimeter wall. He understood my meaning but was confused as to the nature of the clothes line. He shook his head, but looked up at me again when I made a facial gesture that implied I would like to continue speaking. I indicated that perhaps we could go outside so that I could show him the clothes line. He turned without demur towards the door and walked out. He stood in the shade of the perimeter wall. I stood in the doorway of the cell. I waited for permission to come out, rather than risk an accident with the Kalashnikov, which must be there. After two or three seconds I was given a sharp order by First Day, who motioned me to join him. The low mutterings of the other guards quickly ceased on sight of First Day, and they stood around diffidently, awaiting an order.

I walked past First Day as I had been bid, and turned the corner of the building with the intention of mounting the low brick wall that retained the garden, and showing First Day the clothes line. My heart started pounding as I rounded the corner as there, bang in front of me, was the Black Kid with the Kalashnikov in his hands and a look of real malevolence in his face. Who was the more surprised, I do not know. I was certainly the quicker to recover. As little as a week of practice at not getting shot had made me by far the quicker as I had a great deal more to lose. Not taking any chances, I just went back around the corner again and slipped back into the cell, my heart still pounding at the momentary shock. To my surprise, First Day followed. He had obviously been edified by my indicating the clothes line. But then I was disappointed. It seemed as though my gambit hadn't worked. First Day told the guards to close the door and I reconciled myself to another day of mental puzzles, saxophone exercises and anxiety, when just as they were about to hammer the bolt home on the door, First Day told them to put the metal bar down and leave the cell doors ajar, but to remain on guard. First Day disappeared.

I had sat down on my mattress by the time he had got back, his hands unchanged in clutching his shawl. He gave a quiet order for the door to be reopened and told the guards to usher me out. Upon stepping forward, I was yelled at by the Black Kid to go back, and he prodded me with the gun barrel. Now I was confused and frightened. Another almost silent order issued and a different guard came in and motioned to my blanket. I picked it up and started with very deliberate movements to walk outside. As I reached the corner of the building, the Black Kid was nervously fiddling with the machine gun. The other guards were nervous too. It was clear that they were under very strict orders that nothing was to go wrong.

The raising of a finger from an otherwise motionless hand, told me to proceed with hanging my blanket over the line.

The clothesline was high and I'm not that tall so I held the blanket in both hands like a bull fighter and gave a mighty heave and the blanket caught the air like a sail and went anywhere but over the clothes line. I gave another mighty heave and the blanket still went anywhere but over the clothes line.

First Day stood motionless. The guards shuffled with embarrassment. The Black Kid grunted and thrust his free hand at me, and I handed him the blanket.

He took the blanket and whirled it with his free hand to lasso the clothes line and entirely failed to do so. He whirled it again and entirely failed again. I just stood there, taking it all in, trying not to smile. The Black Kid realised that something more was needed.

But the clothesline was high and he was not that tall so he held the blanket in both hands like a bull fighter and gave a mighty heave and the blanket caught the air like a sail and went anywhere but over the clothes line. He gave another mighty heave and the blanket still went anywhere but over the clothes line.

But wherever the blanket did go, it got tangled up in the machine gun in his left hand. First Day stood motionless. The guards shuffled with embarrassment. I grunted and thrust my left hand at the Black Kid, and he handed me the machine gun.

Even First Day moved now. Panic spread across the faces of the guards as they looked on in silent horror, all movement stalled. I rotated the gun, butt towards my shoulder, left hand on the furniture, right hand approaching the grip and the trigger. They'd been caught with their trousers down and they knew it.

Time stood still.

I had done what I'd set out to do and it had been funny, but now was the time to stop. So, in one seamless sweep, I transferred the machine gun from my left hand to my right, and from the Black Kid to First Day - and for all the world no-one could say that I hadn't intended to do just that all along.

First Day was the quickest to recover and he took the gun. Unlocked, the guards were almost dancing with fear. The Black Kid looked at me knowing he had just been conned but not sure how.

The tallest among the guards made a fine pair along with the Intelligent One - Tweedle Dum and Tweedle Dee - a lifeless, disinterested pair, about whom it is difficult to say anything. One is left with the impression that the two of them were plucked off the street one day because they were hapless enough to be there when the press gang came along, and were given the job of political jailers. Tweedle Dum, the taller, now took the blanket from the Black Kid and with one movement hung it squarely over the clothes line. First Day's shoulders dropped.

I kept the initiative. I raised the palms of my hands towards the sun, and inclined my head towards First Day and then towards the sun. Then I put my tongue very firmly in my cheek, and said, "Quaise." "Lovely weather, what?" And then I wondered if he would let me stay out in the sun for a while? That would be a real treat. I motioned the palm of my hand back and forth between the First Day and the sun. First Day inclined his head. "Could I just stand here in the sun for a moment?" Quiet orders were issued. I was surrounded. First Day glided off and disappeared into the side door. Two minutes later he was back. "Fifteen minutes," he said. Fifteen minutes! I couldn't believe it! And the Black Kid still had the machine gun!

I stood motionless, head slightly bowed. I now had fifteen minutes to take in the detail of my surroundings. I looked at the shadows of the air conditioners on the wall of the building opposite. Half past eleven. First Day disappeared.

The house was a four bedroomed, Italian, colonial mansion. The front door at the centre of the building faced north and was recessed in the spacious porch for shade. Fourteen marble steps descended from the porch onto the broad, concrete pathway that led about 30 feet to the high, wide, double, steel gate that reached from the ground to the height of the perimeter wall. The garden was a jungle, which was unfortunate, because clear, decorative lines had been laid out by skilled gardeners years before.

With any turn of the light breeze, the scent of Jasmine permeated the nostrils. Bougainvillea, palm trees, the wall, the gate. The smell of rotting rubbish, Jasmine, Capability Brown, the concrete pathway, the gate. The buildings next door, the buildings across the street, air conditioners and their shadows, the steps from the porch, the gate. The minaret of the nearby mosque, its loud speaker bolted to the wall of the parapet, the gate, 400 yards to the Italian Embassy and freedom, the gate.

A mosquito landed on my neck. I raised first my eyes and then a finger to indicate to the Black Kid that I was going to move. He was now alert but calm. Then I raised my hand in an open palmed gesture which he acknowledged, and swatted the mosquito before it bit me. I had learnt to avoid getting shot.

First Day returned. I took this as my signal to go and started to move. It was too much to believe that when they had said fifteen minutes they really meant fifteen minutes. But First Day raised a finger and I stood still. The raised finger did not worry me, but the accompanying look on his face of severe reprimand did. What had I done wrong? Then I saw that the look was not directed at me. It was directed at the Black Kid who had become bored with guarding me while I took the sun. He had started playing with the machine gun again. He had removed the clip with his left hand and was currently using the muzzle to chisel out mortar from between the bricks of the building. I thought that if he tried to fire the gun now before it was cleaned, it would probably blow up in his face. Here was hoping. Then I realised that in its present state, the gun would not fire anyway. Examination of the clip in his hand revealed that it contained no bullets.

I went and stood beside First Day.

I heard a motion at the window of the office. I looked up without appearing to do so. It was White Shirt. That at least explained the relative orderliness of this morning's proceedings. He had come to look out of the window without appearing to do so. I saw him look at me and he saw me look at him. We both saw each other trying to appear not to look. So honour was satisfied. Then White Shirt moved away from the window as if he had never been there.

An unspoken conversation between First Day and me continued for several minutes until two more crisp words were heard from the office. It was White Shirt. There was no sight of him and I guessed he was sitting at the desk. I caught sight of the shadows of the air conditioners on the walls across the street as I turned to walk to my cell. I had had my fifteen minutes.

I walked the few paces through the relative darkness of the shadow of the building, and then turned into the almost total blackness of my cell. I seated myself as usual on the mattress and awaited the closing of the door and the deafening hammering home of the bolt. Then peace.

With my new found intelligence, a plan started to form in my mind.

I'd had my fifteen minutes alright.

That night, I heard a lone set of feet coming out of the front door.

"Mudir! Mudir!" I called out. "Mudir!"

The well heeled soles of leather ceased their pacey clatter as they hit the bottom of the fourteen steps and, to my delight, turned towards the gap at the top of the window through which I now looked.

I saw a pressed blue shirt, and a well fed frame. The owner stooped to look in through the gap. A face appeared.

"Inte Mudir?" I asked, knowing that if he answered, I had no further Arabic with which to address him.

"It is alright," he replied, looking but without smiling. "I speak English."

My shoulders dropped.

"What do you want?" he said, as his eyes narrowed and his face showed interest in the possible answer.

I was afraid of losing his attention. But I didn't know where to start. So I tried at the beginning. I gave him the potted version of my arrest for which no reason had been given. He asked what I wanted him to do. I told him I had heard that the mudir was the only man who could get me out of here. He said he was not the mudir, but that he would ask. He would come back and see me. Tomorrow, God willing. Maybe the day after.

Bukra, inshallah. Bad bukra, munken.

So that was it then.

After two harrowing days filled with mathematical puzzles, jazz tunes and walking, during which all I had achieved was an opportunity, he was, to my surprise, back.

Stooped once again at the window, he said in clear, if ungrammatical English, that he had asked, but had been told, "This not you problem."

"So there is nothing you can do," I said pointlessly.

"No," he replied apologetically. "This from very high manager, Mudir. Sorry."

I thanked him for trying. We shook hands. He went. I never saw him again.

The following day, Friday, brought stresses of a different kind. All week, I listened for sounds that might presage freedom. On Fridays there were no sounds. Friday was prayers. No Mudir. Nothing. I wasn't going home. I came to regard Fridays as a waste of a day. Nothing ever happened. It made it all the more difficult to stay focussed and sane than on any other day of the week.

Days later, when they took me for morning ablutions to the Hole in the Floor, I asked the guard if I might go to the Pink Bathroom.

He said, "No."

I explained in dumb show that it was not possible to wash properly downstairs.

Sedate in his authority, in his late twenties, good looking for a Libyan, scrubbed and filling the confined space with an exotic and not unpleasant perfume, he agreed after only the briefest reflection.

The sweet smelling boy made me wait outside the Hole in the Floor with the usual armed escort and went off to check with the office. While I was waiting I saw Michael again through the open door to the basement. Once again Michael was sitting on his bed apparently doing nothing. My earlier concerns about him now included whether or not he could stand the psychological pressure. At least he had company. Two or three others if my estimate was correct.

But I was shocked when I saw the Sudanese Lawyer, for his arm was in a sling.

"What happened?" I spat out.

"Oh, they beat him so badly they broke his arm," announced Michael.

At this point, the Sweet Smelling Boy returned and took me to the Pink Bathroom. This was a small victory but a tremendous psychological fillip.

I never saw the Sudanese again. Later, Michael said that the Libyans had deported him back to the Sudan.

That evening after dinner, I went to the window of my cell upon hearing an unusually rowdy group leave the front door of the mansion. I managed to attract their attention in spite of the absence of any appropriate Arabic and, to my surprise, they came to the gap above the steel plate and listened to me.

After the customary handshakes through the four inch gap, I said, "Mudir," pointing at the nearest.

"Mudir...? Mudir...?" they all jabbered quizzically to each other.

"Inte mudir?" I enquired.

"La," he denied, with an incredulous smirk creeping across his mouth.

"Inte mudir?" I stressed, now turning to the next

"Inte mudir?" someone cried with hilarity, pointing at the same fellow.

"Aiwa!" agreed someone else. "Mudir Ali!"

They all roared with laughter, repeating "Mudir Ali", and slapping Ali on the back. They walked off cackling with mirth, elbowing each, and out of earshot.

In the middle of the following morning, a number of low, chatty voices emerged from the side door, and approached.

I kept walking, relaxed physically, opened my mouth and focussed on infinity, ready to withstand the din of the door being opened. The door opened, and in sauntered four guards. I stood still and mentally raised my eyebrows as they disregarded me and turned to the short piece of wall on the left hand side of the door. One of them carried a lamp fitting. They held a discussion for a good ten minutes. One of the men then turned to me and explained that the lamp fitting was to provide me with light so that I could see when it was dark. My mental eyebrows rose a little further and I looked down without responding. His face hardened. When I continued to ignore him, hurt appeared across his face. Then his face broke into a laugh - more for his own reassurance than that anything was actually funny.

As with most Libyans over the age of about forty, he had one eye that was badly diseased. He was black haired, muscularly built and slightly shorter than me. But he was possessed of a peculiar crouch, probably born of a severe squint that exacerbated his lack of stature. He always therefore appeared to look up at me. He also appeared to look up to me. During these, the early days of his first six week tour, he would approach me with a slightly fearful demeanour, as did most of the guards. As time progressed, he increasingly sought reassurance that he and I were equals.

"You - me," he would say. "Same - same."

And he would rub his index fingers together in a gesture which I understood in Mediterranean climes to associate shame with sexual intercourse.

What else was I to reply? "Er... Yes. You - me. Same - same."

Laughing Boy took a pace closer to me and looked up.

"You," he paused. "James Bond."

"No," I said. "Not James Bond."

"Inte," he repeated. "James Bond."

"Oh! Christ!" I thought. "They think I'm a spy."

The rest of the day was spent with a tradesman and his Black and Decker wiring up a lamp fitting, and the guards constantly on standby. The switch was mounted in the office on the floor above my head.

That night, for the first time, I could see what I was eating for my dinner.

It didn't matter, though.

The penalty for espionage is death.

I wake up. I can hear my own, regular breathing. I am warm, comfortable, and floating. The blankets do not weigh on me, and neither can I feel the rotting mattress beneath me. It is dark, so I cannot understand why I am awake.

A second burst of machine gun fire breaks the night. The bullets fall uselessly into the mirror-like surface of the harbour water. I doubt that they hit their target. I smile inwardly to myself at my own joke. Some inert object within the harbour boom had been spotted by one of the soldiers patrolling the harbour, and he had loosed off a burst of automatic fire. They work on the basis that there shouldn't be anything in the water, and that if there is it has to be arrested. Or shot. It also livens things up to shoot at things in the water - in the middle of the midnight shift. I concentrate on keeping my breathing regular. My little joke warms me. Sleep overtakes me.

Over the silent city wafts the call of a Muezzin. The call is so familiar that I can sing it. "Allahu ..." He sings a colourfully melodic line that ends with two punctuating syllables "... Ak-bar!" and then the silence of eternity. I hope I will not wake up fully. To wake up fully is to have my body surge into near panic, all senses screaming at the daily realisation of my predicament. Today I am lucky. My body stays mostly asleep. The second "Allahu Akbar...," is as far as he gets before being joined by another wafting voice from a different suburb of the city. Another voice joins, then another, and another, and another until the whole city is covered in a blanket of electronically propelled, bitter sweet mysticism from the minarets of a myriad or more of mosques. The melodies and harmonies, the clashes and discords of this celestial cacophony, unique each time it is sung, that is a transport of delight. This mystical moment persists and rises like a bubble from a child's pipe and, for the while, diverts you from the realities of your existence. Then the mystical bubble is burst as the switch is thrown in the local mosque. The proximity of our prison to the mosque and its minareted loudspeaker drown the voices of other clerics across the town. And, so far from making a "heavenly sound" intended to make the faithful want to come to prayer, by his tuneless bark, it seems that our Muezzin's task in life is to destroy any vestigial desire to come to prayer that may lie in some wavering Muslim. I smile inwardly to myself. That is a good sign. To smile means that I am not fully awake. My little joke warms me. Our neighbourhood Muezzin abruptly ceases his tuneless call, and snaps off his microphone with an earthy bang. Silence follows but it is silence no longer. The ineffable, city-wide meld of calls persists, but is ineluctably subsumed into a crescendo of city traffic noise. More traffic joins the ever noisier fray and in five minutes nought can be heard of the waking calls that have served their purpose. Nobody can hear the moment at which the last Caller ceases his Holy invocation. The traffic noise rises now to its peak as the earliest risers make their tolerant way about their business. Tolerant - there is no sound of car horns. The plateau of traffic noise persists for five minutes and then dies rapidly to a low mutter. It is no longer the silence of a sleeping city, yet the low mutter is near inaudible. Sleep overtakes me.

I wake up. I try to fight it. But I wake up. Can I just keep my breathing regular? Can I just keep my eyes rolled upwards to the limit of their sockets? Can I just keep my heart beat down? Can I just lose myself in prayer? Can I just fool my body, for a few more blessed minutes, that it is not awake?

No.

I wake up.

I wake up fully. Eyes hunting, dark cell, bright daylight, light and dark and shadow and brilliance, looking for a hint of shadows outside that herald the silent approach of a guard. I'm half naked. They mustn't see me so disadvantaged. Smell the jasmine and the refuse and the sewage and the dust and the harsh smelling sweat that lies in a pool upon my chest. Blood pounding in the ears. Blood pressure up through the roof. How much of this will my heart stand? Tongue tastes salt from dried up sweat upon the lips and promptly mixes it with foul city dust, blown soft across my face by night and now encrusted. Rushes of air in my wind pipe sounding like a bellows. Can you just hear your self breathing? Man, you're frightened. Yes, I know. Wouldn't you be? Striving to keep the breathing regular. Mind cartwheeling in spontaneous thrusts of uncoordinated thoughts. All of them tearing at me with unassuaged anxiety. Head dipping and turning and weaving, a baby's mouth searching for the nipple. Where's

Mummy? Get control, Robin! Get control! The weight of oppression pressing down on burning neck, sweat sodden shirt collar now cooling, burning bladder, hungry, thirsty. Bastards! Right arm dead and unresponsive where I lay my head upon it to augment a useless pillow. Ear still burning from this too hard pillow. Dead arm something tangible to focus mind on. Work it, Robin! Work that arm, tease those fingers. Get blood moving! I get the blood moving. Shoulder working. Ah, good! Responses coming. Keep control, Robin! I get the arm working. Collar freezing, sweat drying, elbow bending, fingers working. Still no tactile sensation. I force my fingers to work by pulling on trousers. Trousers on. Do up shoes. Keep concentrating. The volume of the solid of revolution generated by a curve, rotated about the x axis, whose equation is.... Ah! You remembered. Right now you're OK. You're dressing and have twenty minutes of exercise to concentrate on. God, my bladder hurts. Bastards! They've got to let me go to the toilet today. No, they haven't. Shoes nearly laced now. Fingers mostly responding. Finished. Good. Up! Blanket folding. Fill the time with graceful movement. Fold it carefully, don't be sloppy, don't throw away an opportunity to have something to concentrate on. Keep control. Blanket folded. Place it over left arm. Mattress up and on its edge. Lay it against the wall away from sweat soaked spot upon the floor on which I lie at night. I let the bottom of the mattress dry out during the day. I place the blankets in a neat pile and stand and face the window. Narrowed eyes with lowered eyelids, senses alert, mind still reeling, don't lose it, Robin. Keep concentrating. Arms up and down, one, two, three, four. Breath control. Transcendental moment. Twenty minutes exercise. Bladder bursting. Bastards! I hope they let me go to the toilet today. Look at shadows of the ACUs. It's too early for shadows yet. God! It must be early. Christ! I could have another two hours before the guards bring my breakfast. Then they must let me go to the toilet. Jesus Christ! I'm going to pee myself. Sit. Do mental puzzles. Concentrate. No! Mental puzzles are too diverting. Concentrate on bladder. Don't go to the toilet. That is your over riding objective for this morning, until they come. How long will that be? It doesn't matter how long. You mustn't pee yourself. That is the goal today for as long as it takes. Why not pee through the gap between the door and the wall, as you did yesterday? Some of the water in your bladder will be reabsorbed into your system as the temperature rises and you get thirsty. It will not be so bad then. No, Robin, stop thinking. Concentrate. There is nothing to be done but not go to the toilet. There is nothing else to do, so it doesn't matter. I do not attempt to get up to take a look at the shadows to determine the time. It is of no importance. Concentrate. I concentrate for a while and I will the discomfort away. I concentrate for an hour. The side door opens. Thank God! Then the side gate opens and somebody throws a bag of rubbish out onto the stinking pile on the pavement just outside the gate. No, don't let it wind you up, concentrate. I concentrate for another hour. The side door opens. Nothing. Foot steps in my direction. With a slight scraping movement, somebody places something metallic on the ground just outside my cell door. My breakfast tray! Steel yourself, Robin! I steel myself for two, very trying events. One is the taxing din of the bolt being hammered off the cell door. The other is the Pavlovian reaction to the door being opened - the enhancement of the desire to urinate. The painful demand upon my body caused by the clangourous freeing of the bolt is countered by total bodily relaxation. The other painful desire, to urinate, is made worse by relaxing. The iron bar is laid on the ground. I can tell by the way the iron bar is laid on the ground that my breakfast has been brought to me by the Hajji. Thank God. The door opens. There is a huge influx of light. The light is indirect because it is morning and the cell door is on the shaded side of the building. But the brilliant sunlight is reflected off the flat, brick wall of the vast building across the side street from the prison, and straight in through the open doorway of my cell. I avert my gaze. The newly intruding radiance is in such stark contrast to the almost impenetrable gloom of the cell whenever the door is shut, that the bedazzlement is painful for several minutes. I avert my gaze. Another, much more sinister outcome may result if I do not avert my gaze. I might get a beating from some unknown revolutionary who, upon entering, takes umbrage at a political hostage who dares to raise his eyes above the dirt and look directly into his. I remain motionless. The Pavlovian effect is testing every ounce of my resolve. But I am blessed. The Hajji sees me and mutters "Salaam Aleikum". He laughs his conciliatory laugh, steps aside and ushers me with both hands, out through the door. I remain motionless, testing his bidding. But he laughs that laugh again and reassures me with his chiding mimickery of "To-a-lett, to-a-lett." I rise with determination to give no indication of my plight. I wait for him to accompany me. I do not want to breech the protocol lest the breech delay my arrival at the lavatory. I clutch the thirty inch trouser waistband with my left hand and I mount the steps that lead to the side door. The Hajji tries to precede me to check that no-one is about that I should not see. But I just keep walking. Nature has taken charge now. I try the door of the pink suite. O Mercy, it's free. Zipper undone, I stand astride the beautiful pink lavatory bowl and, Oh, beautiful steaming release. I am breathless with the exertion of the release, and I am panting like a four minute miler. I pray that the Hajji is not the one on duty on the day I make my escape. He is too good a man to want to kill. No. Escape will have to be at about three o'clock in the afternoon on a week day, not Friday, in the third week of Ramadan, when nobody will be about because they will all be asleep, too exhausted to do anything else. I am still urinating. The pain and the pressure start to subside. They no longer occupy my entire thoughts and my mind starts to wander. Keep control, Robin. Don't let your thoughts wander aimlessly, for that way madness lies. Concentrate! Now I can listen for the sound of anyone who might be about. There is a distinct movement, but it is just the Hajji shifting his position on the long settee in the entrance hall where he usually sits while I am washing. Somebody clears his throat. It is a discrete clearing, not a hacking, hocking sound. If I could just find out who is in the room adjoining the Pink Suite. It's just too risky to attempt to look with the outer door to the rooms unlocked. Now I have got control again. The practised mental process of maintaining a constant stream of carefully and deliberately selected thoughts takes over and a mental catalogue of actions to complete, and thoughts to most fully occupy my brain, unfolds. At last I finish urinating. I sit on the seatless toilet to perform the other bodily function. The pink porcelain of the lavatory bowl is slippery enough that I have to be careful to stay on it, but this is a small matter. At least I am not compelled to do my ablutions in the filthy, stinking, fly infested hole-in-the-floor of the toilet downstairs. I laugh inwardly at my present, short term fortune, and thank God that my right leg has so far held out long enough that I haven't fallen into the besmirched hole downstairs. I turn to the wash basin and run water, cold from either tap. I fill my cupped hands and scrub my face as well as I can in the absence of soap or flannel. Eyes open for as much of my wash as I can manage; my attempts to scrutinize my face in the mirror are still fruitless as my eyes continue to dance from side to side. As the layer of nightly grime is finally scrubbed away, I switch to polishing my teeth and gums with a wet index finger, wishing that I could have this small luxury after I have eaten breakfast. Washing finished, I turn off the taps and turn myself around to the lavatory for the second pee of the morning. No point in raking my hair into place - it is matted solid to my head. Another eternity of peeing, and my ablutions are over. Now I stand and listen. Not for so long however that the guard will become suspicious, but for a few seconds which may be enough. Nothing, today. Let's try again tomorrow. My routine complete, and the guard unaroused, I pace evenly and silently to the bathroom door and open it. I take the two paces to the outer door and try the handle. In the time it takes to feel the door locked, the Hajji is on his feet and turning the key. I step back, the door is opened, and I step through at the Hajji's minute bidding. The return to my cell is the reverse of the process. Once inside, the door is shut and the hammering begun. I ignore the banging with great difficulty, seat myself and draw my breakfast things towards me. Today I am lucky. I have a whole loaf of bread instead of the often times half or sometimes none, two pieces of processed cheese instead of the sometimes one, and a fuller than normal half cup of milk. Plainly the Hajji is on duty this morning. I eat my cheese, drink my milk, gently sloshing it around inside my mouth to help wash the cheese off my teeth and gums, and then eat my bread. The delicious, rough flour scourges my mouth and further assists dental hygiene. I figure that the roughage will also help to keep my bowels clear. I do not eat all my bread - just half the loaf. So I save half a loaf each meal whenever I have surplus. Hunger takes hold. The limbs feel heavy, shaky and faintly feverish as my body eats into its reserves. I crave. Breakfast over, what do you do with the rest of twenty four hours?

I woke in darkness to a commotion outside my window. The fall of feet suggested a fight but, although someone was in some distress, there was no sound of blows.
Instead, I heard an antipodean voice utter some expletives, and also what sounded like an Indian voice asking, "Are you alright, Sir?"
Then the antipodean voice said, "Just get these fucking handcuffs off me! And let me see where I'm fucking well going!"
Later that night the same body of people and the antipodean came back.
I figured that it would be useful if I could see out. The gap above the steel plate was sufficiently narrow and sufficiently close to the top of the window, that while it was possible to twist the head to see out, it was also ungainly, uncomfortable and unsustainable. I needed a mirror.

If they had been going to shoot me through the gap above the window, I would have to have been quick to avoid getting hit. And when they came through the door, they had up until now come in mob handed, and I would have had a fight on my hands.

I was awakened by the rib shaking clangour of the bolt being knocked off. As I awoke I noticed that the light in the cell had been switched on. In the time available before the door was opened, I had myself fully dressed and sitting on my mattress. In strode a Libyan. He was well into his thirties. His black moustache matched his close curled top, and the barely adequate lamp bulb picked out deep lines in his face, made deeper by an anger that only the Libyans can fabricate. He walked straight at me. No "Salaam Aleikum" - only revolutionary fervour, and the iron bar brandished above his head.
I rolled out of my seated position and sat Japanese style. As the bar was raised and started to descend towards my head, I raised my arms, crossed them above and in front of my forehead, and relaxed to receive the blow.
Half way through his blow, the iron bar hesitated, raised and threatened to descend again and, once more it stalled in mid air. Each new appearance of a blow was met with immobility from me. His eyes narrowed and his brow creased. The iron bar stayed above his head, no longer shaking.
He bellowed "Inte! Bucra! Britanien!" and tailed off with the gesture by his left hand of an aeroplane taking off.
So, I was to go home to Britain tomorrow.
Instead, I said, "Look, I'm terribly sorry. If you want to tell me something, you'll have to put it into English."
His eyes bulged with anger again as he bellowed back, "Arabi bes!"
So, I was to speak only Arabic.
Instead, I said, "Look, I really am most terribly sorry, but I don't speak any Arabic. If you want to tell me something you really are going to have to put it into English."
Then he repeated, "Arabi bes." And again bellowed, "Arabi bes," followed, as he turned and swaggered out the door, by, "Arabic only. Speak only Arabic."

When the Hajji brought my breakfast, I described the events of the previous night. Neither the Hajji nor the two other guards with him had any news of my imminent departure. The Hajji's faint but perceptible body language indicated an apology. The guards left after I had been to the toilet and been returned to my cell, and I ate my breakfast somewhat more slowly than at any time since my capture.

The cell door was pounded open once again in the middle of another night. In burst a different revolutionary, slightly earlier in his thirties than the previous one.
He looked at me and bellowed, "Inte, Zowjetye! Your wife is dead!"
It was possible that she was dead. She wasn't well. A little improbable, however. But, in any case, I would need confirmation. Until such time as I had confirmation, she must be assumed to be alive and kicking and living in Royston.
And soon she would be coming to get me out.

"No," I replied and just looked at him.

"Yes," he hectored. "Your wife - dead."

"No," I replied. And looked away.

He turned on his heel and stormed out.

When the clanging had ceased, I went to sleep somewhat more peacefully than at any time since my capture.

Later, I was to explain to the others that if the Libyans felt the need to go to these lengths to demonstrate their superiority to us, then we had won already. All we had to do was to recognize that point, and we had won without trying.

"Why doesn't Daddy call any more?" asked Ross.

"Um, I don't know," she lied, in her beautiful, public school vowels.

Already she'd lost weight. What would you expect after three weeks of concealing from your children that your husband, their father, had been kidnapped? And, when all was said and done, he was her husband, and he was their father.

She hated herself for leaving him in Libya. But her sister had died, and she did have her course to sort out. Anyway, the children were probably better off out of it. Tripoli had become too dangerous.

"But he always calls," observed Ross.

"Only on Wednesdays and Saturdays," she said lightly.

Tuesdays or Wednesdays before the Weekend, and Saturdays or Sundays after he'd come back from a dive or something.

She clenched her teeth, pursed her lips and tightened her cheeks.

She swallowed, looked up and away. And wept.

"What's wrong, Mummy?" said Ross, as he walked around to look at the tear streaked face. "Isn't Daddy coming back?"

His face showed care. Why not? His daddy's always did when his mummy cried. Ross stood close, looked up, and reached with his hand to touch her arm.

She sobbed and let out a short moan, the corners of her mouth turned down. Ross put his arms around her thighs, turned his face to the side and held her. Why not? His daddy always did when he held his mummy.

"The soldiers won't let Daddy out of the house."

"Does Katy know?" Ross asked.

"I'll tell her when she comes home from school," she said. "Oh, look! We've got to go and get her soon. Do you want some tea sugar milk?"

Ross skipped, flapped his arms once in a vain attempt to fly, smiled, and let out an unvoiced aspiration of assent.

By mid cup of tea sugar milk, Daddy and the soldiers were far back, but irremediably lodged in his mind.

Then it was time for Katy.

Something closed over Ross. He took the half finished cup away from his mouth and rested. An introvert became more introverted, an acolyte went into purdah.

"Daddy," he pronounced flatly, "will be alright."

A seismic bang, followed by the scattering of a lot of heavy furniture, made me explode from sleep into total wakefulness, heart thumping, breathing difficult. Sudden noises had occurred before but this was different. The anger, the terrified shouts and screams of a young man, had me fully alert and just over the edge into panic. The sound, the screams of a terrified young man, the terrifying bellows of some dread tormentor, a baritone from Hell pursuing, beating, tearing at this boy who was witless in futile attempts to escape, had me choking. I turned from side to side on my mattress, curled up in a ball, stretched out, felt vulnerable, curled up again, got a grip on myself, started to control my breathing and began to think. Get up! Get dressed! And then I started to pray.

There was a lull and a silence.

Then the baritone bellow resumed after only seconds when, I guess, our unfortunate victim had refused to answer a question, quietly put but no less intended for all its quietness, or in mistaking the intent of the question had given the wrong answer. Whatever trajectory this young man had been launched into by our zealous interrogator, it was clear that he had bounced several times and landed extremely badly. Giving no time to recover, the interrogator was upon his victim before he had stopped moving. Brief orders were very rapidly obeyed by other interrogators. They seized the man amid truly alarming protests and more loud movement of furniture.

Then they started beating him.

The ceiling separating me from the office was thick enough to dull all but the loudest sounds. Above the noise of the air conditioner, mounted through the wall of the upstairs office, it was rare to hear the spoken word, foot falls or even the sound of a chair moved noisily. In comparison with the noise of this interrogation it was impossible to tell whether the air conditioner was even on or not. The beating was severe and it made me feel sick in a fashion second only to what I felt upon reading the history of Auschwitz when I was about 18.

The stick was heavy and was landing very hard upon almost unprotected bone and there was no room for his body to give.

They hit him this way quite a number of times, the sound of the beating unaltering.

A question followed.

The answer was wrong.

The bellow followed.

The answer was helpless then terrified, and still wrong.

They hit him this way a number of times again, the sound of the beating unaltered.

Another question followed.

The answer was wrong.

The bellow followed.

The answer was terrified then panicky, and still wrong.

They hit him.

Another question followed, but this time it started with the customary bellow and then, without waiting for an answer, there was another great scuffling sound and the violent moving of furniture now accompanied by a continuous and terrified bleat.

Then they started beating him.

They hit him once a second. The sound was unaltered. They kept hitting him once a second. Half a minute later they were still beating him. I thought that my brain was going to come out of my skull like tooth paste out of a split tube. They hit him once a second. I counted three or four minutes at least. Then the beating stopped and the momentary hiatus left time enough only for one bellowed question and the dragging of him to his feet. A systematic pounding on the floor followed immediately, drowned sporadically by the familiar bellow, and accompanied by a continuous and animal like whine. They were making him run! On the spot. On what? Bare feet? Bare wire? Bare glass? God alone knew. But, though badly beaten, run on the spot he did, and mightily encouraged to run he was by the persistent bellow and occasional slaps on bare skin that followed any indication of slacking. More questions, more wrong answers. The running stopped. They beat him again, once a second for a minute or so. More running, more bellows, more animal whining. Then he was thrown to the floor, and there were sharp movements.

Then they started beating him.

They hit him once a second. The sound was unaltered. They kept hitting him once a second. Now my head was almost splitting, but it promptly turned inside out at what I heard next. His voiced climaxed as he screamed repeatedly, "My legs, my legs, my legs..." He <u>was</u> English. That's it! We've all had it now! And still they beat him. And I prayed. And they beat him. And I prayed. And in the midst of the prayers, for no reason that I could explain, I found myself saying out loud and with an air of total finality, "You don't ever tell me what to do again."

I was taken to the pink bathroom suite on the first floor instead of the filthy hole in the basement. On any occasion that I went to ablutions, I was accompanied by at least three guards. One to supervise and give orders, one to ensure that all appropriate doors were shut so that I could not see into rooms that did not concern me, and one more to usher me as ordered by the supervising guard. On the rare occasions that I was allowed to use the pink suite, the pattern was unchanged, but the guards were more than usually vigilant. This told me that there was something in the room adjoining the pink suite that I was, most emphatically, not to see.

So I was surprised on this Friday morning's visit to ablutions by a number of things. To be taken to the pink suite at all, to have no phalanx of guards checking everything along the way, to be allowed to attend to my ablutions with no guard directly outside the door, to have the guard lock the outer door and go clean away, to be left unattended with something to actually <u>do</u>, and then this very important room next door that I was not allowed to see into!

Even in the briefest of time that I was usually allowed to do my ablutions, I stuck to my routine. This allowed me take advantage of any chance happening that might occur. I would have to be ready. I therefore used to sit on the toilet first thing. Then, having cleaned myself with the usual hose pipe, I would dress. I would then run water into the basin and scrub my face with my bare hands. Then I would clean my teeth.

That would leave the longest possible time to observe anything that might serve to improve my position. On another, rare previous occasion, I took the opportunity to look out of the bathroom window - a very serious offence for which I had previously been castigated. To my delight and amazement, I saw a fellow diver whose company I had kept at a number of social gatherings. He was walking along the road just outside the garden wall and I saw him as he was crossing the road to the next block. I thought of calling him, hoping that if he heard and then saw me he would subsequently tell the British embassy officials where I was. I thought, too, of the danger that I might place him in by alerting him and others, but I was prepared to take that chance. Or was I? The perimeter wall was high and no-one inside the building was likely to be aware of him. But the decision whether or not to call him was made for me. To my horror, try as I might, I couldn't remember his name. As the frustration and impotence at my own poor ability to recall names surged up inside me, the moment passed and he slipped out of earshot behind the building on the next block.

There was a knock on the door. I stood my ground and replied with authority.
"I'm sorry, you'll have to wait. I'm having a crap," is what came out. This declaration had sent whoever had knocked scurrying back into the adjoining room.
When I had finished my ablutions, I guardedly looked out of the window, and saw no movement - it was Friday after all. Turning away from the window, I was conscious that, for several minutes, I had not heard the sound of anyone's presence outside the bathroom door. I resolved to open the bathroom door with great care, and see what I could see. I decided that I was going to have to open the door as naturally as possible in case a guard happened to be sitting on the other side of it. I listened for moment but couldn't hear so much as breathing. I pulled the door slowly, sufficient for me to scan the little entrance hall. It was deserted. I pulled the door fully open, and cleared my throat. That was the signal that whoever had knocked had been waiting for. His eye glued to the minute crack that he had carefully left open between the door and the door frame, he touched the door as a further signal to me and, when he heard my body turn towards the door, he saw me, and opened the door a few inches.
"Was that you who knocked a minute ago?" I whispered.
"Yes. I've been trying to make contact with you for days. I was about to start singing something you'd recognise - Rule Britannia - but I forgot the bloody words. What did you have to talk so loudly for? I thought they'd hear you outside and the guard would come up," he said.

"Oh, I always talk to them like that. It's all part of trying to stay in charge, I suppose. I didn't know it was you," said I.
"Well you do now. Put it there!" said he.

"Where are you from?" said I.
"What, originally? New Zealand," said he.

"What the bloody hell are you doing in here? Are you the B-Cal chappie?"
"Doug Ledingham."

"Yes, but are you the B-Cal Chappie?"
"Yes."

"Thank God! We thought you were dead."
"Oh, charming! Thanks mate! You've cheered me up no end."

"Oh, sorry. Well it's just that you disappeared about a month ago..."
"April 17th."

"The day WPC Fletcher got shot."
"The day they turned the B-Cal flight around and sent it back to Gatwick, you mean?"

"I didn't know that."
"Well you know now."

"Anyway, you disappeared and nobody's seen or heard of you since. We thought you'd been murdered."
"Well as you can clearly see..."

"I really am awfully glad to see you."
"Not half as glad as I am to see you, Brother. What's your name?"

"Robin Plummer. What have they got you for?"
"Hostage."

"Yes. That's what I figured they've got me for."
"Where have they got you? Are you in that tin box outside?"

"Well, it's not a tin box."
"Well, outside, anyway. I keep hearing this incredible noise. At first I thought they were giving someone a beating. Then I realised that they're simply knocking the bolt off someone's cell door. Is that you?"

"Yes."
"What's it like in there?"

"Rotting mattress, concrete floor."
"That's terrible. I mean, are you eating? Do they let you out?"

"Oh, I'm eating OK. No real appetite."
"You're telling me. I've lost pounds."

"Yeah, so have I. I have to walk around holding my trousers up I've lost so much weight. Did you hear that beating the other night?"
"Hear it? It was right outside my fucking door. They were throwing that poor bastard straight down on the marble slabs. They even had the poor bastard running on the spot for ten minutes after they'd been beating him!"

"Yes, I know. They brought him down to my cell afterwards. They'd beaten him so badly they broke one of his legs."
"Jesus Christ! The bastards."

"It was two days before they took him to hospital. He came back with two great big plaster boots on. What did they think they were doing?"
"Trying to tell us what we're in for. Trying to put the fear of Christ up us."

"Well, they succeeded in doing that."
"You'd better believe it, Brother!"

"Did it scare you?"
"I was absolutely shitting myself! As long as I live I shall never forget the sound of that animal doing the interrogation! I don't want to meet the bastard that runs this place."

"What's it like in here? Bloody Hell! You've got a table, and a carpet. Sheets! Who's that?"
"He's Tunisian. He's a devout Muslim, would you believe? And the bastards are holding him too."

"How come they put him in here with you?"
"They figured that because he doesn't speak any English and I don't speak any Arabic that it wouldn't matter."

"But, of course, it does."
"Well, yes! Just to be in the same room with another human being. Someone to smile at occasionally."

"You'd better believe it!"
"Is...isn't there anyone in with you?"

"I'm in solitary confinement."
"Bloody Hell! What's it like?"

"Every bit as bad as it's cracked up to be. Look I'll have to go now. I've been here long enough."

"What do you do all day?"

"Nothing."

"They'll come now you've tapped on the door. Nothing? You must go spare!"

"I do mental exercises and play my saxophone."

"I haven't heard it."

"No, in my head."

"What do you mean? Look he's coming now."

"It's going to be a bloody sight easier knowing that you're up here."

" 'Ere, do you know what day it is?"

"Yes."

"It's Friday the 8th of June."

"I know. I write a calendar in the dirt. Does he come whenever you knock?"

"Oh, yes."

"Do you knock often?"

"Whenever I need to."

"Bloody Hell! There are times when they won't even let me out for the toilet."

"I've got a toilet of my own here."

"Bloody Hell! You don't want to swap do you?"

"No thanks, Sport."

"Look, if you can get out, then do so. I'll make my own way out."

"That's good of you, Sport."

"...Ledingham?"

"Yes, Doug Ledingham. Robert Plummer, right?"

"Robin Plummer. Take it easy."

"You too, Sport. You're going to need it. Put it there, Sport."

"Don't worry," said I. "I'll get the bastards."

We shook hands, Doug eased his door shut and I turned to face the outer door. By the time the Sweet Smelling Boy had unlocked and opened the door, I was standing alone, silent and with studied indifference.

The following day, Saturday, the 9th of June, the usual uncertainty about whether or not a working day would bring activity was forgotten as footsteps heralded new visitors.

Quiet authority could be felt as the bolt was beaten loose. Guards entered accompanied by a man of bearing, refinement, and a buff coloured uniform.

The discourse was brief and faintly friendly. The uniformed man asked me in articulate English to confess to everything that I had done wrong for which I had been arrested. I said that I did not know why I had been arrested.

"Even so," he said without threat, "you must confess to what you have done."

Upon my momentary silence, he took from a guard and calmly passed to me a blank sheet of paper and a pen, and told me that I must write down anything that I remembered for which I had been arrested, and that I had no choice in the matter.

He stood there in silence, desiring not to be oppressive in spite of the very clear threat he had just made, and then proceeded to pass the time of day with me, asking if there was anything that I wanted. The guards were uncomfortable, and I was mystified.

I kept the mood light. "Inte," I said, feeling my pockets for a packet I knew I didn't have. Then, I imitated the act of him smoking, and offered, "Cigarette?"

"La," he declined, discreetly touching his abdomen. "Ramadan."

When he was satisfied that I was not going to confess anything to him there and then, and that I had all that I wanted, he turned and left, the entourage in discreet tow.

I put a blanket over my shoulders and walked back and forth along the diagonal of the cell, looking at the blank sheet of paper, and asking myself where all this was going. It was a relief to have activity but not by way of an invitation to the state of rigour mortis. I wrote my name on the piece of paper and left it otherwise blank.

An hour later, the officer was back. The calm, measured core of steel of a professional army officer, even a Libyan army officer, stood head and shoulders above the insidious mendacity of the revolutionaries. I had no choice. I made a scant reference in illegible handwriting to making a U-turn in the entrance of the university, and left it at that.

But I now knew that Ramadan had started. If my escape plan was to come together, I needed to be almost anywhere but bolted in a basement storeroom.

Sunday, the 10th of June, started earlier than usual. Activity in the office above my head was business like, with strange footsteps. The air was more resolute, authoritative and forbidding than usual.

Just in time, I finished dressing. A now predictable succession of noises told me that they were coming. I was more scared than usual. I stood away from my usual seated position and waited.

The door was opened as usual and the "officer" from the previous day came in accompanied by the usual three or four guards but not by the Kalashnikov.

I was accompanied rather than led upstairs. The beating sticks were not in their usual place, which alarmed me, and my alarm was heightened as I saw an upright chair situated in the usually empty middle of the entrance hall, and a low table beside it covered in stainless steel tools. At first glance I took them to be implements of torture. My skin crawled at what they were about to do to me.

In the next breath it was clear that they were not implements of torture but barbers' impedimenta. And the barber, who I had initially taken to be part of the interrogation team turned to address me with a white cloth and a warm smile that extended all the way to his eyes. The guards melted into the background. An overweight man in a blue shirt and glasses stood by.

The first attempt at conversation was led by the man, now close enough for me to see the immaculate, regimental creases in his freshly ironed, blue, uniform shirt. He sounded as though he didn't know where to start a conversation, and my responses were indifferent to the point of being dismissive. The conversation fizzled out under the combined weights of my indifference and the sheer impossibility of sensible communication while I took a shave and a haircut. The barber kindly asked in dumb show how closely I would like to be shaven. Careful to avoid his use of a straight razor, I stated that he should trim my beard into the fashion of an Elizabethan sea captain. The uncomprehending barber promptly trimmed my beard into the fashion of an Elizabethan sea captain. The man in blue stood by with commendable patience until I had been professionally and excellently coiffed. It felt good to have four weeks of coiled and plastered matting trimmed away to allow my scalp to breath. And in spite of myself, the rare treat of inadvertent physical contact by the barber after a month of forced abstinence was almost ecstatic.

The barber removed the cloth and shook it, and smiled to me a graceful obligato, as I was led into the office for who knew what.

Guards stood around at a respectable distance anywhere that there was a blank area of wall. The blue shirt seated himself behind the desk, on one corner of which sat a pile of several polythene bags containing new, western style clothes. The blue shirt's left hand indicated that I should look at them. Somebody closed the door. Others closed the blinds. "God, this is it," I thought. But his demeanour was not right for a man who was about to supervise a beating. And I was invited to try on the clothes. There was nothing there of any account, but I stalled for time to try to figure out what was coming. When I had selected some poorly made Chinese T shirts and ill fitting trousers, which I had no expectation of ever wearing, I was invited to sit, and the guards invited to leave. The door closed behind them, and we were alone.

He opened up without preamble. "You may be in prison and you may or may not have done something wrong," he said. "But whatever a man has done, whether he is guilty of some crime or not, all men are entitled to human rights."

I was mentally slack jawed with disbelief. But he was absolutely serious. He proceeded. "What are your demands?" Demands? So now it is I who am the terrorist! What? What are my demands in order for you to release me? I felt that the joke might be wasted on him so I let it pass. Then I thought about the perversion of logic that they should lock me up and then ask what my demands are. Then I thought under the present climate that maybe they think I am a terrorist (they certainly think I'm a spy) and they want to know what are the demands of my terrorist organization. I thought of asking for fifty million and a helicopter to Cuba. But this man didn't have a sense of humour. I could see that this interview was going to go badly. How badly depended very much on me. Better save the wit for when I got home. I knew I was going to get home but, the way this interview was shaping up, it was going to take a great deal longer than I first anticipated. A void opened in my heart.

"What do you mean by demands?" I countered.

"Your demands! Your demands!" he barked.

"I have been arrested and locked up for no reason that I know, and allowed no contact with anyone. What could I possibly demand?" I said perfectly reasonably and with a core of steel.

"You are entitled to human rights. You must have demands," he explained.

The penny dropped, but he was quick to add, "What do you need, want. Do you have any problems?"

Still incredulous, I probed. "Well, my skin is starting to suffer through being dirty. I need a bath. But there never seems to be time for one."

"There will be time," he said, looking away.

"There never seems to be time," I threw away.

"There will be time," he insisted, looking at me.

The lecture on human rights was over.

He called out for the Hajji, who presented himself before the call had ceased, and issued an authoritative stream of Arabic.

The Hajji bubbled his soporific Arabic at me, beckoned and, with a nod from the man in blue, we left the room. There was no threat.

On the first floor of the mansion, there was a fully equipped, if decaying, bathroom. A hot bath was drawn from a wall mounted heater just above the tub. There was no plug and, as the hot water ran down the plug hole, Laughing Boy appeared and demonstrated to me how to use the fabric of a lattice work, plastic, shopping bag, as a scourer to wash myself. I blocked the plug hole with my heel. I luxuriated, soaked, scrubbed, overstayed my welcome and got shouted at by the Hajji. Dried and dressed, I was returned to the office.

After a few seconds of silence during which he just looked at me, I raised my head and said, "I understand that the Mudir is the only one who can get me out of here."

He said, "The only way I can get out of here is if your wife is ill or pregnant."

Oh! She was ill alright, but not in any way that would be meaningful to this barbarian.

"My wife is ill."

"What kind of illness?"

How could I tell him? It would be wasted on him.

Why should I tell him? I hadn't told anyone else. That was the way Pat wanted it. Therefore there was no way he could check my story, short of talking to Pat herself.

"Is it physical or mental?" he rapped.

How do you tell an animal like this, something of such pendulous gravity?

"Is it physiological or neurological?" now he surprised me.

I was wasting my time. I ran an index finger around the side of my head, the universal sign of 'loco', as I spluttered to stifle the truth. It was more important to me to keep Pat's secret, than to squander it on such a man as this.

And if I did tell the Mudir what was wrong with her, and he didn't let me go, then I had shot my bolt – and betrayed Pat into the bargain.

I squeezed out half of the word, 'neurological', and my shoulders slumped. I was here for the long haul.

In unchanged tones, he repeated, "The only way I can get you out is if your wife is ill or if she is pregnant."

I was pretty sure she wasn't pregnant. We'd had a fright a couple of months back, but it was a false alarm. I wondered if she'd get pregnant, and by whom. I wondered how I would get a message to her to do it. I wondered if she would agree.

The interview was over.

The interrogation began.

"Where is your written confession?" he began.

I gave the Gallic Shrug and said, "Maffeish." He accepted that it had probably got lost.

"Why have you been arrested?" he continued.

People who don't want to give information, and who are skilled at not giving it, are damnably difficult to interview. Mostly, they block by feigning ignorance. Oh, the interrogator can generally trip them up by his own knowledge of what he is looking for. But first the interrogator has to know what he is looking for. My first task therefore was to find out how much the Mudir knew.

"I don't know," I replied.

"You must know," he shouted. "You were arrested."

Two thoughts crossed my mind. First, this wasn't England. They don't tell you why you've been brought in.

The second thought was that I had heard that shout before. Calm, controlled, no rancour, and capable of great volume.

"I may have been arrested," I continued. "But that doesn't mean I know why."

"You must know why," bawled the Mudir.

He doesn't know. Let's see how far I can push him.

"Everything said to me was spoken in Arabic. I do not understand Arabic."

"There are translators!"

I took him to mean 'there were translators'. He need only check the transcripts of the first interrogations and I would be caught in the lie. I had to stick to something resembling the truth.

"But they spoke French," which was true. "My French is unreliable," which was not.

He sat back.

He didn't know anything.

"What was in your bag?"

Oh! Maybe he did.

"I can't remember. It is a month since I was arrested," I said.

"Oh, come!" he bellowed. "You must know what is in your handbag."

Women don't, I thought.

"I will see if I can remember what was in my handbag when I was arrested. Let me think."

I leaned back, adopted a pensive look, regarded the ceiling, and took the opportunity to weigh up the interrogation so far.

He was calm and relaxed.

He never took his screwed up eyes off me.

He thought he had softened me up with the bath, the shave and the haircut, the new clothes and the courtesy of shutting the blinds while I changed into them - and the lecture on human rights.

He had been expecting me to talk. I'd been in solitary confinement for a month, for Christ's sake. Anybody talks after a month in solitary. Particularly since they had been systematically trying to soften me up - the iron bar, going home tomorrow, your wife is dead - culminating in the beating the other evening. That would soften up any normal person.

The look in his eye was beginning to say, "This man is either very, very good, or he is telling the truth."

Then his body language started to say, "This man must be telling the truth. Nobody stays silent after what he has been through."

"When I was arrested, I had my pink card, my glasses..."

"You wear glasses?" he interrupted.

I paused, "Sun glasses."

I took the opportunity of the interruption to stop talking and to force him to make me restart.

"What else?" he snapped.

"Oh, I don't know. Money, I expect - a few bits and pieces. I really can't remember."

Now I was going to have to be careful.

The first requirement of a good liar is a phenomenal memory. You have to be able to remember what lies you have told. You then have to be able to reproduce those lies. If you indicate that your memory is unreliable, and then show an uncharacteristic grasp of detail, then you expose yourself.

And so the interrogation dragged on.

Each time he interrupted me, I went silent, forcing him to make me start talking again, and then I would dissemble into a non-answer. After the cycle had been repeated a few times, he got the message, and stopped interrupting me.

I now had control of the interrogation. While I talked, he stayed silent. While I talked, I told him what I wanted him to hear. Whenever he asked a question, I gave an answer that was either uncheckable, or checkable only in transcripts of previous interrogations which I figured he would have access to if they were organized - and at this point, I had to assume that they were organized.

But there would come a time, as there does in all interrogations, when the target runs out of lies and diversions. The only thing that then remains to come out is the truth. The skilled interrogator simply has to wait for that time. The real skill of the interrogator lies in knowing how long to wait, and what the signs are that that point has been reached.

Sooner or later, therefore, I must tell what actually happened. To remain in control of the interrogation, however, I had to start telling what happened sooner rather than later, so that I did not waste precious ammunition that I might need in case I really needed to start lying later on.

I did feel the need, however, to stall long enough to make the switch look convincing, and also to see if I could find out exactly what they were after.

I fluffed and bumbled my way around a few more aimless questions. Until I started to see signs of boredom - which told me that he knew there was nothing here to get excited about.

Then I made the switch.

"Look," I said.

He sat up. He knew the truth was coming now.

And it was.

My version of the truth.

So I started with an innocent account of my wrong turning into the university, claiming that I was lost and seeking only to do a U-turn and go back.

Then I told him that I was held and questioned at a number of locations over several hours for no reason that I knew.

Then I gave him the bit about the maps that I'd been carrying in my handbag. Everybody carried maps. None of us spoke any Arabic, nor could we read the road signs or street names.

By the time my version of events was exhausted, the Mudir had shown neither signs of surprise, nor any real interest. But he wasn't finished.

"What else have you done?" he said with only some insistence.

I demurred.

"Is there anything else?" he said with more insistence.

I thought about the rackets among the expatriate community, and wanted to explore how much he knew so that I would know what to cover for.

All I had to do was to make him interrupt me.

"Well, I don't know..."

"You must know," he barked.

"Well...," I started to say.

He grew impatient - and interrupted me.

"What happens to you depends on what you say now. If you have done nothing wrong before God, then you have nothing to fear."

It took his cue. I straightened myself in my chair and said, "I have nothing to fear."

I was taken back to my cell. I walked my usual walk, agonizing over how I'd handled the interrogation. In fact I kicked myself for days afterwards over the way I'd handled it. Should I have told him anything? I know I was right not to have told him everything. Should I have toughed it out? I certainly didn't want a beating. I wasn't going home any time soon, and I had to give them something other wise they would know I was lying.

As I was walking around my cell, the sound and feel of the mansion was different. After a few hours the Hajji came, alone, and brought me most of the clothes that I had selected. I changed into the fresh, ill fitting clothes. They smelled sweet after the discarded shirt and trousers, unwashed, in the filthy conditions for four weeks.

An hour later, the Hajji was back. This time he took me to a new room. The new room was slightly larger than my old one, on the opposite wing of the mansion, and on the ground floor. But it was a formal reception room with lights, a large casement window that opened inwards, a ghibli, bars on the outside, and a wall mounted air conditioning unit beneath. I had day light and could look out! There was a carpet, a chair, a tall bureau in an alcove beside the door and, luxury, a bed with a mattress and pillow, which the previous incumbent had situated beneath the air conditioner outfall.

My mind was reeling at the possibilities of where this move was taking me. The insecurity still screamed at me from within, and I still had to concentrate to stay sane. But I now had unknown additional possibilities coupled with the loss of the few possessions, including my own clothes, that I had accumulated in my previous cell.

After a routine dinner, the Hajji came and got me again, and returned me to my old cell. I was dispirited as it was now getting dark and I concluded that the move to the new room was spurious. I bit hard and started to settle in for another night in the basement.

A few minutes later, the Hajji was back and again took me to the new room. Ten minutes later he returned and took me back to the basement cell. Now, I was getting fed up and remonstrated with him. He cooed his usual burble of incomprehensible Arabic, only this time, he motioned to my blankets, clothes and water jug. I picked them up quickly, not wishing any delay for fear of being shut in again. I left the knife blade, I snatched at the sock hanging drying – and tore a big hole in it as it caught on the nail. Cursing silently, I swept up my stinking shirt and trousers, swept out of the cell, and followed the Hajji's beckoning arm back to the new room. As I rose from the stairwell I encountered the unwelcome sight of the Mudir. He studied me as I measured my way across the marble floor. As I drew abreast of him, he indicated the new room with a wave of his right arm. "Better," he said. I nodded and kept walking. "You want?" he added, and looked at me. I paused, turned and said with a voice pleading deference but not submissiveness, and eyes that did not meet his, "A toothbrush. I wonder if I could have a toothbrush – please." And, with a faint bow, turned back and continued to my new room. "Toothbrush," I heard behind me. And at the third time of being locked in the room, I heard the keys being left in the lock on the outside of the door.

The next day was devoid of activity. But, the tuneless bark of the muezzin in the mosque next door had been replaced. I expected to shudder, ready for the familiar but deadly wail. Instead, to my astonishment, a melody broke forth that attracted my ear. Perhaps the previous muezzin had indeed died of cancer, and his place had been taken by this altogether different young songster.

When I was taken to ablutions, it was to a bathroom different from the pink one. This one was on the left hand side of a narrow corridor that ran past a kitchen to the back of the building. The First Day Guard was not in evidence. Instead, the Sweet Smelling Boy was in charge. I counted it a loss that I could not use the pink bathroom, but none of it mattered because I now had the runs, presumably from some maggot ridden apricots of earlier in the week.

The changes in the regime also brought a collection of men in the early twenties who, presumably, wanted to be revolutionaries. As I was being moved about by the Sweet Smelling Boy, in one of the few, diurnal peregrinations, a handful of them actually greeted me in the main entrance hall with warmth and enthusiasm. I thought they were going to ask for my autograph. What is the Arabic for "Bond - James Bond"?

"If there is anything you need," enthused one of them, "all you have to do is knock."
An hour later I knocked. They unlocked and opened the door in seconds. Could I go to the toilet, please? Yes, I could. And upon my return, I was told that I could go whenever I wanted to. Just knock. Under the circumstances, that was a relief. Every time I knocked at hourly or two hourly intervals for the remainder of the day, the enthusiastic amateurs let me go to the lavatory, until my bowels and my energy were both completely drained.

At the request of Ian Ridout, a meeting was held, on the 13th of June, 1984, in the office of the Head of Consular Department, at the Foreign and Commonwealth Office, the FCO, in London. Present at that meeting were the Head of Consular Department; one of his staff, Fleur Fraser, who took minutes; a representative of the Near East and North Africa Department, NENAD; and Ian Ridout and Mike Peace of BT. The meeting proceeded with clinical and tolerant conciseness.

The Consular Department of the FCO in London was responsible for providing assistance to British subjects in distress abroad. NENAD was part of the department of the FCO that was responsible for political matters in international affairs - in this case the Near East and North Africa Department.

Pat had telephoned Fleur at the Consular Department late on the 12th of June and asked whether the FCO thought it would be worthwhile if she travelled to Tripoli with Christopher, and tried to persuade the Libyans to let her see me. Pat thought that this approach might appeal to the Libyans. Fleur had told Pat that such a visit would probably achieve little or no results, judging by the lack of success encountered by Doug Ledingham's wife in her recent visit. In any case there was little point in travelling to Tripoli for such a purpose until after Ramadan was over. Ian Ridout and Mike Peace agreed that the visit would be non-productive at the present time. They had no idea where I was being held. They confirmed that, through a fixer, they had at one time located the British detainees who were being held together in a flat but that the group had been moved almost immediately afterwards.

A discussion took place of the possible ways to secure access to the prisoners. The Head of Consular Department pointed out the difficulties faced by the two British consular officers in Tripoli and although consular access had been agreed by the Libyans on the 12th of May, no visit had yet taken place. The Consular Head mentioned that on the 27th of May, the FCO had been informed by the Second Consul in Tripoli, George Anderson, that owing to the crowded conditions in Libyan prisons, no foreign embassies were being allowed to make prison visits for the time being. It was agreed that British Telecom in Tripoli would also pursue the matter through their own contacts in the Libyan Ministry of Communications. Consideration was given to backing up any such approach on access to me by producing a letter from my British doctor certifying that I needed special shoes for a leg condition resulting from two car accidents. This certificate was held in Tripoli and Ian Ridout would use it when he returned there on the 20th of June.

Ian Ridout asked what approach had been made by the FCO to the Home Office to try to bring forward the date of the trial of the Libyan bombers, detained in the UK. The Head of Consular Department said that he had in fact asked the Home Office on several occasions when the trials of the Libyan bombers were likely to take place. The present understanding was that the hearing was likely to be towards the end of September, 1984..

Ian Ridout also asked whether the FCO regarded the British detainees as Tripoli as political detainees. The Consular Head explained that the FCO's understanding of a political detainee was that the detainee had been engaged in political activity. The British prisoners might have been arrested for political reasons but they were not political prisoners as such.

The NENAD representative asked about the morale of the British expatriates working in Libya. Mr Ridout said that although perhaps those working in Tripoli itself might find life difficult, those working outside the capital found life much as usual. It was normal for expatriates to work four weeks and then have three weeks' leave.

It emerged at the meeting that there was a feature among the British detainees in that most of them had somehow come to the attention of the Libyan authorities before they were detained without charge in the middle of May. I, myself, it appeared, had done no more than drive somewhat incautiously and had made a forbidden U-turn. I had been questioned about it, the meeting heard, and then released but later re-arrested. Messrs Ridout and Peace said that I was the sort of person who tended to drive erratically and had not been surprised that I had been stopped. Ian Ridout said that I had been on my way to an underwater club meeting when the U-turn was made. Ian Ridout believed that there was a collection of hand drawn maps of the Libyan coast line in my handbag at the time and they could have given the Libyans cause for suspicion.

Messrs Ridout and Peace expressed their thanks to the Head of Consular Department for arranging the meeting. It was agreed that all those present would keep in touch so that information could be exchanged.

It was Friday, the 15th of June. The Sweet Smelling Boy was in charge. Under different circumstances I would have allowed myself to like him. But I wasn't here to like people. I was here to stay sane and to win the psychological war with the guards.

After lunch, he came and took my dishes away. He also escorted me to the toilet.

On the way back from the toilet, White Shirt was standing in the entrance hall. He had just changed into a clean, white shirt, ready to go to Friday prayers. He just watched as I walked back to my room, but followed at a safe distance and quietly spoke a few words to the Sweet Smelling Boy who had yet to shut my door. White Shirt looked up at me, and I took the opportunity to step into the doorway of my own room.

"Why are you here?" he asked.

"I don't know," I started. "No-one has ever told me."

"What do you want?" he said.

"I want to see the British Consul," I said.

"Yes," he said.

"I want to see the British Consul now," I said.

"All in good time," he replied.

"Your room," he said. "How long have you been here?"

I told him. And, recognising the education in the man, I also told him that I would like to get out of my room and do some exercise.

"You wait. One hour," he said, and started to turn away. "Exercise in the garden." But I'd heard it all before.

"No," I replied, and started to turn away as well.

"Yes," he said, turning back briefly and, showing me his watch, he added, "After one hour. Prayers. Then exercise." And he walked off.

As he did so, the Sweet Smelling Boy looked at me, cupped his hands to his ears to indicate the act of praying, and nodded vaguely in the direction of the White Shirt before stepping forward to shut and lock my door.

To my astonishment White Shirt was back in one hour - to the minute.

He himself unlocked my door, showed me his watch, and walked with me across the entrance hall. We walked down the stairs and out into the sunlight.

We turned left towards the back of the building and paused as we reached the corner. White Shirt stepped into the scant, June shadow of the perimeter wall.

I was at a loss to know quite what to do with my exercise period. So I looked up at the post noon sun, and thought that with less than a week to go to midsummer's day, and being only a few hundred miles north of the Tropic of Cancer, this was probably as high a sun as I would ever see. Then I remembered getting out of my car a year previously, just to experience midsummer sun. I had marvelled at just how nearly non existent my shadow had been.

I looked down at my feet to another almost non-existent shadow. After weeks in the darkness of solitary confinement, the sun felt good.

And I said so. "Samas quaise," said I, looking up at White Shirt.

"Samas mush quaise for Libyan," he replied truthfully. I remembered the afternoon walk that I had taken a year previously on the beach with a friend, and even at five in the afternoon I had eventually burnt, after a long day in the sun. The tropical sun is bad for you if you're out in it all the time.

I flicked my chin at him, in request for what I should do. He replied by both looking at the garden and indicating its direction with a wave of the back of his hand.

I turned around, stepped off a kerb, and walked across the ten yards or so of the concrete hard standing until I reached what had once been flower beds. I examined the undergrowth. Why do they call it "undergrowth" when it is always overgrown?

Then I saw a sole and solitary flower. It was extraordinary for its splash of colour in the other wise bland, dusty green of a desert edge garden.

I put my hand around its stem, turned to see White Shirt dispassionately observing me, and flicked my head up, with a return glance at the flower. White Shirt nodded. I picked the flower, cradled it and later put it on the bureau in my room, where its incandescent, red petals lent a pin point of glorious Technicolor to four, further weeks of solitary confinement, until it eventually withered. Michael Berdinner later told me that that particular shrub only ever sprouted one flower at a time. Now that I had picked it, it would produce another sole and solitary flower.

As I walked with my treasured flower back to where White Shirt stood in the shadow, I saw him observing my built up shoe. He asked me. I showed him the damage. When he enquired, I plummeted my right fist into the palm of my moving left hand to imitate a car hitting a motorcycle - a Mercedes doing thirty miles an hour hitting me full in the side while I was riding my Laverda in London, six years previously. I'd spent five months in hospital.

Exercise over, I was escorted back to my room. I shook hands with White Shirt, who assured me that there would be further periods of exercise.

I never saw White Shirt again.

Quiet but clear and crisp orders were issued to us to go outside and into a waiting van. I was already dressed and my heart was pounding at the prospect of release. In spite of my practiced, measured way of moving, I had difficulty containing the excitement. I changed back into my own clothes and went for the door. And, lastly, on instinct, I grabbed one of the hideous, striped, Chinese T-shirts, clenched it tightly in my fist, and walked out the front door to the van.

The back door of the van was opened by one of the Tweedles. As my eyes were adjusting to the gloom, I recognized Michael Berdinner. Another fellow was sitting there, elbows on knees, hands clasped, head down near his hands.

"Hello, Michael," I said, firmly.

"Hello," said he, with a tone and an eye, both upturned and cautious.

I couldn't gain the height of the step into the van. After the second vain attempt, I quietly asked the two in the van if someone could help. Michael looked to weigh up the situation and said and did nothing. He was beaten to the draw by the other fellow, who silently reached out a hand for me to grip and to pull myself in. Seated, I asked the other fellow who he was. He announced that he was Doug Ledingham. I apologised for not recognizing him. He turned and said that he would be surprised if I had recognized him because he had never seen me before.

"On the contrary," said I. "I'm Robin Plummer."

Doug's head shot up, electrified.

"Bloody Hell! I didn't recognize you," he punched out.

"I daresay I've lost even more weight. I've had all this lot shorn a bit, too - the other day."

I turned and shook hands with Michael next to whom I was seated, and asked him how he was. He replied, cautiously, that he was OK.

Expecting nothing definite from Michael and not being disappointed, I returned to Doug.

To my relief, he opened. "So you got a hair cut too, Sport?"

We quickly summarized recent events, which really meant the writing of our "confessions", and our respective haircuts, baths and interrogations. Michael concurred that this had been how his time had been spent too.

"Do you two know each other?" ventured Michael curiously.

I started to bumble that we had known each other only as long as I had known Michael. But Doug had jumped in much more precisely with, "Not before this started we didn't," and then asked Michael why he wanted to know. Michael said that he just thought we got on very well together, that was all. Doug and I both looked quizzical, and let it pass.

I went back to Doug and asked where he thought we were going.

"Another prison, I expect," he replied.

"You haven't brought anything," I stated.

"What do you mean?" he shot.

"You haven't brought your stuff."

"Didn't have time. Didn't have any warning." And, looking up with a faint smile, he added, "You brought a T-shirt, then?" and gave a brief snort.

Having no idea how long we were going to be together, or how long we would get away with talking to each other, Doug and I tried clinically and economically to extract from each other what information we could. The almost fruitless conversation continued until we heard the approach of footsteps. We ceased talking, sat up straight, lowered our heads slightly, and glazed our eyes.

The driver's side door opened and a gun barrel was poked in. I had visions of death camp Jews being carted off by the bus load to be murdered on the way to burial in the forest. I thought we were dead. I tensed to dive for the floor, Doug likewise. I can't speak for Michael. But the moment passed as Tweedle Dee (the Intelligent One) stepped in front of the muzzle and into the driver's seat. All business like, he did his driver's checks, while the other door opened and the jump seat became occupied.

The unseen holder of the gun told us in unequivocal English that there was to be no talking while we were in the van.

The voice then asked if we had understood.

Well, we had just been told at the point of a gun not to say anything, so we didn't.

The voice became filled with raged and bellowed the question again.

We remained silent.

The bellow started again, but somebody outside the van spoke quietly, and everything fell to silence.

The driver started the van and we were off.

I was able to navigate the first part of the journey into the suburbs, but soon became lost. Twenty odd minutes later, we stopped outside a white wall at least ten feet high.

Doug, Michael and I were ushered out of the van and into a building behind the wall. After a few paces into the entrance hall, a single, open door to the left gave onto a room, furnished and dominated by a large table set near the window. Both the window and the table occupied almost the length of the room. Six men were already seated, two Libyans at the head of the broad table, and two more just around the corner from them on the window side, one with the phenomenal carrot coloured hair. All were suited, open necked, impassive and silent, with hands clasped in front of them. The man with carrot coloured hair had papers. Two more men sat at some distance down the table, aloof from the others, also suited but wearing fixed diplomatic smiles and smiling eyes. I heard the words, "Hello, Robin," which I refused to acknowledge. Only when the incongruously un-Libyan-like, soft, refined, Edinburgh accent sunk in, did I look up. The remains of carrot coloured hair, incongruously Libyan-like, still had me confused as the sharp, lean, moustachioed and bespectacled physiognomy of George Anderson raised itself to greet me. My heart surged.

I reached across the table, still unsure. But when he stood up and, with his right elbow clamped to the side of his ribcage, and his right hand swinging in a lengthy arc from outside to clap into the hand that I now offered, we shook hands, all doubt disappeared. His impish eyes looking out from under lowered brows eased more of my tension.

"Hello, George," I said. "Nice to see you again." I was glad of the human contact, but alarmed at the rigidity of his hand shake. George was shaking like a leaf. Not surprising. He had done almost four years in Tripoli, a year longer than a standard, FCO stint, because they couldn't find anyone brave enough or crazy enough to replace him.

I introduced George to Michael and Doug. Michael said, simply, "Hello."

Doug shook hands and politely snapped out his name.

George then introduced the two suited men from lower down the table, as Italian diplomats from the British Interests Section at the Italian Embassy in Tripoli. My look to George conveyed the question, "What the Hell are they doing here?" He explained that, officially, they were the diplomatic presence at the meeting, since we no longer had diplomatic relations with Libya.

I sat down on the opposite side of the table to George to avoid being trapped against the window, and a little down the table from everybody so that I could see them all at once, and not have anyone behind me, except the Italians, who were at least on our side – or supposed to be – and some of the guards who were dotted around the walls.

George referred to the three Libyans at the table as representing the Libyan Foreign Service.

George started by getting confirmation of our names and stating that he was expecting two others.

"Two others," I said, trying to stifle a gasp. "How many of us are there?"

"There's always a number of people in prison," he said, looking down. "I've currently got fourteen I'm trying to get out."

"Well, who's holding us?" I asked.

"And why?" chimed in Doug.

"You are being held by a revolutionary committee. They have no legal powers. Unfortunately, they have a lot of political power."

"That sounds dangerous," I said. "You're quite sure we're not being held by the Libyan government?"

"Quite sure. By a revolutionary committee," replied George, looking at me. "These men represent the Libyan administration." He turned his head in the direction of the three remaining men at the table.

"Can they do that?" enquired Doug.

"They've done it," said George, with characteristic Scottish economy. Then he added, more usefully, "Quite in defiance of international law."

At last. We were not being held by the formal authorities, but by a bunch of illegal revolutionaries. That meant that we would be out soon. My relief was palpable

A few seconds of silence followed as the import of George's revelation sunk in.

Then George proceeded to ask each of us how we were.

"Well, I'm alright," shrugged Doug

I just shook my head from side to side with my mouth open at the vacuity of the question. George gave me a sympathetic look, which told me that we both knew he had to ask the question. I nodded my assent with pursed lips. But I took my opportunity.

"I'm in solitary confinement," I said factually.

"What have you done?" said George.

"I don't know," I said. "Something about some maps."

"What did you do to get into solitary?" said George.

"I've been in solitary since day one. They call me James Bond," I marked out.

"Well, we'll see what we can do about that," said George.

Meanwhile, Michael said nothing.

George solicited messages for our wives and, in Michael's case, his sister.

"When will you be giving them these messages," asked Doug, smelling a rat.

"As soon as I get back to the embassy," replied George.

"Why can't we give them?" hit back Doug.

"I'll make sure they go out tonight," asserted George, lightly.

"So, we're not going home today," I concluded as much a question as a statement. My shoulders dropped as the realisation sank in.

"No. I'm afraid not," said George, levelly.

"Not going home?" clarified Doug.

"No," confirmed George, looking up.

"Who would like to pass on a message? Robin?" George continued.

"You go first," I said to Doug. And Doug dictated a message to his wife that incorporated the inevitable joke.

"Robin?" said George.

"Do your course. Use all the resources of the estate to get me out," I said, cryptically. And added sotto voce, "I'm griping. I need a doctor."

"Noted," said George, without looking up.

Then it was Michael's turn. "I don't think I want to send a message." He paused. His body language contrived to demand continued attention. "I want my brief case."

Doug's head came up. "What do you want that for?"

"I want my brief case," Michael repeated.

"Why do you want that," enquired Doug genuinely mystified.

"I don't know – I just want my brief case."

George sought to understand why and received the same reply. George then asked where the briefcase was, and Michael told him exactly where he had left it in his office at the university.

George again asked why, was there money in it?

"I just want my brief case."

George sought to point out the chances that, after 4 weeks, the authorities would probably have it anyway, and that getting it could be a problem.

I stepped in. "What is so important that you need your briefcase after all this time?" But any answer was truncated by the sound of foot falls in the entrance hall.

Two Caucasian men stood in the open door way. Their heads were slightly down, their mouths open, their faces darkly lined. Their eyes hunted, eyelids and eyebrows strained to the limit of their travel. The older man smoked a battered cigarette, his hand shaking violently along with the rest of his body. They looked around them, warily attempting to take in those already in the room.

"Are you Alan Russell and Malcolm Anderson?" asked George calmly.

"Aye. This is..." faded the younger one, to the accompaniment of a basso growl from the older man. And, in the exquisitely flawless mutilation of the English language that only Geordies can achieve, the younger man finished "I'm Malcolm Anderson."

Malcolm looked at me momentarily and away to George. His face invited an explanation. "What's goin' on?" he asked.

"This is George Anderson..." I started, but Malcolm cut in, emphasizing his Christian name, with, "No. Malcolm Anderson."

I tried again. "This is George Anderson, British Consul at the embassy," I said patiently.

"Second consul," corrected George. George shook hands, first with Malcolm and then with Alan.

"We've met," said Alan, turning his cocked head down and smiling momentarily all the way to his eyes.

Then I gave Alan and Malcolm a ten second summary of proceedings to date, as they sat down amidst Doug and Michael.

"I just want my brief case," continued Michael, unperturbed.

And knowing that he had our attention again, "It's got my passport in it," he climaxed, dispassionately.

I shuddered. Now the Libyans knew where his passport was.

"Your passport's not going to do you any good in here?" said Doug incredulously.

"I just want it," finished Michael.

"I'll see what I can do," assured George.

"They want to shave wor heads," came in Malcolm, looking worriedly between George and me.

"That's something we may have no control over. It's common in most prisons," correctly pointed out George.

"We've had our hair cut," said I, looking Malcolm straight in the eye.

"Aye, but that's not shavin', is it?" Malcolm had a point.

"If only I had something to read!" declared Alan, with animation in his face, voice and hands.

"Can ya get wor some decent food?" asked Malcolm, more in hope than expectation. "All we get is pasta."

"That's what they eat in this part of the world," correctly pointed out George.

I was seeing the waste of opportunity, talking about minor details. So I cut straight across. "Look! None of this is important. There is only one thing that is important and that is "out"." George stated the last word simultaneously, with a firm nod of assent.

"HMG is fully aware of your situation. The FCO is working night and day to get the situation resolved."

"What situation?" grabbed Doug. And, "HMG? What's the FCO?" enquired Malcolm, simultaneously.

"Her Majesty's Government, and the Foreign and Commonwealth Office - the diplomats," I said, turning to Malcolm. But George choked.

Then, "What situation?" demanded Doug and I simultaneously.

"Some Libyan's were arrested in the UK. You are being held against their release," said George. "The details aren't clear."

"Hostages," said Doug rhetorically, and crisply nodded assent at his own conclusion.

"Can you get some clear details?" I asked with only a hint of sarcasm.

George nodded with the voiceless movement of the lips so commonly used when there is nothing useful to say.

From near his feet, George pulled out a large, white, plastic bag. The lettering on the side was from a shop somewhere in Knightsbridge. He disbursed to each of us a pair of white plimsolls, a couple of car magazines, and a carton of two hundred cigarettes. The thought was touching, as it made me, at least, feel cared for. But it was no substitute for what we really needed.

The pastoral care over, the three Libyans rose from their seats. Smiling with effort, but careful not to engage our eyes too boldly, they offered their hands, which I made no move to shake, and I disregarded their exit into the small entrance hall.

Malcolm and I remained where we stood.

To our good fortune, every Libyan in the room, and one of the Italian diplomats migrated in a group into the hallway. Doug and Alan were with them - Alan holding the group's attention through discourse. Alan's aggrieved growl greeted me as I saw the group of attentive Libyans gathering up his garrulousness. Malcolm and I were left alone with George and the other, the more senior Italian diplomat, Mr Amuso.

In the seconds that we now stole alone with George and Mr Amuso, I blistered out my impromptu message. At my first words, George sharply cautioned me that some of the Libyans understood English well, and the Italian standing beside him understood some. So I said to George that I would talk as fast, quietly and quickly as I could, and use the longest and most complicated words I could think of - and did so.

The thrust of the conversation was simple, however.

"Do you know where we're being held?" I asked George.

"No," he said not wasting time.

"Sharah Türkiye, Turkey Street," I said, and George looked quizzical. "Four hundred yards west on the road that runs on the south side of the Italian embassy."

"Shh," said George, eyes down, but nodded as a claim to know the location. "Some of them understand English." But George's face cleared.

"George, can you get us out?"

"Of course. As soon as you get to the embassy."

"But can you get us out?"

"Yes." Then he realised what I was asking. "When?"

"Now."

"No."

"It says 'Her Britannic Majesty's principle secretary of state requests and requires....' "

"I'm afraid that no longer applies any more. Borders are closed now. They're not open like they used to be."

"It's only four hundred yards."

"Don't try it. You'll probably get shot."

"I thought you lot carried an arsenal of small arms at British Embassies."

"That all went at the end of World War II. In any case, once they knew you were in the embassy, they would just rush in and grab you and put you straight back in prison. They are no respecters of international law, or of diplomatic privilege."

"So you can't help us."

"No. Not until you're officially released."

"So that's it then?"

"I'm afraid it is for now."

"Thanks anyway," I said, and meant it. And then, "Get us out! And tell these smiling spaghetti benders to do something useful and earn their bloody salary."

George looked me straight in the eye and assured me that he was doing everything he could - in spite of all impediments.

We shook hands. Although he was still shaking like a leaf, it was a warm, strong, affirmative and trustworthy handshake. I had developed an instant, permanent and trusting affection for George at the time I had first met him in August the previous year. I needed no persuading that he meant what he had just said.

I made the effort to thank the Italian and bid him farewell in his own language. In answer to my compliment, the Italian's practiced and convincing smile and twinkle jumped into an alive expression of human warmth and recognition that only served to bang home my misgivings.

With a final look and an accompanying "George", I turned on my heel and stepped past an open mouthed Malcolm, passed through the door and into the hallway. Alan was still talking to the small group of Libyans.

Not wanting to stand still while in the presence of the Libyans, and thereby allow them to take the initiative, I looked each of Alan and Malcolm in the eye and shook them in turn by the hand while wishing them well and looking forward to seeing them again soon, preferably when we were all out of here.

Then we trooped blankly back to our vans for the return to our respective prisons. As I did so, I contemplated the height of the van floor above the ground.

On reaching the van which stood in the late afternoon sun, I opened the rear door unbid, and clawed my way into the back. I knew it was going to be as hot as Hell in there. But I had raced the guards to try to steal as much time as possible alone with Doug and Michael, in an attempt to analyse the meeting.

Having slammed the door shut behind me and assured myself that there were neither doors nor windows open, nor guards close enough to hear, I spoke in a low unhurried voice.

"What did you make of that?" I asked.

"What did I make of what?" asked Michael back.

Oh, Lord!

But I ran out of time.

All three van doors opened simultaneously. There was no probable line of fire so I froze until, to my surprise, I saw Malcolm at the front, nearside door, with Alan in the background. I caught his eye and felt happy at seeing them again so soon.

An unintelligible order was shouted. I remained frozen. I didn't know how many guns there were about. A repeat of the order made us disengage each other's eyes. What was this?

The possibilities flashed through my mind.

We were going to be set free. No. They'd have turned us over to George. No. That didn't automatically follow.

They were going to put us all in the same prison. Whose? Ours? Theirs?

They were going to take us to a new prison. Where?

We were going to be taken out and shot. No.

Malcolm still looked frightened, although somewhat reassured to see us again. Alan still shook like a leaf.

We assumed correctly that the two were to get in, and made way accordingly. We shuffled in the small van. Malcolm sat against me, to my right. After all these weeks in solitary, I was glad of the physical contact.

The doors clanged shut. Remarkably, we were alone.

The decent, socially acceptable hiatus lasted about ten milliseconds. Michael's head was up and aloof. Doug's head was bowed and listening. Alan's head was level and waiting. My head was level and scanning. But it was Malcolm who spoke.

"Do ya think we're gonna get out of here?" he said. This was at least as much a gambit, as we were to find out in a minute, as it was a serious question.

"Well, we all got in a minute ago. Don't you think we can get out of here?" quipped Doug.

I was always grateful for wit, but there was no time for it now. Malcolm tried again.

"No. I mean ..."

"I know what you mean," I interjected to save time. "Yes." I struggled around and looked him squarely in the eye. "We are going to get out of here."

"How do ya know?" He looked back at me.

"When this is all over, we'll have a few pints together in Piccadilly Circus. Do ya think you could manage that?"

"Aye, I think I could manage a few pints."

"What about the rest of you?" I tried.

In the soft chorus of assent was included, "Too bloody right..." from Doug. "Whisky..." from Alan, and "Yes," from Michael.

"Where's Piccadilly Circus?" said Malcolm.

"Oh, it's in London," I smiled.

"So we are gonna get out, then," pressed Malcolm, looking around at everyone.

"Why Piccadilly Circus?" asked Doug genuinely confused.

"Oh, it's the only place I could think of," I said and, turning back to Malcolm, I realised that there was more to come. "You're frightened," I said, just to get it on the table.

"Howway, man!"

"I'm frightened too," I confided. "But I don't tell anybody."

"You don't?" he looked at me. "Aye, well, I'm frightened too, then."

"We're all frightened!" asserted Alan.

Malcolm needed leading. "Well, I prefer to call it being very insecure," I said.

"Well, I'm frightened," Malcolm continued.

"Why particularly?"

Malcolm looked around at everyone again, lighting last on Alan. "We've been beaten," he said.

"Well, don't complain to me," said Alan, piqued. "I told you to tell George while we were in there."

Now we knew. Malcolm was terrified of going back to their old prison. And clearly Alan wasn't all that keen, either.

I put my arm around Malcolm. The build of his frame matched his height of six feet three, and my arm could not encircle him. But I pulled him to me, nonetheless. His first reaction was one of surprise, and he inclined his turned head away from me, homophobia on his face. But it was obvious that he needed the hug. He later said that that was the most reassuring moment of his life, when he really believed we were going to make it. I was glad that he believed it. Because, at that moment, I didn't.

I turned and looked out the back window of the van, to see if there was any evidence of George. I was prepared to risk a beating myself to tell him this news.

"What you looking for?" rapped Doug, in his staccato manner.

"George," I replied without looking.

"His car's gone," growled Alan. "I saw it leave as we were getting into the van."

"Which car?" I said, testing the intelligence.

"The Jag. - the ambassador's car," he offered with studied nonchalance. "It's a white XJS," he added for effect.

We were all suitably, if silently, impressed.

"You'll just have to tell him the next time you see him," I said, inwardly sinking as the news sunk in.

"You talk as if you know him," Malcolm stated. "Do ya know George?"

"Yes," said I, briefly, "I spent an evening alone with him during a beach party once, among other things."

"So, you're one of us, li'e?" said Malcolm, genuinely relieved. "I thought you were one of them. You seemed to be in charge."

"What about these beatings?" I asked.

The detail of the beatings of Alan and Malcolm was unfolded until Malcolm ran out of time. The front doors swung open, the Intelligent One and another guard swung in, and we swung out of the car park and were off. Silence reigned.

I contemplated the detail of the beatings and compared it to the comeuppance of Monostatos. How we'd laughed, Ha! Ha! at the way the soles of his feet must have hurt. I felt sick at hearing of it being meted out to people I now knew and who, as far as I could see, had done nothing to warrant such barbarity.

I did not relish their prospect of return to their prison with its probable aftermath. But I relished return to my prison and further solitary confinement to no greater extent. Not a choice I would ever want to have to make.

Upon return to my new room, the guards had washed the floor of the kitchen, that I was shortly to discover adjoined my new room through a door that was kept permanently locked. The washing water had run under the adjoining door and soaked my carpet for a distance of eight or ten feet. In the seconds that I stood looking at it while the main entrance door to my new room was locked behind me, another wave of water gushed under the adjoining door and soddened the already wet area completely.

Having yet to learn the Arabic for "You bunch of fucking idiots!" I bellowed the English version instead.

Within seconds the main entrance door was unlocked, and although initially the guards looked as though they were going to assault me for shouting so loudly, they quickly started to look sheepish as I diverted their attention to the mess they had created. I folded the corner of the carpet back for some ten feet. It took ten days to dry out.

Over the remainder of the day, I banged on my door every time my bowels informed me of the necessity. On each occasion, the youngsters let me go with alacrity and generosity.

Partly out of necessity and partly out of testing the boundaries of the new arrivals, I asked as often as necessary. But the self evident truth of my repeated visits to the toilet informed the guards that something was definitely not right.

Evening meal was heralded by the fourth call of the day. The key turned in the door, and the jolly faced youngsters of earlier in the day appeared behind the Sweet Smelling Boy. With the gaggle of amiable youngsters all around, the Sweet Smelling Boy placed my food on the flat ledge of the office bureau in the alcove. Then, standing back from the food and resting his arms at full length by his slim sides, he addressed me in English. His speech, broken and halting but a good deal better than that of many, asked if there was anything I needed or if I had any problems. I indicated the constant need for the toilet, that whatever was wrong was not righting itself after all this time, and that I needed a doctor.

I suggested the Oil Clinic, which would have put me in touch with people I knew I could trust. The idea was promptly rejected.

I repeated, "Doctor, doctor."

With barely a nod and no apparent reply, he turned silently, and started to leave the room accompanied by the gaggle.

I turned to the flat working surface of the bureau and was glad for the Libyan soup as a means of re-hydrating my body. I ate, but the familiar call of nature was back again in no time. I knocked. Mercifully, the Sweet Smelling Boy was back as soon, presumably, as they had all had their own dinner.

The following day, tradesmen were back in the building, erecting a shower cubicle in the bathroom down the corridor. I was constrained to use both the shower and the toilet down the corridor and not the pink bathroom. My heart sank further at yet one more indication of the increasing permanence of my situation.

I tried to persuade the guards to let me use the pink bathroom for the obvious reason of Doug but was told by the Sweet Smelling Boy to cease asking. And yet, the idea of a shower did have some appeal. But after a couple of attempts with laughable water pressure, temperature, and an intermittent flow rate, I gave up showering.

As increasing dejection took over, and putting one foot in front of the other, both metaphorically and physically, became the norm, I played my saxophone in my head – two hours morning, two hours afternoon.

In between time, I walked across the diagonal of my room – eleven paces one way, eleven back, being careful to avoid the wet part of the carpet, which now smelt.

I still had the runs. I had already lost enough weight by the end of the third week in the basement cell that I had to hold my trousers up as I walked. But since the runs had started, I was losing weight even faster. I reckoned I was down to under ten stone.

Then the door opened and my lunch arrived.

I spoke to the Sweet Smelling Boy. He nodded.

A car was brought round and I was escorted by three guards. I was taken only a few hundred yards and the car was parked.

The doctor's surgery was in a curious little building which sat at the apex of other buildings at the confluence of a side road and Sharah Ben Assur, a normally busy main thoroughfare leading into and out of central Tripoli.

The entrance to the building was apparent with wrought iron, and the hallway had a mosaic floor. The quarter lights above the interior doors, and the main, casement windows gave abundant light inside. In fact it was odd to see a house without the ghiblis down. The Italian influence was no more than to be expected in this, a once affluent part of town. In the rising heat of late June, the marble floors were still cool.

We waited in the hall as one of the guards stated our business to the doctor, after which I was shown into the surgery. I entered and was invited to sit down. The slightly built, Malaysian doctor took me in, in the first sweep of his eyes. He was about my age – a few years older perhaps, wore a pale blue, short sleeved shirt, open at the neck, tan slacks and a stethoscope, hung by the ear pieces around his neck, in the traditional mode of British trained doctors. He had the looked of a seasoned and experienced physician, and the lined face of an expatriate on contract in Libya. But, in spite of a genuine professional bearing, a rasp of his breath rattled his otherwise inscrutable exterior, as he proceeded to be seated. And while he continued to survey with a professional look, there was fear in his eyes. Instantly, there was something about him I felt I could trust.

He asked me in calm tones what the matter was. I started to reply with a bumbling explanation and vague wavings of my hands to indicate my stomach. Realising that he was getting nowhere, he told me to get on the couch, came out from behind his desk and drew back a fabric curtain to expose a cramped examination room. He pointed at the couch, upon which I sat down, and he advanced as a man who is in charge of his own consulting rooms. The guards bridled. That was my cue.

"Imshi," I said, telling them to go away. They all went away and stood around in the mosaiqued hall way. The door was closed and all was silence save for the rare car buzzing past in the Ramadan, afternoon sunlight.

As soon as I was alone, I told the doctor that I was being held in prison as a hostage, that I had been there for several weeks and that I had the runs. The food was terrible and things were very difficult. Could he diagnose me as having a heart problem that required me to be sent home?

His eyes widened, his lips parted and his face tensed. He told me that he could but that if he were discovered, then he would get a beating. I told him of my heart murmur. He said it wasn't enough.

Could he get a message to the British Embassy for me to tell them what was happening? He would have to think about it, he told me. He could not just walk up to the British Embassy. He would be noticed.

I told him that if he would agree I would give him the details of who to contact and what to say.

"OK," he said. "Now what is the matter?"

I described the maggots in the apricot. He nodded quickly but not peremptorily.

He told me that he needed a stool sample and gave me a specimen container with my details clearly marked on the label outside, and a small plastic spatula inside. He also gave me a small bottle of emulsion to take each day until they knew exactly what I was suffering from.

He looked me squarely in the eye, shook hands warmly and firmly, and we said goodbye until next week when the results would be back. I told him that under the circumstances, there was no guarantee that these idiots would bring me back next week – especially since it would be the third week in Ramadan. He said that he would tell them personally. I asked him again if would diagnose me with a dangerous heart condition. He said that he couldn't do it. He went and spoke to the guards. By the time he had finished, the Sweet Smelling Boy was nodding clear affirmatives in my direction and repeating the return visit in Arabic, for the next week.

We walked back to the car and drove back to the Italian mansion.

The now familiar pattern of visits to the toilet was repeated for the rest of the day. I took the requisite stool sample at the first available opportunity, and handed the specimen container to the Sweet Smelling Boy as the most likely candidate to actually take it to the Malaysian doctor.

By the second or third use of the toilet that day, however, I had become aware of boot marks on the toilet seat. Unlike me, the Libyans had not graduated from the traditional and commonplace hole in the ground. Their cultural, almost defensive modesty prohibited them from anything as unhygienic as sitting on a toilet seat, and they had resorted to acrobatic lengths to maintain the status quo. But the Libyans had also cottoned onto the ease with which other waste matter could be flushed away and, with the increased numbers now living in the villa, had started to use the lavatory bowl as a kitchen waste disposal unit. On a daily basis, scrapings of tomato paste, spaghetti, lamb bones and bread from the Libyans' meal time plates and catering sized aluminium pots, were being emptied into the lavatory pan and flushed away. But as June wore on, and the public water supply became increasingly intermittent, the daily scrapings from the Libyans' plates and pots remained in the pan unflushed, along with an increasing quantity of excrement - and flies were duly attracted. Yet, still I was constrained to perform my bodily needs there.

One day, I walked to use the toilet, exercising my diaphragm ready to hold my breath for the vital minute or two that it would take me to evacuate my bowels and bladder, only to find that the porcelain lavatory pan had been smashed. The rim, gone, would never again channel flushing water around the pan. Spikes, capable of cutting a man's thigh to the bone, were all that remained of the once proud piece of pink porcelain - and a buckled and broken, boot-marked lavatory seat rested dolefully against the wall, complete with its eviscerated hinges.

The fly flown tomato paste, lamb bones and excrement still lay at the bottom of the lifeless lavatory bowl. I thought for a second, pressed the flush button and, stepping smartly away, walked back to my room shaking my head in pure disgust at these filthy pigs whose disgusting habits no amount of good example would modify, and in pure delight as two gallons of water gushed their expectant way out of the cistern and emptied themselves all over the floor.

Now that the lavatory pan was permanently out of commission, the guards were forced to concede against their better judgement and their orders, and I was allowed to use the Pink Bathroom in Doug's suite. This breakthrough afforded me privacy and quietude, briefly away from the stress of solitary confinement on one hand and the unpredictability of the guards on the other. It brought me the luxury of relief from the smell of an increasingly hot city and an increasingly inadequate sewage system - in the form of pine scented disinfectant. And most importantly, of course, it gave me the opportunity to snatch a few words with Doug.

I tapped on his door, and got in a few whispered words to get up to date. But like an idiot, I neglected to observe whether or not the outer door had been locked with me inside – and the Sweet Smelling Boy came in and caught me in the act.

The Sweet Smelling Boy looked reproachful. I tried not to look sheepish. The Sweet Smelling Boy drew breath and parted his lips, but thought better of saying anything. He escorted me back to my room.

Doug told me of his relief that I was still being held in the mansion. Not wishing to indicate that he was glad that I was still there, he was quick to point out, but instead relieved that I was OK, since he had heard neither "that terrible banging for a while" nor my movements in the Pink Bathroom, he was glad to know that I was at least safe and in one piece, as he hadn't known what had happened to me. I told him that I understood completely. He also told me that he had said to the guards on more than one occasion that "that man should not be locked up on his own outside like that. It isn't good for him." I thanked him for his solicitude, and we agreed that it might have been the reason they brought into my new room.

Now, knowing that I was still in the mansion, Doug set about the Hajji to find out exactly where I was.

The following day, the Hajji opened my door in the middle of the morning. In both hands he held a rolled up magazine. He handed it to me and purred his usual purr. I flattened it out gratefully but discovered to my horror that it was in Italian - bought by the Black Kid - too genuinely ignorant to be able to distinguish Italian from English - with a five Dinar note given to him by Doug out of B-Cal's float money. My senses reeled to figure out what kind of trap this was, and I looked back up at the Hajji with one hand turned palm up. But the Hajji was genuine and he continued to purr indicating with his hand that I should just enjoy it.

The boon of having an up to date and credible news magazine was a major asset. The challenge of translating from the Italian was great. The intellectual stimulation was totally absorbing. All provided for hours of concentration, and dissipation of the situation for the next several days. But the shock of the first news item that I read served to confirm yet again how downward, depressing and increasingly inescapable was the path we currently trod.

Mrs Indira Ghandi, the prime minister of India, had been assassinated.

When I saw the front page, I was horrified. An explosion of emotions ran through my head as I read the lengthy article in the magazine. What a waste, what a great woman, the end of an era, idiotic Sikhs, it was too easily announced, the Libyans must have had something to do with it, what does it mean to us, the statesmanlike leader of the world's most populous democracy - murdered by extremists, what hope was there for us, the vanished? The news was devastating.

But in the same magazine, there was a lengthy article about the return to the "Vingt-Quatre Heures du Mans" of the racing team Jaguar. After so many years away they didn't win of course but, as the article concluded, they put in such a good showing and conducted themselves so professionally that they would be very welcome back again. Good for you, Jaguar!

The emergence of the Hajji with the magazine was as surprising as it was novel. But later the same day, the door opened again a few inches, in the middle of the afternoon just when you would expect all good Libyans to be taking a siesta. The Hajji appeared. He didn't cross the threshold, but just stood there. After a few words of whispered Arabic, and some indeterminate pointings over his shoulders, he asked me a question. I totally failed to understand. After two or three more attempts, during which it became clear that the Hajji was genuinely trying to hold a conversation and, with the best will in the world on both our parts and both our languages, it also became clear that any attempt at verbal communication was pointless.

So we just stood there and looked at each others eyes for twenty minutes. He smiled as a tender father would. And I was momentarily lost from the grip of solitary confinement in the warmth of another human being who stood not as much as twenty inches in front of me.

The same episode was repeated most days over the remainder of Ramadan when, presumably, all the other guards were asleep, but the Hajji was obliged to remain on duty.

Doug told me that the Hajji would come all the way into his room, and hold lengthy conversations with the Tunisian cleric who would translate the Hajji's Arabic for Doug where relevant. On one such occasion, the Hajji was translated as saying to Doug that he thought it was a disgrace that such nice boys as us were being kept and held in this way.

The next few days were kept occupied with the longest article in the Italian magazine – about the bespoke fabrication of top quality shot guns from beautiful blocks of wood and hexagonal, bored, steel tubing, for individual owners.

Then during one of his silent visits, the Hajji produced two paper backs. One was a bona fide gunslinger adventure, complete with cowboys "feelin' fer the makin's to build themselves a quirly"; and the other, a fictional play about the American experience of a post nuclear winter. I read them a dozen times each over the next while. I then set about learning by rote and devising how to direct the play while. Every day that the Hajji was on duty, I benefited from the wordless, human visits for twenty minutes or so, or until footfalls were heard and the Hajji was compelled to go or be caught "talking" to me.

Add to that the four hours a day of mental saxophone exercises - I was now note perfect on 17 songs - and the daily sweeping of my carpet whenever they would allow me a broom, and my days were more fully occupied. The constant search for something to be doing to avoid the onrush of insecurity became, to some extent, diminished, but by no means eliminated.

A few days later, the Hajji brought me a copy of Time magazine. The copy of Time magazine - the one I had read and re-read until I knew the editor's inside leg measurement. I told the Hajji that I didn't want it. He protested mildly, but I didn't want to waste the opportunity to read something I hadn't seen before, in the face of something I had.

Doug cursed to himself after the Hajji brought the magazine back to him. Unknown to either the Hajji or me, Doug had taken the risky step of inserting a handwritten note to me, inside the pages of the magazine. And I had refused to take it!

Later, the Hajji brought me a book of poems by Yevtushenko. I almost forgot where I was when I started to read, once again, the seductive sounds of the Russian language, inadequately transliterated in the book though they were. Then to flick through "Zima Junction" and be transported to the edge of Lake Baikal away from the filth and heat of Libya to the sterile cold of Siberia - mixing with souls so parochial that they knew not of the Bolshoi Ballet.

Then I turned to the bald and harrowing reality of "Lies":

"Lying to the young is wrong.
Proving to them that lies are true is wrong.
Telling them God's in his heaven and all's well with the world is wrong.
They know what you mean.
They are people too.
Tell them the difficulties can't be counted,
and let them see with clarity these present times.
Say obstacles exist they must encounter, sorrow comes, hardship happens.
The Hell with it.
Who never knew the price of happiness will not be happy.
Forgive no error you recognize, it will repeat itself a hundred fold, and afterward our pupils will not forgive in us what we forgave."

I had to get out. I had to tell people what really goes on.

Then the Hajji handed me a paperback of the Poems of St John of the Cross. As ever, I tried to determine any significance, such as, which previous prisoner in here had turned to religion for his salvation. Then I remembered seeing this book lying on Michael's bed when I asked him if he knew any poetry.

I opened the book and found to my delight that not only were the poems written in English, but also in the Spanish, as originally written by St John of the Cross during his imprisonment throughout the long hot summer of 1578, closely confined in a narrow, stifling cell. If nothing else, he and I had that in common.

The poems meant that I could now read in both English and Spanish. The practice would be useful in its own right, but the absorption in the study would keep me going for hours – days. And so I read.

Ramadan wore on. Day was slowly turned into night and night into day, so that by week three of Ramadan, everybody was tired and had become nocturnal.

But I concentrated on the poems. The translation into English was more doggerel than poetry. It often lacked rhyme and scansion. The Spanish was far more absorbing. Rhyme in Spanish is easy because of the highly consistent patterns of endings to words. But that didn't stop me polishing my Spanish.

Neither did it stop me developing a fascination with the religiosity of St John of the Cross. In spite of the book's almost obsequious preface written by a Jesuit, the mysticism of St John's religion shone in the lines of the Spanish poetry and, as I read and re-read them, I found myself becoming drawn in by the charismatic description of his religious experiences while in detention.

I read the lines, which described his own assent into ecstasy as he climbed and climbed in his knowledge of God. And I was astonished to find that the whole of my own body was also filled with an ecstatic sensation that was close to sexual but somehow not. The sensation that I was experiencing paralleled that which St John of the Cross was describing. But as he talked about his upward journey to ecstasy, he also said that the higher and higher up he climbed the more and more frightened he became. Now he and I had two things in common.

I put the book down and I sat for a number of minutes.

The ecstasy and fear faded and an inexplicable calm descended over me.

And, in a moment of mystical revelation, for no reason that I could explain, I found myself saying out loud and with an air of total finality, "It's going to be alright. We're going to get out of here."

It was the middle of the morning. The door opened. The Intelligent One came in and indicated that I was to come with him.

"Why?" I choked out.

"Information," he said.

"What do you mean information?" I felt myself blanching.

"You go. Big office. Information," he said.

"Information about what?" I said, fighting to keep my voice level.

"About you problem," said the Sweet Smelling Boy from behind.

I was escorted out to the white van. Doug and Michael were already inside.

We went to an inelegant, monolithic building just outside old Tripoli and parked.

Inside, we were shown to a waiting room and told to sit. There was no indication of how long we were to wait. There was no indication of what we were waiting for. There was no clock. There were no magazines.

Michael sat with his legs crossed and his arms folded. Doug sat with his head almost between his knees and his hands over the back of his neck. I sat with my mind swirling, my mouth dry and my eyes incapable of alighting on anything.

Over an interminable and inestimable period, while indifferent, minor officials drifted in, out or simply past the waiting room, we smoked, sweated, drank water, took our bladders to the toilet only for nothing to come out, and felt the blood pounding in our ears. We found ourselves unable even to look at each other for mutual support as we each sat in our own private, uncertain, head spinning Hell, waiting to give 'Information'.

In time, I was called. I walked on wobbly legs to an office. In the office were three men. Two were roughly suited. The third was dressed in desert garb. Two sitting and one standing, they gave the impression of milling around with no real direction.

I was ordered to sit.

The two at the desk spent the next eternity examining and cross examining me.

The questions were all about the maps. The detail that they sought bore little reality to what I did or to anything that I had done.

The assumptions that they were working on spoke of a paradigm in their minds which bore no comparison to reality. I tried to say so and was bawled into silence by the man who was standing.

I now had the multiple problems of not knowing what they wanted, of not being allowed to state my own position in my own words, but of implicitly being accused of things that I had not done, and had no intention of doing. Whatever they thought I had done, they obviously took a very dim view of it. Either that, or someone had done something pretty serious, and they were looking at the wrong man.

The unreasonableness of it all was quite literally breath taking.

With many a baffled glance at each other, as it started to become clear that I did not appear to fit their paradigm, the seemingly directionless interview dragged its stressful way towards no real conclusion. When, finally, they had covered all the same ground as the interrogations of the night I was arrested at the university, I was told to leave, with no progress in my opinion having been made, and no explanation of my position having even been requested.

I went back to the waiting room. In the few seconds that all of us we there together before being escorted to the van and silence, Doug and I quickly agreed on the common format of our interrogations. Michael nodded.

One night, I had dozed off on my bed, fully dressed. There was a knock at the door. The key turned and a tall, good looking guard, who I'd never seen before, simpered in.

It was not his disdain or indifference that got my attention. Alarmed at what I saw, I rose at once, measured my way across the floor, and gave the appearance of offering him my right hand to shake. He passed the automatic pistol from his right hand to his left hand, and started to stretch out his right.

Instead of taking his hand, I made an expansive gesture to my right inviting him into the room.

"You are sleep," he said indifferently and turned to go.

I had no desire to talk to him. But contact is contact and he might have known something new.

"No, no," I said in my best BBC. "Please." I sat down in the chair by the bureau, raised my face with my chin slightly forward, and just looked at him. After several silent seconds, he turned back to me with a shrug, and said, "As you like."

He made some vague noises, vague gestures with his free hand, and vague glances from side to side. Eventually, he discovered the floor, and sat on it, with his back to the wall more or less directly in front me. He passed the automatic from his left hand to his right, and cradled it pointing at me.

Now looking down the length of my nose and over my crossed legs at the automatic, I said "Afwan."

He didn't mind. "As you like," he said, and lowered the muzzle.

The automatic blended into the black of his tight slacks, which in turn revealed the musculature of his buttocks. The off-white shirt was unbuttoned to mid torso, and a heavy plait of gold chain, that matched his wrist watch, hung almost to his navel. The short sleeves revealed muscular, but not over developed arms.

I asked what was afoot. "Shuney?" I said, and looked indifferently away.

"You have food, shai?" solicited The Gigolo, without looking at me.

"Yes," I said curtly, without looking back.

"What you want? What you need?" he asked.

"I want to see the British Consul," I said resolutely and without having to think.

"Munken," he said, indifferently referring to the Muslim ideal of possibility if God chooses. "Inshallah."

"Why am I here?" I preferred to get straight down to business.

"Munken..." he started.

"Yes?" I pressed, raising my chin.

"...Some Libyan boys - problem in you country," he said, still avoiding my gaze.

"No," I said, testing the intelligence.

"Some Libyan boys in England - Secret Bolice," and he crossed his wrists together in the universally recognised sign that means "handcuffs".

"We do not have secret police in England," I said.

"Bucket of water at six in the morning."

"Where?" I said, unconcerned.

"Prison....," he replied. But I cut him off.

"No," I said. "We do not treat prisoners like that." But I was worried at the implications.

"Yes," he said. "Six in the morning, every morning. Bucket of water. Sshhhh!" And he imitated the act of throwing a bucket of water, quickly returning his right hand to the automatic in his lap. "And they are not allowed to pray."

"No," I said.

"You not treated that," said he, now looking at me. The irony plainly eluded him.

"We go home soon," I said, raising my chin as I spoke.

"Maybe," he said indifferently. Then added, "They get – you get. They go free – you go free. They get.... – you get....." And at each unspoken part of the equation, he placed his left hand around his own throat, lifted the hand, and poked out a flaccid tongue. His right hand stayed around the automatic.

"What have they done," I enquired flatly, testing all the while.

"Revolution," he answered, with a shrug.

"Look. I'm terribly sorry. I've got to go to bed," I said, and stood up putting the chair under the bureau.

"As you like," said The Gigolo, and stood.

I abandoned him as he stood at the door, turning to walk to my bed. Without a flicker he wheeled right, left, and shut and locked the door.

I lay on my bed with one wrist on my forehead and contemplated twenty five years more of this.

A few days later, a Friday, soft, quick, even footsteps – heel and toe, heel and toe – approached, and ceased. It was the Sweet Smelling Boy. The key in the door was turned. Once, twice. He bid me come out of the room. A few seconds later, I found to my surprise that I was standing in the fresh air, at the foot of the staircase, in front, the North side, of the mansion, in what little shade was offered in the mid-day, mid summer sun. With no signal from the guard, I just stood about, turning and "taking my ease". A round, wicker table sat incongruously bedecked with steaming tea and a large, transistor radio that was on and playing, although it took several seconds for me to realise that fact, on account of the low volume and of the programme being mostly drowned by a low but all pervading hiss. The atmosphere created by the Sweet Smelling Boy was one of afternoon tea in an English Country Garden.

After a brief silence, the Sweet Smelling Boy opened up. "You like tea?"

"No," I obliged him with a courteous incline of the head.

"You want, er, inte asma radio?" he went on.

"No, I don't want to listen to the radio. I would like to walk up and down if I may," and I accompanied my request with the two fingered dumb show of a man walking.

I walked the length of the front wall of the mansion. And back. And repeated. At the third pass, I proceeded to walk around the right angled bend where the narrow concrete footpath turned to go down the East side of the building, directly under the casement window of my room. I was told to come back and limit myself to the run of the front path, and did so. Asked if I wanted to come in, I indicated that I would like to continue walking for a bit longer. And did so. Then I went in.

Then it was Doug's turn. Initially, I only heard movement. But I opened my window and stood in the shade of my room to see what I could see. The first time Doug reached the end of the designated run, I could see him clearly, and waved furiously at him. He couldn't see me in the dark of the room. At the next pass, I called his name. He heard me, but could not identify the source of the sound. Next run, I stepped forward into the light. He saw me.

"Ok?" I aspirated.

"Yeah. You?" he replied.

I nodded.

"I've got a radio!" mouthed Doug.

I cupped my hands to my ears, and shook my head.

"I've got a radio!" he repeated, slightly aspirated this time.

My mouth fell open. Doug drew his lips back into a manic grin and nodded his head several times, vigorously.

Then he mouthed, "I've got to go." And walked back.

I was pleased for him, but down cast with incredulity.

The next pass was indicated by the footfalls. However, Doug's footfalls had changed to soft, quick, even heel and toe. Too late I saw the Sweet Smelling Boy. Too late he saw me.

Seconds later the key turned and the Sweet Smelling Boy confronted me, admonishing me in Arabic at the point of a wagging finger. He counted out the three times that I had been doing something that met with his disapproval, all while making contact with Doug, and that if I did one more transgression, I was going to get the Mudir. It was all in erudite Arabic, but I knew what I was being told and I did not under any circumstances want the Mudir. I assured him that it was Malleish, and on the second Malleish, he softened.

He locked the door on the way out. Once, twice.

There were no more walks in the front garden after that.

It was the middle of the morning. The door opened. The Intelligent One came in and indicated that I was to come with him.

"Why?" I choked out.

"Information," he said.

"But I have already given information," I said, pointlessly.

He shrugged and said, "Information again." And imitated writing on a pad.

Breathing became difficult.

We got into a couple of cars. The others were there.

As we walked from the cars to the side door of the large, monolithic building, we were further disconcerted to see an army sergeant cutting a four foot switch from the base of a birch tree, to be used, a guard confirmed with a single nod, to administer a judicial caning. Breathing became more difficult.

We sat around in the waiting room as before, this time with the odd Libyan or two, presumably also waiting for interrogation. We found ourselves wanting to drink water and go to the lavatory just as before, but not quite as much this time.

I was called.

I was accompanied to an office door on the right hand side of a corridor. The guard knocked. I was told to wait as the guard stuck his head in. Then I was told to go in.

I entered an office and walked past a small, screened off section into the main void. There sat two older men. One sat behind a large, imitation wooden desk, the other, to his right, on an upright chair at the end of the desk.

Both wore suits over their corpulent forms. The man at the desk was dark haired, heavily bespectacled, crumple faced, and sat with his hands clasped on the table in front of him - his eyes screwed up so that you couldn't see where they were looking.

The man on the upright chair wore a mature suit and tie to match his mature years and voluminous, grey hair. His glasses sat upon a Nubian nose. Immediately behind him was the partitioned off section. He sat up and back, with his hands resting on his thighs, although he had the end of the desk to rest his left arm on if he'd wanted to. The desk bore little more that a telephone and a couple of piles of paper. But also a blank writing pad and a pen, beneath the hands of the incumbent. The remaining width of the office was made up by the cheap, Chinese, metal-framed chair on which I was now invited to sit, with a little more than enough leg room that I would not be cramped.

I sat down and back and crossed my legs.

I was immediately upbraided by the grey suited man to sit up straight. And promptly did so, heart pounding.

"What is your name?" said the magistrate through the interpreter.

I told them.

"Where did you do your police training?" they asked.

Not constabulary duties..., but police of the secret type - MI6.

Right from the beginning then, I thought. Better play this very cool. And I decided that I would look up only long enough to answer a question, and then never directly into their eyes.

"I have never had any police training," I said.

"When did you do your national service?" they asked.

"I have never done national service." I thought of my two years in the Air Training Corps. I'd learnt to be a dead shot with a rifle. But that didn't count.

"Never?"

"Never."

"How did you avoid National Service?"

"I didn't 'avoid' National Service."

"Yes you did. You just said you never did National Service."

"That is true."

"Then how did you avoid National Service."

"I didn't have to do National Service."

"Everyone has to do National Service."

I ignored his statement.

"Everyone in the world has to do National Service."

"We don't."

"Oh! Come on, of course you do!" he cajoled. "Everyone in Britain has to do two years National Service."

"No we don't."

"Yes you do!"

"No."

"Of course you do!!"

"No."

"Why did you not do your National Service?"

"Because we don't have to do National Service."

"Why not?"

"Because National Service was abolished in 1963."

"You still have to do two years?" they said.

But I could see that they were trying to draw me into vehemently denying something which they already knew to be false, in order to see what I looked like when I was telling what they knew to be the truth. I refused to be drawn.

I just said firmly, "No, no." And disengaged.

They paused and just watched me.

"Then where do the soldiers come from?"

"All our forces are volunteers."

"So it is a professional army?"

"Yes."

"OK," he said mildly, and watched me as I disengaged even further.

They had both been closely observing me all the while. Now they knew what I looked like when I was saying 'No' honestly. They also knew what I looked like when I was recounting facts - honestly. Both of these would make it easier for them to spot if I should turn to lying.

"Where do you live?"

I told them.

"How big is your family?"

I told them.

"What do your brothers do?"

"I don't know."

"What are your antecedents?"

"What?"

The translator leaned forward not only to rebuke me but also to establish the magistrate's credentials. He said, "His honour has attended a course in legal terminology."

The translator rephrased the question in more prosaic English.

"What does your father do?"

"He is retired."

"What did he do before he retired?"

I couldn't tell them that he worked for a newspaper. After all, newspapers are controlled by the state.

"He was an artisan."

"What does your mother do?"

"She is deceased."

They sat back. The was a momentary silence

"Why did you come to Libya?"

"To do good work, to get paid and to go home again."

"What work do you do?"

"Engineer."

"What are you an engineer doing?"

"Laying a huge telecommunications network."

"Who are you trying to communicate with?"

"Telecommunications."

"That is still communications. Who are you trying to communicate with?"

"No. Telecommunications."

"Where have you hidden your communications equipment?"

I was in disbelief.

"I do not have any communications equipment."

"You said you are laying a huge telecommunications network. What is this network?"

"Telecommunications. So that everyone in Libya can have telephone and television in their house."

"Why do you want them to have telephone in their house?"

I was reeling in disbelief at the bias of their questioning. I now had to figure out a meaningful answer.

"Because the contract says so."

"What contract? Who is your contract with? Which government department do you work with?"

Now I had to be very careful. British Telecom was still effectively a government department. Not for a few more months would it be a plc. But there was nothing I could do to convince these two that it did not mean that I worked for the government in any accepted sense - far less the sense of being here to accumulate information for a department of the British Government.

"I work for BPOCO."

"What is that?"

I told them.

"So you do work for the government?"

Well, they had started this interrogation by finding out what I looked like when I am saying 'no' in a truthful and honest way. So I simply had to remember what I looked like while I was denying National Service, and laid it on with a trowel.

"No, no," I said, shaking my head with an irritated frown on my face. And disengaged.

They sat back

"How do you get paid?"

"In London."

"How do you live in Libya? Where do you get money from?"

"Company loan account," I said.

"Who do you contact in your work?"

"Sirti."

"What is Sirti?"

"The main contractor."

"Where does he come from?"

"They are an Italian company from Milan. Look them up."

"Who are your friends?"

This was going to require care. Any names I gave the magistrate would spawn all manner of supplementary questions and, with little doubt, find my friends in the same situation as me. They wouldn't thank me for that. I had to close down this line of enquiry immediately.

"I don't have any friends."

"You must have friends. Everyone has friends."

"I don't have any friends. I am a loner."

"You must have some people you meet?"

Close it down, Robin.

"Look. One of my men comes to Libya to do his nine weeks duty. When he gets here, he sits for that nine weeks in his caravan at the cable head, checks the job, does the paper work, smokes his pipe, plays with his pet scorpion, and doesn't talk to anyone for nine weeks. I don't have any friends. I am a loner. I had my wife and three children with me. I spent my time with them. I keep myself to myself."

"Where are your wife and children?"

"They left Libya three days before I was arrested."

They sat back.

"What were you doing out on the Saturday night?"

"I was ill. I needed some fresh air. I went out for a drive."

"Saturday was not a time to be going out for fresh air after the events of the week."

"I heard that there had been an incident."

"What incident?"

I was talking too much

"Some incident in the city."

"What incident?"

"I don't know. It is not my business. I don't ask. I told you. I am a loner. I do not ask about things that don't concern me."

They sat back.

"What is this dive club? What is this meeting?"

"I don't know."

"But you have a map with this date on. You must know."

"Look at the date. It is over a year ago. I cannot remember what meetings I went to a year ago. Can you?"

"What is this dive club?"

"It is some people who are interested in swimming. We meet at the beach to talk about it."

"The Beach Hotel?"

"No the beach - beside the sea."

"Who do these people work for?"

"I don't know."

"Whose house is this?"

"I do not know their names, but they work for Whinney Murray."

"Ah! So you do know who your friends work for," leapt in the translator.

I was talking too much.

At this point a few things became clear. All my answers had to fit into the following categories.

What I had told them before.

The truth if it didn't matter

Lies if they were uncheckble.

If I could tell truth and lies, intermixed with each other, they would have great difficulty telling when I was lying.

Give each answer only after several seconds pause. That way, when I did not know what to say I would have a few seconds in which to think. And when I did know what to say, I would pause anyway. That way they would not know when I was making something up and when I was not.

"Whinney Murray are BPOCO's accountants."

They sat back.

The magistrate pulled out the photocopies of the maps I had been carrying.

"Why are you carrying maps?"

"I have to find my way around. I do not read Arabic. I cannot read the street signs."

"Why do you want to read the street signs?"

I didn't know whether to laugh or cry.

"I don't want to read the street signs. I have a map."

"Why would you want to read the street signs?"

"To find my way around Tripoli."

"Why do you want to find your way around Tripoli?"

"So that I can get to and from work and the shops."

"Why does the map contain details of strategic locations?"

"I don't know what you're talking about."

"The GP Post Office. The GP Post Office is a strategic location."

"Is it?"

"Why does your map show the GP Post Office?"

"Everyone knows where the GP Post Office is. It is easy to navigate by."

So continued a grinding routine of patient question and answer - question to tease out an inconsistency, and answer to give them nothing to go on, nothing on which to base a supplementary question, nothing that wasn't either true or uncheckable.

After two and a half hours, the translator told me to sign the transcript of the interrogation. It was in Arabic. I told him that there was no point in me signing something that I could not read. I said so, but had no choice. I signed. Now I could go, I got up and shook hands with the translator. The magistrate showed no sign of recognition, so I turned and stepped out the door.

As I walked down the corridor to the waiting room, I realised that there was nobody in sight. No guards, no hostages, no officials - no-one. All I had to do was to keep walking - along the corridor, down the stairs, out the door, across the car park and into the bustle of Tripoli. No-one would know I had gone. Unfortunately, as I got towards the end of the corridor, Tweedle Dee (The Intelligent One) saw me and called me in.

But in the car on the way back to the mansion, two essential pieces of intelligence about the locality of the Italian mansion finally became clear to me.

The first was the geographical layout of the Italian Embassy, including the location of the entrance gate and the street on which it lay a mere 400 yards from the Italian mansion.

The second was that the streets were deserted, and that all the goons who normally patrolled the security block with or without their Kalashnikovs were absent, it being the middle of the afternoon of the middle of the third week in Ramadan.

It was the day for my return visit to the doctor. The key turned. In strode Red Head.

It all happened so fast that I was still in bed under my sheet, with my clothes neatly piled on the floor beside me, stacked in the correct order for speediest dressing. Red Head strode to within a few feet of me, and I just had to sit it out. The exchange that followed occurred solely in Arabic – his being rather better than mine, but his English non-existent. He wanted to know why I wanted to go to the doctor. I struggled to tell him that it was agreed. He wanted to know what was the matter with me. I struggled to explain. He pointed out, that I was not a doctor and therefore couldn't possibly diagnose myself.

"Inte mush doctor," he observed unnecessarily.

"Aiwa," I agreed. "Ana mush doctor."

He rose to leave. As he did so, I told him what in fact I was.

"...Ana Ingineer, Berid (Post Office) Britania," I said to his departing back. And then told him in English the implication of being an engineer, "and therefore probably know a good deal more about it than you do." And finally, I stamped out, "Doctor! Doctor!"

He turned, looked at me, and beckoned me with his left hand to follow him.

I waved him out of my room with the back of my left hand. He didn't move. I pointed to my pile of clothes, look up at him and waved again. Muslim modesty cut in. He looked at the clothes, nodded to me and left.

I dressed and stepped out of the door. Any suggestion of making headway with Red Head was soon cut short as he locked me in his vice like grip to escort me to the waiting car.

We drove the few hundred yards as before and parked. We crossed Sharah Ben Assur with barely a car in sight and no vice like grip. Instead, we walked side by side.

I started to shake hands with the Malaysian Doctor, but he quickly disengaged and said, "What do you want me to do?"

I wasn't ready for such simple directness. In a split second, I ran through the plan in my mind to tell him of my exact location, and that he was to go to the Italian Embassy and tell George Anderson what I had told him. But in the seconds as I was thinking, I realised that whole thing was futile. George already knew where we were, and I was pretty sure that he was doing everything possible already to get us out. This would just risk the Malaysian a beating. Besides, it was altogether too convenient that the he should just come out with it like that, and what with Red Head's unexpected presence,

I got the impression I was being set up. I told him, "No. Nothing." And got on with the other matter in hand.

I told the doctor that I had taken the emulsion daily as prescribed and that the constant diarrhoea had largely abated. He nodded without surprise. He gave me a plastic drum of tablets and told me to take them at the prescribed rate until I was free of symptoms for at least twenty four hours.

We shook hands, and Red Head and I stepped out of the office, off the kerb and into Sharah ben Assur.

It being the third week in Ramadan, there was absolutely no way that the driver of the car would have been able to avoid a collision and Red Head would undoubtedly have been killed. In the split second allowed to me as we started to cross the road, I weighed up the possibility of assisting Red Head into the path of the one, oncoming car and seamlessly started to act. But he detected the movement of my left hand as I started to secrete it into the small of his back, and as he turned to face my open and vulnerable body, further unsighting himself to the car, I realised that there was nothing I could do to achieve my plan, and I switched to his front - catching him full in the solar plexus. It was a good shot. But he was as tough as he appeared, and although he stalled in his stride, he was quickly upon my hand, presumably with a view to braining me. But in the next millisecond, one of the tyres on the fast moving car polished the toe caps of his shoes, and all became clear to him. While still stalled, he looked first at me with some surprise that, contrary to the will of Allah, someone had chosen to save his life, and then looked to his left to avoid a repeat of the same hazard. He let slip my left hand from his own left hand, but, far from relinquishing it completely, he retained it in his right and, as our hands fell naturally to our sides as we started to cross the remainder of the road, I felt the start of the dread interlocking finger grasp of the first day of my arrest. And yet it did not materialize. Instead, he took my hand in his, as lovers do - and Arab men alike when they are fond of each other - and paid me the incongruous tribute of this open display of affection until, as we reached the opposite kerb, I gently disengaged.

On the short run back to the Italian mansion, I observed, exactly as expected, that no-one was about. Upon approaching the security area and the mansion, not so much as one of the usual goons was about, no guards, no lazy sentries, no guns - nothing. In another few hours it would be the middle of the afternoon in the middle of the third week of Ramadan.

At my cell door, I took my life in my hands once more by mentioning the religious aspects of the forthcoming Eids. The Eid al Fitr, the Festival of the Conclusion of Fasting, the end of the month of Ramadan, celebrated by a huge feast, a mega pig-out by all fasting Muslims everywhere - Hari Raya. And the Eid al Adha, the great celebration when Abraham was commanded by God to sacrifice Isaac, but instead sacrificed a sheep. Red Head was flat out astonished at my knowledge of his religion at the Eids. He paused and allowed a moment's conversation. But glaringly and defensively corrected me from Abraham and Isaac, to Ibrahim and Ishmael, before moving on. After the moment had gone he continued to unlock my room and make me go in, but not now with any threat.

Lunch came and went. The Sweet Smelling Boy unlocked the door, came in, and took away the dishes. I now settled down to the middle of the afternoon in the middle of the third week in Ramadan when everybody would be asleep. For the previous hour I had only heard one set of foot steps anywhere within earshot. And now I heard the sound of the gentle heel and toe footfalls on the staircase on the far side of the building, and the door to the main basement where Michael was kept, being opened. Further, familiar noises told me that the Sweet Smelling Boy was moving into the basement proper. Still having no real idea of how many men were being held here, it was only a probability that he was collecting more plates. But I was as certain as I could be, short of standing next to him. I estimated how long I had. All the time I needed, I concluded.

I tried the door. To my surprise and yet not, the handle turned and the door opened. It wasn't possible. The Sweet Smelling Boy had left the door unlocked. This is what I had planned for, and this was the bit of luck that any improbable plan needs to succeed.

I opened the door to the fullest extent necessary to listen, while not standing in the way of the door so that I could shut it in a split second if necessary.

There was nothing. No footfalls, no breathing, no snoring, no television, no radio, no cars, no air conditioners. Nothing. And in the absence of any of these, I could hear with complete satisfaction the Sweet Smelling Boy moving around in the basement.

And, Holy Mother of God, the front door was ajar. It wasn't possible.

I left my door open. I spread my arms slightly, breathed through my mouth, and walked on the outsides of my soles, pace at a time. I listened for any echo off the marble floor and walls of my first few footfalls. There was none. I made the few paces to the door of the sitting room that adjoined my room to look for off duty guards, who would in any case be asleep.

There was nobody in the sitting room.

I walked to the front doorway. The left hand door was sufficiently ajar to allow any but the fattest person through. But the right hand door was shut. And I had no idea of who might be sitting on the other side of it asleep on the cool marble in the Ramadan heat.

But I still had calculations to do. The steel gates at the end of the garden path were closed. God alone knew how they were to be opened, and how much noise they would make in doing so. And who they would attract and how long it would take them to wake up and react and it's only 400 yards to the Italian embassy.

It was all so improbably easy. I felt as though I was being set up.

George's words rang in my ears, "Don't try it. You'll probably get shot."

To go or not to go?

Everything in my plan had come together. The middle of the afternoon in the middle of the third week of Ramadan when everybody would be asleep. But the imponderables of who might be asleep outside the closed front door, and of the outer gate, made it far too risky. In the 400 yard run to the Italian embassy, anything could happen. And I still had to get down the side street on either side of which were the main entrance to the central police station and, directly across the road from it, the entrance to the Italian embassy.

"If you are going to go, go now. If you're not going to go, then go back to your cell, now."

"And if you are not going to go now, then do not mention again the topic of escape. You had your chance. You made a decision. You cannot talk again about escape."

This, then, was a defining moment. And the man defines the moment.

If the man does not define the moment, then the moment defines the man.

I did not feel as though I defined the moment. So what did this moment say about me?

Or <u>did</u> I define the moment?

If I had still been twenty one, unmarried, no children, and never been to hospital, I would have gone, climbed over the gate and taken my chances. But I wasn't twenty one any longer. And I was married. I had been to hospital. And I had three beautiful children who needed a father. If it took me 25 years to get out of here, I would still see them again.

No hero to me is he who gains honours by easy shedding of blood. The true hero is he who continues to function effectively whilst terrified out of his wits.

It's easy to be brave when you are surrounded by your friends - sitting there in the green fields of Hertfordshire. Try being brave when you are in the mental Hell of solitary confinement and listening to somebody being beaten past the point of broken bones and having no idea of who is next.

When all is said and done, I am still here, alive, sane, unwounded, and my children still have their father. So the decision to stay put was certainly not the wrong one. Which decision took the more courage? To go, and risk getting shot - and lose my children their father? Or to stay, and face further interrogation - and who knew how many years of continued solitary confinement?

I thought of my children. I weighed it up. I walked back to my room and shut the door.

*** *** ***

1. Skinning a goat on the side of the coast road. May 1983.

2. Hangover Cure. Dead Cow Beach. May 1983.

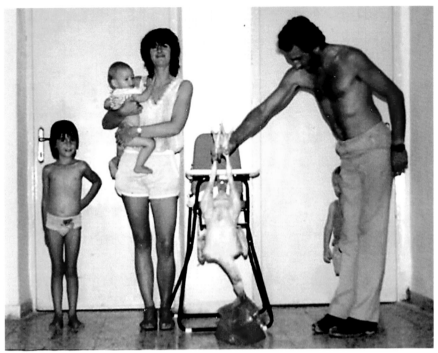

3. September, 1983. After 3 weeks in solitary, I was 10kg lighter than this.

4. Katy, Ross, Chris at one of the Italian Contractor's Camps. Spring, 1984.

5. Diving. Tank Bay, Tripoli. Autumn, 1983.

6. The crowd stoned us for taking this photograph. Eid Al Adha, Sept, 1983.

7. Coast Road, Bay of Surt. WWII tanker. See the two torpedo holes? Sept, 1983.

8. Italian Foreign Legion Fort. S. Libya. 6th Dec, 1983.

9. Katy's Nativity Play. The British School, Tripoli. Christmas, 1983.

10. Christmas, 1983.

LATITUDE AND LONGITUDE OF LOCATIONS

Italian Mansion

32º53'33.71" N
13º11'20.45" E

Local Mosque (Sidi Issa)

32º53'33.99" N
13º11'24.67" E

Security (Interrogation) Centre

32º53'33.23" N
13º11'22.92" E

Grand Hotel

32º53'36.21" N
13º11'05.28" E

Meetings with Pat, Terry, Carol Service

32º53'30.67" N
13º11'18.85" E

Italian Embassy

32º53'36.20" N
13º11'32.65" E

Central Police Station

32º53'35.99" N
13º11'32.25" E

BPOCO Main Office

32º53'34.42" N
13º11'31.18" E

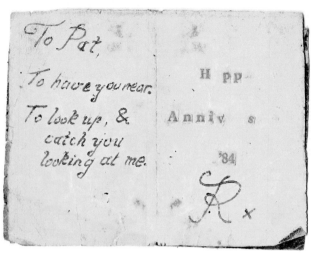

11. The "I Love You" card. 8th Aug, 1984.

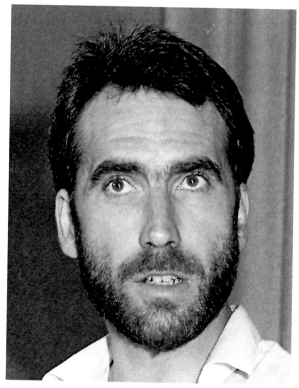

12. The Thousand Yard Stare did not leave me for 4 months after release.
7th Feb, 1985.

13. Malcolm.
Butter wouldn't melt in his mouth.

14. Michael.
Snappy

15. The Iconic Group Photo during the punch up. 7th Feb, 1985.

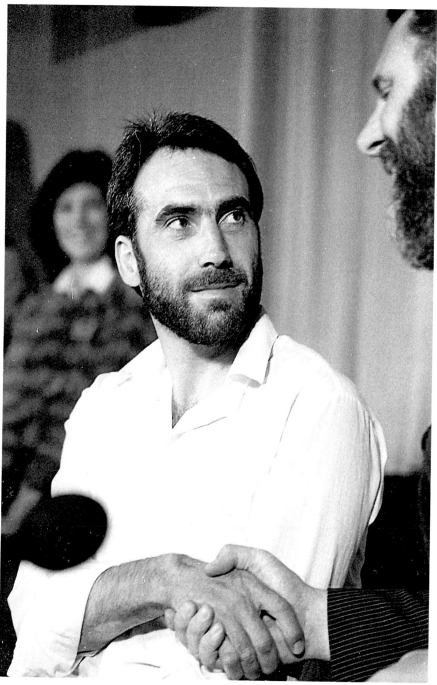

16. Man of the Match. 7th Feb, 1985.

17. Barry, Robin and Andrew. 7th Feb, 1985.

18. Result!

PART THREE
3rd Week of Ramadan to 31st August, 1984

It was now late enough in Ramadan that all fasting Muslims had become entirely nocturnal. Accordingly, on the Thursday night at the end of the third week in Ramadan, the guards gave every impression of having a party, and I could not sleep. I sat on my bed and played my imaginary saxophone against the deafening Arab music as counterpoint. That itself was an achievement, because Arab music is like the desert. It goes on for ever, it never resolves, and in the end it starts to drive you mad.

Those fasting were catching up on their sleep when they could.

The following day, the Gigolo was catching up on his sleep - at the wheel of his car. He missed the bend in the road, turned his car over, wrecked it, killed his wife, and induced a compound, spiral fracture with complications in his right tibia.
The revolutionary committee that was holding us flew him to Switzerland where he stayed for the next six weeks in a skiing injury ward that specialises in spiral fractures. Plastered, plated and screwed, he returned to Libya with his immaculate, form-fitting, black slacks slit to the thigh, a carless widower.

The key turned in the lock. With all the other guards still stupefied by the abstinences of Ramadan, and therefore asleep during daylight hours, the Sweet Smelling Boy had taken the view that allowing Doug and me some time together would not be noticed.
Thus the first time I was allowed into Doug's room, the Sweet Smelling Boy gave Doug and me an astonishing thirty minutes together.
I walked in to find Doug bent over the bathtub in the Pink Suite. I asked Doug what he was doing.
"Cleaning the bathroom," he replied. "Why? There's nothing else to do."
"Do you want to ...?" he said, indicating the lavatory.
"No," I said, with my thumb pointing over my shoulder. "He said we could chat."
"Bloody Hell, Sport," said Doug, putting down the cleaning cloth. "Come in, then."
The Tunisian Cleric occupied his several square feet of floor space in the corner directly facing the door and in full view of anyone entering. His personal world consisted of a couple of white sheets laid out neatly on the floor, an army grey blanket, a copy of the Koran and what looked like a set of Rosary beads, and a tea cup. Doug's bed ran along the wall with the door at one end and a tall, glass fronted bureau occupying the corner, at the other end of his bed. The next wall around bore a window with Venetian blinds, ghiblis raised, and light pouring in. The other outside wall bore a similar, casement window and the ubiquitous wall mounted air conditioner which purred quietly away. But what dominated the room was a massive, imposing desk, the size of a six foot billiard table, at which Doug now seated himself with his

back to the brilliantly illuminating window.

I sat down in action position on the armrest of an armchair, ready to get to my feet in an instant if the door should be opened. I did not want to give the guards any impression of having got too comfortable.

There was also an urgency in me to be warm and not pushy, something I was not very good at. So I looked Doug full in the eye for the duration, except when acknowledging the Cleric, in order to extract the maximum information in whatever time we had available.

We exchanged brief accounts of how we'd got lifted.

"Well, now you know about me," he concluded. "What about you?"

I told him. And concluded by saying, "I took a wrong turning on the way to a party. Drove into the university. Couldn't tell the Libs where I was really going for fear of dropping my mates from the diving club in the shit.

"Took the rap myself," I said. "Won't get any thanks for it, I don't suppose."

"Your right there, mate. So you're an unsung fucking hero?" he concluded.

"Yep."

"And all that bullshit about a U-turn was bullshit?" he summarised correctly.

"Total bullshit. It's not a very good cover story, but it's the only one I've got."

"Well, all that matters is that the Libyans believe it, and you're off the hook," he said.

"And the more people go on about a U-turn, the more chances there are that the Libyans will believe it," I said. "But I don't think it matters anyway. I am now as sure as I can be that we're hostages. And we're all gonna look the same dancing on the end of a rope."

"Thanks a fucking lot, Sport!" said Doug, looking up. "You sure know how to keep my spirits up."

"It's odd you know," I said. "But there are times in solitary - times when it is really bad - that I find myself saying, 'What difference does it make? We're all going to dead a hundred years anyway.' And for a few hours, somehow things don't seem quite so bad."

"That's a bit grim, isn't it?" said Doug.

Then I told Doug about the Gigolo's visit to my room late at night. "They get ...., you get .....," complete with the automatic.

"Yeah. That's what the bastard told me," jumped in Doug. "He even took the clip out of the Browning and showed it to me. It was full of Dum Dum bullets!"

"What, flat nosed or sawn?" I said.

"Sawn," said Doug. "With a cross!"

"Fucking Hell," I said. "The bastards did them themselves. That's worrying."

"I'm permanently constipated," he said. "I can't seem to pass anything."

"I don't think it's constipation," I observed. "I think that with the limited amount of food that we're getting, their simply isn't anything to pass."

Doug felt relieved.

Thirty minutes was up.

I was told to go back to my room.

The following day we got two whole hours together.

We quickly agreed that this detention was the toughest thing that either of us had ever done in our lives.

"We just got to stiff upper lip the bastards," I said.

"Well, whatever it is, we've just got to keep sticking at it," he said

Tucker's principle was that strategy is defined as "Keep firing - even when you've run out of bullets." Unfortunately, Tucker tended to keep firing long after the brighter amongst us had seen not only that he had run out of bullets, but also that the ammunition store had long since rotted and fallen down.

Well, of course, the Libyans held all the cards. There was nothing I could do except to stiff upper lip the bastards. And it was going to take a lot of stiff upper lip. Let's keep firing and see how far it gets us.

"Well, that's when we were young enough and good looking enough that you could shag anything you set eyes on," I lamented.

"Yeah," went on Doug, "and kept the shagging up until your balls ached with emptiness!"

"And for a while after that you can't do any shagging," I lamented further.

"On the contrary!" looked up Doug. "I thought the definition of strategy is to keep firing even when you've run out of bullets."

Doug asked, "So what's been happening?"

I filled him in on the month that he had been missing between our kidnappings.

After the British broke off diplomatic relations with Libya. Britain's affairs were handled by a skeleton staff of British diplomats, at the British Interests Section at the Italian Embassy. All except the skeleton staff of the FCO packed their bags and left. In the time it took for all these decisions to be made and effected, one FCO member took to his bed and stayed there for a week.

"Just the sort of person you need to protect you," observed Doug accurately.

The other side of the coin, I told Doug, was that while the FCO representatives and their families were sitting at Tripoli airport waiting for their flight out, the leader of the evacuation, Julia Miles, wife of Oliver Miles, the British Ambassador to Tripoli, got the entire diplomatic community singing endless choruses of Rule Britannia at the tops of their voices, all the while surrounded by a cohort of militia men bearing the Kalashnikov. This act of defiance was not regarded in diplomatic circles as perhaps the most prudent thing that Julia could have done. But this act of defiance certainly succeeded in letting the whole world know exactly where the British stood.

And what was not generally known, is just how actively involved in our situation were the FCO and the most senior members of government.

By mid June, Sir Geoffrey Howe, the British Foreign Secretary himself, was regularly engaged in correspondence to Britain's friends in the diplomatic world, with a view to putting pressure on the Libyans to grant consular access to Doug Ledingham at least, that was promised on the 13th and again on the 21st of May.

In fact the Foreign Secretary's involvement was rather larger than was in any way known to the public.

The FCO didn't recognize the hostage element at the outset. They thought that some expats had been arrested on bona fide criminal charges.

"It can't be assumed that any arrest of expats is automatically other than bona fide criminal," Sir Geoffrey later said to me.

"The whole hostage affair is covered by the Report of the Commons Foreign Affairs Committee, in which an enquiry was held to establish whether or not HMG had handled the hostage situation as well as they might have done. Under the circumstances, the government was judged to have done everything reasonable.

"You don't break off diplomatic relations easily," Sir Geoffrey told me. "The FCO had no realistic idea of just how crazy were the gang in the Libyan People's Bureau in London."

"Why the Italian embassy?" asked Doug. "I thought the Italians had three forward gears and four reverse gears. Why not someone like - say - the Swiss?"

"Well, it works out," said I, "that the Libyans and the Italians have been historic trading partners for centuries. I mean the two countries face each other across the Mediterranean. If you think about it, Malta, the crossroads of the Mediterranean, is directly between the two, and the Maltese language is essentially a cross breed of Italian and Arabic.

"Everything in this country is either Peugeot or Fiat. The motor cycle police even ride Laverdas, for Christ's sake."

"So the British could rely on the Italians as having probably the best relationship as anyone at the moment with the Libyans," completed Doug. And while he was nodding, he made a connection and frowned. "How far is the Italian embassy?" he solicited.

"Don't worry. I've thought about that," I said. "Four hundred yards."

I went on to tell Doug about the assassination attempt on the 8th of May. Doug then recounted that he was initially held in a different building, and that one day, gunmen started firing at the building he was in. He thought that they were coming to kill him. Instead, one of his guards shouted at him to get down, and proceeded to return fire. Doug indicated that the incoming fire seemed to be coming from a shorter and shorter range, and that he genuinely feared for his life for a number of minutes right there on the floor, until his guards apparently drove off whoever it was that had been firing at them. He was soon afterwards moved to the Italian mansion.

I also recounted to Doug the shelling on Sunday, 13th May. He told me that he had heard it, but didn't have a clue what was going on. I indicated that that was odd because the people in the BPOCO main office building only 400 yards away claimed not to have heard it.

Frowning, Doug, "You seem incredibly well informed!"

"It's my job."

In the first dozen weeks of our detention, the Black Kid demonstrated himself to be mindlessly zealous in the discharge of his duty as jailer. At first we believed that his behaviour towards us was typical of what we could expect to receive from the guards. That prospect was grim indeed. But he was not in fact a mindless zealot at all, just mindless, and the zeal came not from revolutionary fervour but from blind and fearful obedience of orders because he was too stupid to do anything else.

He gave every impression of being a thoroughly nasty and violent piece of work, and as such did Doug describe him, and also very dangerous and unpredictable. In fact, he was immensely stupid. In the end this worked in our favour, since it transpired that he was not typical of what we might expect from the guards, and he later turned out to be the butt of the other guards' worst jokes. It took a lot of routine observation of his behaviour (and that of the other guards) to spot the patterns and to establish potential weaknesses in the way they each conducted themselves. The upshot is that for all his animal cunning and natural watchfulness, the Black Kid was remarkably lax when it came to turning his back on me. It only required him to be satisfied that he had finished a particular chore, such as bringing me my food, for him to turn his back once he had walked out of the cell, but before he had closed and bolted the door. By the time it was important, the Black Kid was observably the guard with the most predictable weakness - and I was able to walk on the marble floors totally silently. His weakness would have to be exploited if I was to escape, and in doing so he might have to be killed. I have to say that he had shown himself to be so despicable in the early days that it would not have cost me too many scruples to kill him if it came to it. Oh yes! I would have hit him twice with the iron bar to make sure he was dead. He would have been dead alright.

"You mean, 'Ugh'?" spat out Doug. "That black bastard? I'd kill the fucker if I ever got a chance." Doug told me that the Black Kid had ordered him to wash up his dinner plates that were covered in tomato paste - without the benefit of hot water or detergent. And stood there and bellowed cave man like noises until Doug had totally failed to clean his plate. Doug found it all the more distasteful that he would have to eat his next meals off an inadequately washed plate.

Our two hours together were interrupted by the arrival of food. It was all in one piece. As Doug held the spoon, we looked at the food, individually trying to decide both how to and who would apportion it.

As I looked on, my blazing eyes gave Doug a false message.

"Do _you_ wanna do it?" he asked, offering me the spoon.

"Nope. _You_ do it." I said.

"Do they look even?" he asked about the bisection, impressing me with both his precision and his good manners.

"They certainly do!" I replied.

"Which one do you want?" he asked, sealing my bond to him.

"The one nearest me," I smiled.

A day or two later, two sets of footfalls stopped outside my door. As I awoke, my first response was the usual heightening of anxiety. My second was the practiced response of getting into seated position on my bed by the time the door lock had been turned even only once. Two Libyans, a guard and one other, walked in. The guard turned around immediately and walked out, and closed and locked the door.

Without looking, I took in the second Libyan from head to foot. His well fitting suit, and his clean, open-necked shirt collar set him apart from the usual. His hair was straight, parted and well groomed. He bore himself well.

My first reaction was that he was a Libyan diplomat come to tell me that I was going home. Then I noticed that he carried his shoes in one arm instead of wearing them. He acknowledged me with the briefest of unseen courtesies that I knew to expect from the better bred Libyans, but he uttered not a word. Instead, he sat on the floor and leaned against the wall, opposite my bed. I prepared myself for an oblique interrogation.

We sat there for several minutes. Then I realised that I had seen the guard indicate with a pointing arm that the newcomer should sit precisely where he now sat.

I lay down again and affectedly went back to sleep.

The afternoon slumbered on. The Muezzin called the faithful to prayer. The door opened. Two guards entered carrying a made up bed. The newcomer got up. The guards placed the bed along the wall where the newcomer had been sitting. The newcomer sat down on the bed. The sun went down. The Muezzin called the faithful to prayer. Food arrived. We cleared out plates. The guard came. The newcomer took my plate and left with the guard, and returned with the plates cleaned. We sat and ignored each other. Then the body language started. He was going to speak. After the initial ice breakers, a story unfolded.

He had been to a love tryst. The girl in question was respectable. He had conducted himself correctly. They had enjoyed each other's company. He had gone home. He had broken no law. Next day he had been arrested, questioned and brought here. Just because her father was a major in the army does not give him the right to arrest and imprison people for a love tryst.

My mind raced. What a story to be told unsolicited. And, then, just exactly where does a Libyan get an expression like "Love Tryst"?

And, then, what kind of idiot was he to think that he could get away with trying it on with the daughter of a Libyan army major? Because he plainly wasn't an idiot. A love lorn loon, perhaps, but not an idiot.

It was all too convenient.

After he had told the story, he looked at me for comment. I made none.

He told the story again. This time with more detail, anguish and eye contact.

He looked at me for comment. I told him that I was married so love trysts were unknown to me. The irony eluded him.

Then he asked me why I was being held. I told him that I didn't know.

We turned the lights out, he bid me the peace of Allah, and we went, surprisingly peacefully to sleep.

The following morning, the Hajji opened the door and brought in our breakfast. After breakfast, the newcomer was allowed out to the toilet.

140

When he came back, he sat on his bed looking sorely depressed. Following the same body language, he told his story again. Again he asked me why I was being held. I told him that I didn't know.

Then the cycle was repeated. Only this time when I indicated ignorance of why I was being held, he told me that perhaps some Libyan boys were being held in England, and that was why I had a problem in Libya. Now we were getting there. More than ever it was important to remain silent. I concentrated on ignoring his presence.

After two more days and several repeats of the cycle, the guards came and took him away. This confirmed him in my mind as a plant. But thirty minutes later he was back to pick up what few belongings he owned. The guards followed him in and, out of keeping, picked up his bed. With his shoes once again in his arm, he paused until the guards had left with his bed. When they had left I motioned to him for the first time, the interrogative "Shuney?" He patiently explained that he was being taken down to a cell outside. Putting two and two together, I concluded that maybe he <u>had</u> done something wrong. But it was still too convenient.

Later I discovered, from Doug, that he too had had exactly the same bizarre story cyclically recounted to him.

In the two days that followed the departure, I heard on several occasions the faint sounds of someone pounding on a metal door, and shouting in Arabic at the top of his voice. On the fifth day, my door opened and in walked the newcomer followed by the Sweet Smelling Boy, and other guards who were carrying the bed back again. After they had replaced the bed, I was told by the Sweet Smelling Boy to get up, bring my stuff and follow him. I had nothing to bring and told him so.

Release? No.

We trooped out, the Sweet Smelling Boy, another guard and me. Down the outside stairs we went and into my old cell. I nearly died. Whoever this newcomer was, he had obviously pulled some strings to get himself out of here after only three days.

The Sweet Smelling Boy stood authoritatively in the gloom of the cell.

I know not what I was expecting to achieve in the second and a half that followed, but I started to turn my body away from him and back again as if to say with exaggeration, "No, I'm not being put in here again." Then something came to my aid.

As I turned away from the Sweet Smelling Boy, I saw my old mattress leaning up against the wall farthest from the door. I pointed out by calm dumb show that this degradation of my circumstances was something that I would not tolerate. In response, the Sweet Smelling Boy ordered the other guard to help him get my bed from upstairs. They left. After they had gone, I went to the mattress and saw to my disgust that on the concrete floor behind the mattress were several piles of human faeces and a large pool of urine. Unusually for a Libyan, I thought, the newcomer had tried to be discreet where waste matter was concerned.

When the guards returned with my bed, I was holding the mattress away from the wall with one hand, and my stomach with the other. I looked back and forth between the Sweet Smelling Boy and the pile of faeces and urine on the floor until the Sweet

Smelling Boy came over to look for himself. He stood there impassively, and awaited a sign of capitulation from me. My contempt for the Libyans and their way of life was never greater. They could live in filth if they wanted to, but they shouldn't expect me to. When I showed no sign of capitulation, the Sweet Smelling Boy, to my astonishment and delight, ordered my return to the upstairs room, following which he confirmed that the newcomer would be staying in the basement.

I discovered from Doug that the guards had deliberately ignored for days at a time the newcomer's pounding and shouting to be allowed to go to the toilet.

After two or three more days the pounding and shouting stopped. I never saw the newcomer again. And, for just a couple of days thereafter, solitary confinement actually had an appeal to it.

Now that the lavatory pan on my side of the building was smashed and permanently out of commission, the Libyans were constrained to getting rid of the increasing volume of kitchen waste by a different route. They did this by the simple expedient of ejecting it through the open window directly above and behind the ground floor, kitchen sink. The growing pile of putrescent kitchen waste now lay, discarded through the open kitchen window, festering in the July and August heat.

I was sitting on the floor with my back to the wall, just beyond the foot of my bed. The door opened. I was confident by now - almost cocky, because I could hold off the insecurity at any given moment, by sheer effort of will and by concentrating on my mental saxophone exercises. I ignored the door and carried on playing my saxophone in my head. I figured that the longer I could keep my concentration the longer I was in control.

Red Head walked in.

First he cast a look around the room and, viewing it as empty, started a rumpus with the Tweedle Dum and Tweedle Dee outside. He proceeded to shut the door. I was badly shaken but wide awake, my heart outside my chest wall by now. Tweedles Dum and Dee protested that I must be in there. There was a real row going on. Red Head looked in once more and still did not see me. He remonstrated with the boys again one of whom pushed past him and, casting the door wide open, scanned the entire room. Then Red Head saw me and without looking at me, pursed his lips and beckoned me to get up, with clear danger in his demeanour. Now I had to take the initiative and do something before he did me any damage. I stopped playing my saxophone and stood up to my full height. He'd forgotten how tall I was and he was momentarily wide eyed at me. Then his brow fell and his lips parted as I ignored his further intimidating gestures, and made the 4 or 5 strides to shake hands with him and to offer, "Keffle Halik?" His jaw dropped. Nobody behaves like that after ten weeks in solitary confinement.

But now he was boiling and, though in spite of shaking hands with me in disbelief, he had to recover the initiative before he lost his authority. The Tweedles by this time were very disconcerted by the momentary loss of face. But that was exactly what I had set out to achieve. Red Head recovered his authority after a few seconds. I need not have doubted that he would. Dum and Dee kept their distance from him and he knew it. I was as good as thrown out the door in a very clear rebuff.

We gathered to get into the white van. My offer to shake hands with Michael was met with a false move and a question as to why I should want to shake hands.

"Body contact is very important," I started. "New born babies can die without it. I'm in solitary confinement, and I'm not getting any body contact at all, and I'm finding it very difficult. So I'm trying to get any body contact I can."

Michael shook my hand.

Doug appeared. "You alright, Sport?" We shook hands.

"Yeah. Bastards. You?" I replied.

"Yeah," business like. "You still in...?"

"Solitary. Yeah," I finished.

"Bastards," he echoed. And, "Michael," acknowledging him.

And Doug and I brought each other up to date the limited amount since our last, stolen, conversation together – principally the well groomed Libyan and his Love Tryst. "That's exactly what he said to me," Doug stated, surprised.

The second meeting with George was held in less formal surroundings than was the first. We sat on low, "comfortable", soft furnishings at a low coffee table, which was broad enough to keep Red Head, who was seated on the opposite side of it, well away from me. Red Head's presence throughout the meeting was a constant impediment to free communication on our part, even though he sat there for the whole meeting every bit the polite and respectful subordinate, head lowered, saying nothing and not comprehending a word of English. I wanted to tell George about Red Head, but felt at heart that I would be wasting my time. Beneath the typically gaudy light fittings, a big, non-plussed Libyan who wore an open necked shirt and a jacket, and who appeared to be in charge, was plainly out of his depth. For the entire meeting he looked nothing but confused. As did his compatriot. Also in attendance was the grinning, Italian Consul General, who contributed nothing. One of the Libyans brought up the question of a visit by the families of the prisoners, and told us that such a visit would be considered favourably. Then another Lib told George that he hoped for an improvement in relations. He talked at some length on the subject, and George told him that HMG could not even think about it while they had these prisoners. The small measure of relief afforded by that lever was quickly doused when George went on to say that letters from our families had been passed to the Libyans, but then asked us if we had received them? And then there was George's business as usual style as we passed verbal messages and received bags of, socks, pants, cigarettes and two books each. I couldn't keep the frustration out of my body language as I observed to George that none of these Libyans had been at the first meeting, and it looked as though we were going to have to start all over again at the beginning. George looked at me with his dancing, hazel eyes and indicated with regret that that was no more than par for the course in trying to get anything done in Libya. The event horizon of departure from this whole, sorry mess simply receded a bit further.

The meeting started to break up with nothing having been achieved. We stood up to go.

Malcolm spoke to George about the cigarettes that Alan and he had received at the first meeting. "The guards just stole them as soon as we got back to wor prison."

"There's nothing I can do about that," replied George, quite reasonably. "I hope you get to keep them this time."

Then Malcolm reminded Alan, and Alan told George about the beatings.

"Oh! This changes everything," said George. With his chin down like an aggressive dog and his eyes protected by his eyebrows like a boxer, he blazed over the top of his glasses in the direction of the Libyans. "I want those men moved now. Or Her Majesty's Government will get to hear about this."

The big, non-plussed Libyan looked left and right - and started to go down for the third time.

"Well done, George," I said a few minutes later. "Would you really have told HMG?"

"Come on," he joshed. "I was going to tell HMG anyway but I wasn't going to tell that to these animals. That's the kind of ace we need. They're terrified of HMG getting to hear about anything they do." And, looking up at Malcolm, he nodded and added, "Let's see if we can get you to different prison."

I looked up following this last exchange, and George caught my eye. A frisson of hope ran over my skin.

Malcolm and Alan were returned to their prison in a vehicle separate from our own. Upon our return to our prison, Michael, Doug and I, were escorted into the mansion, shook hands with each other, and went to our respective cells.

Over the next few days, Doug and I were allowed to spend more and more time together. In the end the guards stopped sending us back to our own rooms for meals, only to have to shepherd us back again after chow was over. We soon had all day together, and I got to know and like Doug a great deal.

I even managed to get a bath. The creamed coloured water heater in the Pink Suite had long since ceased to function, but the built in thermometer on it registered twenty eight Celsius, the temperature of a mother and toddler paddling pool. It was bearable once you had slid in past your nether regions. Doug and I shared the joke of howling in pain as the cold water crept up to the important bits, and then at the diminutive size of our wedding tackle upon getting out of the water again. But the luxury of being clean for the first time in two months was worth the pain.

Later, the door opened. Michael was ushered in. He stood and remained a few feet inside the door. "Hello," he said with elongation, and looked up at us with flickering eyelids from within a constantly moving, inclined head. Doug and I avoided looking at each other for the moment that it took both of us to recover.

"Hello, Michael," we replied.

And a moment later, Doug rebuked, "Well don't just stand there. Come in!"

"Oh! Er, thank you," inclined Michael impeccably. "Er, where would you like me to sit?"

"Anywhere you like, Sport," said Doug.

"Is this your room?" asked Michael of Doug. "It certainly sounds as though it is."

"Well, I don't know that we need to get into that," said Doug, faintly bemused.

I ignored the waste of words, as Doug asked Michael, "What happened to you?"

"What do you mean "to me"?" solicited Michael. "Oh, some people at the university didn't like me." And he looked down and away.

Doug pursued it.

"Some people at the university didn't like me," Michael repeated, and continued. "Look, do you think we'll <u>ever</u> get out of here?"

"Why do you say that?" Doug asked, genuinely baffled.

"It's just that...Oh, I don't know..." Michael bemoaned. "Do <u>you</u> think we'll ever get out of here?" he said addressing me. "You seem to know what's going on."

"Yes, Michael," I said. "I think we're going to get out of here. I've already said that to you." And Doug looked at me, realising that there was more to this than met the eye. A number of seconds of silence followed.

Then Michael exploded. "I'm sorry!" he expostulated.

"What for?" asked Doug, frowning.

My engagement with Doug had been as beneficial as it had been delightful. But for the rest, I actually felt relieved when it was time to return to our separate cells.

That night I slept better than I had done for weeks.

The following morning, the key turned in the lock. Rather more guards than normal came in. And, in addition to my breakfast, they were carrying a large table with collapsible legs, an upright chair and what quickly proved to be a table cloth. The damask lent a dimension of refinement. They laid the food out on the crisp, linen table cloth, complete with one cup for coffee, and a second for milk, which they poured very hot from a thermos flask. I drank them separately, resisting the temptation to educate the Libyans about white coffee.

Michael, Doug and I were permitted an even longer period of free association.

And then, "Welcome back to the real world" took on a whole new meaning. The clamps came down as if free association had never existed. I was peremptorily returned to my room as if a naughty boy. Even Doug looked downcast.

The afternoon wore on.

Some time after the third call to prayer, the sound of brakes could be heard, followed by the sound of a vehicle's doors being slammed or slid shut.

Silence followed, leaving me to return to the calm of my saxophone exercises.

But my exercises were interrupted only a few minutes later by several solid footsteps mounting marble steps. This was not the average humble Muslim.

I stopped playing my mental saxophone and just listened.

The multiple footsteps gravitated into a muted shuffle and then ceased. The air conditioner in the office became momentarily louder then softer, then louder then softer again. Words could be heard. Brief questions asked. Answers given – some growled, some with a Geordie accent.

When dinner was being served, I was ordered back to Doug's room. There to my mild surprise, but certainly to my delight were standing Alan and Malcolm glazed, open mouthed, heads turning left and right, and shaking. Doug was his usual seated self, generously trying to engage the newcomers, both of whom were still in the throes of trying to believe that their circumstances had indeed changed.

Almost nothing was said, but courtesy and good manners reigned as we divided up dinner to make sure that everybody, including the Tunisian Cleric had a proper share. We ate in silence.

Then Doug took the lead in what little conversation that followed. Michael tended to defer to Alan, as they were both about the same age – early to middle fifties. Malcolm and Alan were wide-eyed, desultory, sotto voce and guarded in their replies. I sat and watched the dynamics, as this meant a whole new set of relationships with their potential for conflict – prison life notoriously being a pressure cooker with the relief valve screwed down tight.

The following day, shortly after the second call to prayer, Alan and Malcolm were wheeled into my room and stood about at a loss. Two minutes later the door opened again and three guards brought in two additional chairs and put them around the table. One guard smoothed the table cloth, still there from its first use, yesterday.

Food appeared. The same meal as normal. But lots of food – about double the normal portion per person. But also a flask of hot, strong coffee and a vessel of hot milk. And sugar. And, contrary to all good Socialist Peoples' Libyan principles, the guards gave every impression of waiting on us. We ate and drank. The guards departed.

I reached for the coffee and poured myself another inch of scalding rocket fuel, being careful to leave enough for the others. As I eased the flask over, Malcolm gently placed his right hand around the plastic thermos lid that was serving as his cup, and eased it half an inch in my direction. I barely heard the Wallsend vowels of, "Please, Robin," but acknowledged his request with a faint but definite nod, and proceeded to serve him until he nodded a "Stop." I tipped the flask in Alan's direction and looked at him. "No," he growled, eyes down. "Thank you." Manners maketh man.

"D'ya always eat like this?" asked Malcolm quietly. And they both looked at me.

"What, this much food? The content is normal," I said. "But the quantity is about double, and I've never had the coffee or hot milk..."

"Shhhhh!" they both said ducking and looking around. "D'ya always talk that loud?"

I frowned slightly and said, "That's normal speaking voice." And got the same reaction.

"What's wrong?" I said softly.

"We weren't allowed to speak at wor last prison. If they heard us talkin' we'd get a beatin'."

146

"Did that happen often?" I asked.

"Often enough," offered Alan, animation all over his face, watched by Malcolm, anguish all over his.

"No. I mean like this," and Malcolm indicated the table and the white linen.

"No. This is the first time," said I.

"Are ya sure ya don't normally eat like this?" he persisted.

"Alright. Yesterday was the first time, but only as a consequence of the meeting with George. So really this is all new," I said. "I have never had these quantities before."

They were both still looking at me.

I look directly into their eyes. "It's true," I assured them. "I used to eat my dinner off that," referring with my thumb, to the bureau behind me. "Why?"

"We 'ave to eat stand'n' up," Malcolm said, and looked at Alan. Alan raised his eyebrows and nodded his assent. "Some days we didn't get food at all."

"I've had that," I ruefully agreed.

They told me about the over crowded and filthy conditions they had been in - multiple nationalities, forty to a cell, all sleeping on the floor together, filthy ablutions, showers that consisted of a hose pipe and a drum of Vim just long enough to work up a lather whereupon their guards would turn off the hosepipe and Malcolm or Alan would have to walk around for another three days with unrinsed Vim all over their bodies.

And then there were the beatings.

"I was in solitary confinement for ten weeks," I said.

"What by yourself?" asked Malcolm.

"That...that's what it means," said Alan tenderly, turning slightly to Malcolm.

"Aye. We 'ad that," added Malcolm.

And Alan pointed out that the flow of prisoners was high and sometimes the place was empty apart from the two of them.

The guards came and cleared the dishes, and showed all three of us to Doug's room.

We quickly got a lot out onto the table.

Michael taught English as a university lecturer at the Great Al Fatah University and lived on a farm about ten kilometres South of Tripoli.

Alan taught English as a Foreign Language and lived in a camp at Sabratha, sixty kilometres West of Tripoli.

Malcolm was a welder in the oil industry somewhere near Murada, South of Marsa Brega oil terminal, six hundred kilometres East of Tripoli.

Doug was airport manager for British Caledonian at Tripoli Universal Airport and lived somewhere in Central Tripoli.

I was the senior telecommunications, power and buildings engineer on the Libyan Coaxial Cable Project and lived in a suburb of Tripoli, however improbably, called Giorgimpopili – GP.

The conversation soon turned to the use of the English language.

"Do you like Kipling?" asked Alan.

Nobody did the joke. But Alan and I trawled our memories and, in unison while the others listened, we managed:

> "If you can keep your head when all about you
> Are losing theirs and blaming it on you;
> If you can keep your head when all men doubt you
> But make allowance for their doubting too..."

Then we struggled a bit and only picked it up again at:

> "...If you can meet with Triumph and Disaster
> And treat those twin imposters just the same..."

"Well, we've met with fucking disaster alright, Sport!" put in Doug. And while we all roared with laughter, Alan commented, "Yeah, isn't that the truth."

We left "If" alone...

The door opened. We clammed up. Red Head walked in.

Over the next, silent, few minutes, Red Head, backed by Tweedle Dum and Tweedle Dee, never looked at one of us for so much as a second, but laid down the steely law in Arabic. None of us understood the Arabic, but the limited body language was pretty clear. And so, therefore, was the law.

As if his diatribe wasn't hard enough on us, he finished by saying in Arabic and then, for the only time I ever heard him in English, that under no circumstances were we to talk about politics.

When he had finished, Red Head stood motionless and silent as if waiting for questions. They came from Alan. Could we have some cigarettes, please and some - er - books.

Red Head replied in Arabic, and the three guards left.

The instant the guards had gone, I said to everybody that it would be possible to escape. And we quickly agreed on one point. One out - all out. We weren't any longer going to do this piece meal.

But we would not be able to give so much as an inkling of what was going on by, for example, indicating any changes to established routine. That meant that if we were all going to go, we would have to go simultaneously. That would require synchronisation and that would require everybody to be able to count.

"So let's start learning to count at the same speed," I finished, and started to mark out seconds by snapping the fingers of my left hand. "Come on!"

They all joined in, except Michael.

Michael let out a weary sigh, looked for just a few seconds as though he was about to join in, and refolded his arms.

"Come on, Michael," I exhorted. "We've got to do this."

With body language that was rapidly becoming familiar, he indicated his disdain, and then said, "Oh, I really don't think I want to do this." And he didn't.

"If you want to go, you can do so without me," he went on, turning away. But having turned away he turned part way back to see what reaction he had evoked, knowing full well what the reaction would be. He then completed the charade with a throwaway "I'm sorry!" He had spoilt the game and now he was apologizing.

I couldn't believe it. Here we had five people who had no idea of how long they would be here, or even if they would ever get out, and one of them is rejecting at the first hurdle the prospect of a means of escape.

High pitched air started to rush out of my mouth, and anxiety attempted to overwhelm me.

I choked back the panic and took half a pace forward. My experience of Michael's lack of preparedness to face his situation had already convinced me that he was going to take some work. But I wasn't ready for this. The man was his own greatest liability. We were never going to get anything done with this millstone around our necks.

I let counting seconds simultaneously quietly drop.

By the end of the first week together, we had established an important pattern of telling each other what we had done during the day, and of offering the minor congratulations for such, that constituted re-assurance. A slow dance emerged, consisting of reading what little there was, punctuated by meals of prison food, and slowly and circumspectly telling each other what we had done.

Malcolm had been getting ready to go on leave from his oil camp in the desert, where he welded together sections of oil pipe. He was off to Portugal for two weeks' holiday. As he was leaving, Malcolm did what all the rest of us did. He took all the personal outgoing mail from the other expatriates in order to post it in England, or at least somewhere in continental Europe. That knocked up to ten days off the delivery time by circumventing the Libyan postal system.

Malcolm got the chartered flight from his desert oil camp to Tripoli, where he started to go through the normal process of getting a scheduled flight out of the country.

He found himself subject to an aspect of the Libyan airline system that was then unique in the world - a customs check on the way out of the country. This check had been instituted a year or two previously following the successful hijacking of an internal Libyan Arab Airlines flight by a group of Stray Dogs who then forced it to fly to Malta where it landed.

"For the reason of this outgoing customs check," chimed in Doug, "flying out of Libya was the most popular sector with all airline pilots worldwide for more than just the reason that they were getting out of Libya. It meant additionally that there was virtually no chance of there being a bomb aboard their aircraft."

Unfortunately, it also meant that Malcolm was called into an interview room and, after a two hour wait during which he had missed his flight, some Libyan officials came in and he was told to open his bags.

Malcolm could swear that he knew one of the officials but just couldn't place him. More or less immediately the officials went for the pile of letters that he was carrying. They told Malcolm to open them one at a time and read them out loud. Malcolm did so and had read about a dozen letters when he opened the next one and pulled out the contents. A sizeable newspaper clipping fell out onto the table.

The newspaper cutting reported the abortive attempt on Colonel Gaddafi's life on Tuesday the 8th of May, complete with the photograph of the three dead Libyans who had been killed crossing the Tunisian border, and the capture of the leader of the planned assassination, whose capture caused the assassination attempt to fail.

Malcolm started to panic. But he did not panic half as much as a few minutes later when he read out loud the letter that accompanied the newspaper cutting.

The letter was from one of the young secretarial girls at the oil camp to her mother in England. Among all the other things she wrote, she described what she knew of the abortive assassination attempt saying that a large number of people had been involved in trying to kill Colonel Gaddafi, but that "the stupid shits missed".

Malcolm nearly died.

When he looked up with blood pounding in his ears, it was to see faint smirks on the faces of the customs officials.

"That's when the penny dropped," he said. "That's when I knew where I'd seen that face before - as I were pickin' up the mail in the secretary's office. He'd followed me on the flight all the way to Tripoli."

Malcolm was arrested. The ostensible charge was carrying the mail where the Libyan postal system, as with most postal systems worldwide, including the British Post Office at the time, had a monopoly on carrying the mail. Accordingly, it was a bona fide offence, with prima facie evidence, but compounded out of all reason by the content of this particular letter.

No-one knew for over three weeks that Malcolm had gone missing. This was on account of two things. First he was going on leave to Portugal for two weeks and no-one, not even his wife, expected to see him for that duration. And secondly, when he did not show up at work again on the due date, his company assumed that he was just another expatriate who had jumped ship and would never return to complete his contract.

It took a bit of digging by George Anderson to ascertain that Malcolm had in fact been arrested.

The door opened. Red Head walked in. The silent room become more silent. We kept our heads down. Red Head looked about him for someone on whom to exercise his authority. And found it.

The Tunisian Cleric appeared to levitate from his white sheeted world on the floor, assisted by Red Head pulling his left wrist and his left ear. The Tunisian started to squeal and then to shriek. But the levitation continued.

Without looking up from my position on Doug's bed, I said flatly, "Leave him alone."

All the other heads in the room dissembled with embarrassment and impotence. Red Head was unmoved. The Tunisian continued to shriek in terror.

I raised my head but not my eyes, and insisted, "Malleish, eh?"

All heads went further down with reproachful outlets of breath as I walked further onto the thin ice. Red Head turned his face a mite towards me and turned back again. The Tunisian continued to shriek.

I just wasn't prepared to see this bullying go on. Somebody had to make a stand.

Facing Red Head but not looking at him, I snapped out, "Inte mush quaise!"

He was a bad man, but you weren't supposed to tell him that. All heads came up with looks of real alarm and scanned back and forth between Red Head and me. Malcolm's look to me said, "Now you're for it."

Red Head dropped the Tunisian who collapsed in a heap on the floor, motionless except for his terrified sobbing, and came over to me. He feinted by starting to seat himself to my right on the bed beside me. But as he lowered himself, he placed his left hand high on my neck, and started strangling me by squeezing my neck and crushing my head down onto my chest.

I managed to squeeze out, "Let go of me," before my windpipe was sealed.

With my back now bent double and my chin on my chest, I couldn't breathe. And I couldn't get away.

I really couldn't breathe. Distress was pervading my body. Alarm bells were pervading my head. I had to get out of this somehow - and fairly soon.

Then suddenly, for all that the insanity during the brush with madness of my earliest days in detention had been countered by a voice of seemingly random argument from inside my own head, the voice now took on an unparalleled clarity - a deity speaking to me from The Void - that enabled me to remain calm even as Red Head was on the point of choking the life out of me. I heard the voice say, "One must illuminate the border between life and death. Regardless of what may arise, one should be prepared to receive ninety nine percent of an enemy's attack and stare death in the face in order to illuminate the path."

So, I just let Red Head keep strangling me with no resistance and no show of resistance. Where my body went I would let it go until I could find a way to do the switch - unless I passed out first. He kept crushing me. I really couldn't breathe and I became fearful that, sooner or later, he would break my back or my neck.

Then, as he continued to crush me, and my back continued to fold up, I felt the weight of my body go just past my point of balance. That tiny difference made all the difference, allowing me to slide off the bed, and I was able to roll forward, clean out of his unsuspecting grasp and onto the floor.

I came out of the roll into a sitting position, Japanese style with my hands in front of me, facing him but looking out of the sides of my eyes at Malcolm. I held Malcolm's gaze even as Red Head shouted at me to get up and sit again upon the bed. I waited until after he had shouted a second time and he was drawing breath to shout a third time. And, as he started to voice his third shout, I moved and calmly started to do what he had first said. Red Head's mouth fell open and his eyes widened.

But before I moved, he leaned forward to strike me. I remained motionless. He saw something in my eyes. I saw a light in his eyes. He got up and left the room.

There was no more bullying after that.

But there was no more Tunisian either. By the time we were shepherded into Doug's room the following day, the Tunisian had gone. I never saw him again.

I developed Dry Eye – a failure of the fluid that lubricates the eyeball - a condition exacerbated by smoking. Not really surprising - we'd got through the two hundred cigarettes in no time. Doug gave me his bottle of Optrex. It was soothing, but it did not cure the condition. I needed to stop smoking.

Red Head came in, to his usual cold reception. But he threw a surprise onto the big table. The pink paper fell open as it landed to reveal the banner - International Financial Times - and three different editions to boot. Michael was later to explain that in a world of censorship, the Financial Times was generally regarded, even by the Libyans, as being the newspaper of the most even handed reporting in the world.

When Alan asked if we could have more cigarettes, Red Head launched into an Arabic homily on the need for us to ration our consumption. By the time he had finished, it was clear that we would receive another carton, but that rationing would come into force - the very reason why I quit smoking on the first day of captivity.

The following day, Red Head brought another two hundred Winston. Only this time he did some arithmetic, and told us how long the cigarettes would have to last before we would receive more. The schedule was tight fisted, but no-one felt the need to argue. We sighed as he wrote the schedule on the inside of the still full carton, and put it inside the bureau in the corner of the room.

As the door closed behind him, I grabbed the FTs, handed them out, and told everybody to scour them systematically to see if there was anything about us.

There was one short item, but it contributed nothing new to our knowledge.

To our surprise, we got editions of the FT every week from then on. We repeated the same pattern of scouring the pages amongst us to see what there was. There were a few comments or mentions of activity around us, about which we had to be scrupulous in our assessment of what it meant, rather than get carried away with ourselves. Only once did we see anything of significance, an obscure column inch buried deep in the middle of one edition, but the significance was not plain to us at the time.

The door opened. A Caucasian was ushered in. The last vestiges of his fine, straight, receded hair bore the last vestiges of a ginger colour. The last vestiges of slight freckles on his tanned but otherwise colourless face were matched by liver spots. He padded a tentative and undetermined way across the carpet and into the room. His open necked, check shirt and tan trousers matched the blandness of his face.

"George Bush," he announced with raised chin and an attempt at a smile.

George sat down in one of the upright chairs that now surrounded the table, and looked up and around at us, a mouth slightly open, and an eye that lit on nothing.

Doug introduced himself.

George told us his story.

George had been arrested. "Oh, no!" he said in his relaxed Yorkshire tones. "Not just recently. Weeks ago."

"What for?" said Doug.

"Well, I was at the house of the local Major, and they just came and arrested me."

"What did they arrest you for?" said Doug.

"I don't know," said George. "One minute I was in the house having a laugh and joke with the major, and the next thing, when it came time to go, I stepped out the door and there were the police waiting to arrest me."

Remembering the Major in the story of the Love Tryst, Doug continued. "Well you must have done something to come to their attention. What were you doing at the house of the local Major?"

"Nothing much. Just having a bit of fun. A laugh and a joke - you know. I mean we had a few drinks but that's nothing is it?"

"So how come you're here?" Doug continued.

"I don't know," said George.

"Well, I mean, have you been convicted? Sentenced? Drinking?" said Doug in a good imitation of a dentist pulling teeth.

"Oh, no. The last thing that happened was I went to court yesterday and was found not guilty. Then as soon as I stepped out of the court, I were re-arrested and brought here. I don't know why."

"Hostage," said Doug, quietly nodding. "So you got done for drinking, then let go, then re-arrested and brought here."

"I don't know," said George.

"Hostage," reaffirmed Doug, nodding again.

Now we are six.

George later went on to describe the prison that he had been held at all the while.

It was on the Eastern outskirts of Tripoli, he told us. It was more like a row of villas that a real prison. Oh, it had a high wall, on the other side of which was the women's prison. "I don't suppose it would have done much good breaking into there," he quipped. "You could come and go pretty much as you pleased.

"It was funny though," he went on. "They stick you in prison for no reason, and then they feed you off silver plates.

"Anyway, I tried to tell them that I hadn't done anything, but by that time it was Kalass".

The magistrate went through whole thing again from the beginning as if for the first time.

He ignored the questions about my family in England, but went through every single other question of the previous interrogation, with the same minute and tedious attention to detail as before.

And I answered in the same fashion. Tell the truth where it matters. Be clear about significant detail, be hazy about insignificant detail and tell a slightly different version of the insignificant detail each time you tell it. If you tell the story exactly the same each time, then they will know you're lying. Distort the truth where necessary to avoid an awkward detail. Lie only where it is uncheckable. Mix up truth and lies so that they have no clear pattern of what you look like when you're lying. Then when you really have to lie, they will not be able to tell the difference.

And finally, only answer a direct question. Don't complete their sentences for them. Don't answer what appears to be a statement of fact, and don't pick up on inference or ellipsis...

But the biggest problem with telling lies is in remembering what lies you have told.

It was six weeks since they'd asked these questions and they had a transcript of what I'd said. I had no such transcript. That taxes the memory.

After two and a half hours, I signed today's transcript and was taken back to the Italian mansion.

Red Head walked in. He calmly sent me to my room, and told me that I was not to tell any of the others what was going on or why. I was terrified that I was in trouble for opposing him over the Tunisian Cleric. After an hour or so, the Sweet Smelling Boy, Laughing Boy and Tweedle Dee came and got me. They took me to the Pink Suite to wash and shave and to put on a fresh shirt. I scoffed inwardly at the idea of a shirt that was fresh, and that I had already washed and shaved that morning, cutting the skin on my throat with the crummy, disposable razor blades. I pointed out to the guards that shaving again was a senseless exercise. But, against my own better judgement, I took the opportunity of having something to do, and washed as bid, only to open up the morning's shaving cut as I did so. To my surprise, I was shown back into Doug's room.

The three guards all started to groom me, in full view of the others, who sat in their usual chairs.

There were six hands on me at once. They smarmed down my hair. I bridled. They checked the cleanliness of my hands. I told them not to be bloody stupid. They pawed the buttons of my shirt to make sure that they weren't cross buttoned. I drew the line - and tried to wriggle free. "Will you let me go?" I thought. They did not. No, they would not let me go. But, as they worked their way up the already, correctly buttoned shirt, they saw the obvious traces of blood on the collar. Concern, approaching alarm, reigned supreme in their body language. They took a clean towel and started to pat away the traces of blood that still issued from the cuts on my throat. The red mist descended. And, in a bizarre parody of what was probably to become one of the greatest songs written in the last quarter of the twentieth century, if not ever, I found the only swear word in Arabic that I had ever heard, and yet not for a few more seconds ever understood.

"Bismillah!" I spat out. "Will you let me go?" They instantly ceased pawing me, stood back, held their breath, and looked at the floor with their mouths open, totally silent. The effect on the other hostages was the same.

Glaring at the guards, I snatched the towel from Laughing Boy, gave one, definitive wipe of the blood off my own throat, and ejaculated the towel in the general direction of the guards. It bounced off someone's chest and fell to floor. Nobody even thought about picking it up.

There was no more pawing after that.

Taking advantage of my momentary ascendancy, I asked the Sweet Smelling Boy what, exactly was afoot.

"Shuney?" I asked.

"Inte. Zowjetye," he replied.

My eyes widened slightly and my body relaxed.

I was escorted out of the Italian mansion, around the corner and up the road that ran along the wall outside my old cell. In another hundred yards we came to a T junction.

Directly across the T junction stood a dirty-white, rendered, breeze block house, with a small, mature garden, separated from the pavement by a tree lined, rendered wall. The house also had a large driveway, which gave directly onto the footpath. At the far end of the driveway, dark shadow obscured all else.

I was taken through the shadow, through an open door and into a large house. Upstairs, I was ushered into the gloom of tawdry, brown panelling, a yellowing ceiling and gaudy light fittings which illuminated the room inadequately.

At a large desk sat two, suited, Libyan officials. The older one was grey, moustachioed, bespectacled, benign, and overweight. The other was slimmer, better dressed, and attentive to the bits of paper on the desk that they were both discussing. On the wall opposite the desk was a map of Libya. On the wall facing the door was a map of rather more of the Sahara Desert. Beneath the maps, nestled around the right angle beneath them, was a black, leather, sectional sofa, on which was seated a demure, slender, young woman of about the same age as my wife, with her legs crossed beneath a below-the-knee, cotton, summer dress. A small, platinum blonde child was lazily crawling around on the floor.

Following the few additional seconds that it took for my eyes to finish adjusting to the gloom and to take all this in, I recognized Pat. I had to look twice to realise that the child crawling around on the floor was Christopher - now three months older and fully three months more grown.

Pat saw the flame in my eyes - the danger in my eyes. And, as whenever she saw me disquieted, she made no move to do anything. I sat next to her on the sofa, and kissed her. Through the light scent that she had sprayed on many hours before and which had now mostly evaporated, her natural, pungent, hormonal odour penetrated my being - a smell that had always stimulated the primal, animal instinct in me. I clung to her. The two Libyan officials summarily dismissed the guards in spite of their protestations to the contrary, and ostentatiously buried their heads back in their own work.

Knowing how little time we might have, I got straight down to cases, following the briefest of exchanges about the children's welfare. They would be OK. It was hard, but that would have to wait. Getting me out was, for the moment, more important.

"What's happening?" I said straightway, searching her beautiful, hazel eyes.

Pat and Christopher had been on the road since 6.30 that morning. Since then, Pat had engaged three separate taxis to take her to see Col Gaddafi at the Azizia Barracks. The first taxi driver had simply refused to accept the fare when Pat told him where she wanted to go. Subsequently, each taxi that she engaged had dutifully followed her navigation instructions until her destination became clear. At that point the driver simply stopped the taxi, took Pat's money as shown on the meter, and refused to go any further.

Following these abortive attempts, Pat had taken further taxis to locations of known administration officials in the hope of persuading them to let her see Col Gaddafi or, better still, me. The Libyans themselves had brought her here.

The singular and quite remarkable result of her persistence was that she was now sitting beside me.

The twofold and regrettable disadvantages of her persistence were that, for fear of missing an opportunity to be taken to see me, she had not dared suspend her persistence to take even five minutes to change her dear son's nappy, and the poor, dear Christopher had been wearing the same, soiled nappy for many, many hours. Enduring the discomfort with characteristic fortitude and silence, Christopher was nevertheless being a rat. It was totally understandable of course, because at a stage in his life when he needed it most, the attention naturally due to him was being diverted elsewhere.

"What else?" I asked.

Pat said that she was afraid that the two Libyans at the desk would hear her if she told me. I told her to talk into my ear while we gave the impression of canoodling. They were already used to us doing that, so they would be less likely to pay any regard.

"I'll just giggle by way of acknowledgement," I said.

So she did, and they did, and I did. And all the while, Pat went on to tell me about all the frantic activity at the FCO and among all the UK's diplomatic "friends".

When she'd finished talking, I asked, "When did you find out about me?" as I crushed her lips beneath mine.

"George rang after about ten days," she replied.

"What took him so long?"

"He said that there would have been no point in alarming me if this had been just another routine arrest that would have seen you released after ten days or so. Then you could have told me yourself," she explained. "But once it had become clear to the FCO, they decided they had to tell me. Fleur Fraser's been very good."

"Well, it's nice to have someone like George on the case that we know and can trust. It's quite warming actually," said I, without being able to afford a laugh. "We've had two meetings with him."

Pat read the danger signal in my eyes, warning her not to tell anyone of my previous knowledge of George. She just continued to tell all the apparently available news.

And then it was over, and now it was time to play with Christopher.

"Gak-Gak," I called gently. "Come to Daddy." But he kept his head down, regarding me suspiciously from the corners of his eyen, steadfastly refusing to acknowledge my existence.

Time was at a premium, so I just returned my attention to Pat. What little conversation we were making was disappointingly interrupted by the elder of the two Libyans seated at the desk. He spoke only Arabic, but the signal appeared clear enough. So I ignored him. At his second and surprisingly patient attempt to gain our attention, I sighed, kissed Pat and stood to leave. And as I turned to get Christopher for a kiss, it became clear what the Libyan Official had been trying to communicate.

Christopher had crawled in amongst a rat's nest of electrical wiring beneath the desk and, now playing with a live plug, was in realistic danger of electrocuting himself. I stooped, seized the reluctant Christopher around the waist, eased him out of the rat's nest and passed him to Pat. I kissed her again and turned to leave. But after a couple of "malleishes", accompanied by a warm and gentle wave to resume my seat, the Libyan Official demonstrated a compassion rarely seen to date. I sat down again and took Christopher on my lap. His nappy stank to high heavens. He sat with his head against his mum, who briefly explained to him why he shouldn't play with the plug. Christopher ignored me as if he didn't know me, in spite of my kisses. I showed Pat the residual scarring on my leg, for an acknowledgement that it was still healthy. With one look and years of professional training, she nodded a brief affirmative.

Then it really was time to go. I kissed Pat again, and looked her in the eye.

"Get me out of here," I started. "You're the only one who can..."

She nodded another brief affirmative, and said, "OK." Then, "George is trying to arrange another meeting for tomorrow."

I kissed her again, and then found myself in the company of the guards, and walking the hundred yards back to the Italian mansion.

As the guards and I approached the Italian mansion, I swatted a non-existent mosquito on the top of my head and laboriously wiped the non-existent sweat from my brow with the back of my wrist.

Malcolm and Doug saw the signal from the ghiblied window in Doug's room, and told the others that everything was OK.

The Hajji ushered me into Doug's room.

"Can I have something to eat," I asked the Hajji, while moving pinched thumb and fingers in front of my mouth. The Hajji raised his chin, lowered his eyelids and left.

"What happened?" said Doug. "You've been away for ages!"

"Listen carefully. I don't know how much time we've got," said I, "and I'm not supposed to be telling you this anyway."

So, with the sole interruption of the Hajji's momentary return and taciturn but apologetic "maffeish" to say that all the lunch things had been cleared away and that there was no food left, I told them.

George had told Pat about me by the end of about ten days after my capture. She said that George has been jumping up and down for meetings with us ever since day one.

Fleur Fraser at the Consular Department in London was Pat's principal contact at the FCO and was extremely useful in providing up to date information to Pat, and to the wives of Doug, Alan and Malcolm, and to Michael's sister, who they had only lately managed to get hold of.

All five of the women were in regular contact with each other and with Fleur.

Questions have been asked in the House.

Sir Geoffrey Howe was personally involved and taking a highly visible lead in the whole hostage situation.

Ian Ridout has been trying to get me out.

The government has made contact with the UN, the Greeks, the Italian Ambassador to London, the Moroccans and the Tanzanians.

"Yes," I said. "Apparently Julius Nyerere is putting in a lot of effort on our part."

The Italian's have been leaning on the Libyans to allow family visits, and the Libyans appear to be posing no obstacle to the wives coming out here. Apart from getting a predictable run-around this morning, Pat had encountered nothing but courtesy and respect, except from the taxi drivers who she'd asked to take her to see Col Gaddafi.

"Well, that's understandable," chimed in Doug.

But the word is out. There won't be any deals. There have been attempts by the Libyans at diplomatic horse trading, such as deals over visas and that, and recognition of replacement Libyan diplomatic staff in London. But the British government is refusing to budge on anything to do with Libya until we are released. They won't bring forward the trial date of the Libyans arrested on the bombing charges in order to try to get us out. They won't even allow them bail pending a trial.

Pat and the women are furious about that.

The women were going to try to see Mrs Thatcher to see if she can do anything.

The MP, Richard Luce has been on to Sir Adam Thompson.

"Bloody Hell!" said Doug.

"And the reason we haven't been getting meetings with George is because the revolutionary committee that's holding us has refused permission," I added.

But the Greeks have been granted permission to visit us.

"What?" said Doug.

The Syrians are to mention us in Libya, as Arabs talking to brother Arabs.

Another Brit has been picked up for carrying drugs.

"Oh! Christ!" said Doug.

"Yeah," I said. "Apparently, when he came in from Malta, a Libyan customs official asked him if he had any drugs on him. He said that he had a bit of cannabis in his pocket, but that it was for his own personal use. Apparently he's going to go down for seven years."

"The fucking idiot!" said Doug.

They want an MP to come out here.

"Who? The Libyans?" asked Alan. "Well that's a step in the right direction."

It wasn't. It was just a propaganda exercise.

"But, Julius Nyerere..." said Alan.

"I know," I agreed. And then I said, "Alan." And paused to get his full attention. "Carole's coming out."

Alan rolled his head from side to side, batted his eyelids and silently glowed.

"And that's about it."

Everybody sat motionless, except Doug.

"My God!" he said. "I don't think I could have remembered all that lot."

"It is fairly intense," I agreed, and picked up my book.

That evening after dinner, Malcolm and I went over the whole thing again. Only this time Malcolm wasn't as concerned about the diplomatic tangle as he was about Pat. I told him how passionately I loved her, but also how turbulent our marriage was.

And with his seductive grin, he said, "So ya do love 'er then? Aye, well, send 'er a card."

I looked at him. "Make one up out of lett'as!" he ordered.

So I got the old, Italian magazine, and carefully cut letters and a background out of it, glued the whole lot together into a small greeting card, and slid it into the back of a mostly full packet of Rothmans that somebody produced from nowhere.

The following day, the guards came and got me much as they had done on the previous day. This time, however, there was no attempt at either secrecy or trying to smarten me up for the visit.

I was taken to a Spartan office in a different building where, to my delight was to be found Pat once again, this time accompanied by George.

In one corner of the room sat a motionless Libyan. He was leaning slightly forward with his hands delicately clasped in front of him, and his eyes cast tactfully down. He sported a thick black moustache, and an unruly shock of thickly curled black, black hair. But his good looking and obviously well bred face was otherwise properly shaven. He wore a sports jacket with complementary slacks and shirt with open necked collar. The whole, tasteful ensemble was, however, surmounted by a Burberry scarf. I had to work to ignore him.

"That's Kamal," said George without looking up, and George, Pat and I sat down on low sofas. The walls of the room consisted of glass panels atop half height walls. It looked like an open plan office. I would need to speak softly. I took a cigarette and gave one to Pat.

We had covered what I thought was all the current news the previous day, so, fighting to suppress my emotions, I asked about the children. How was Katy...? She's got a new bike. Where was Gak-Gak...? With friends of ours in Tripoli. How was Ross's head...? Pretty much healed now.

I started to tell Pat about the appalling conditions that I had been kept in for the first few weeks. I started to mention the beatings...but looked up at George and motioned towards the Libyan in the corner.

"Oh, no!" said George. "No need to be quiet. Say it out loud. They need someone to tell them how badly you're being treated."

So I continued and found myself in a wholly unnecessary display of tears, essentially for the Libyan's benefit. I told Pat to stand so that we could hug, head to toe. She stood and we hugged - but she plainly felt a little uncomfortable. George smiled benignly. Kamal discreetly pretended that the hug wasn't happening. But the tears kept coming, and finally I let go at Kamal, asking him if he was happy now.

Kamal surprised me by looking slightly sheepishly into my eye. George told me that Kamal was one of the better ones. I asked George what was a good Libyan, apart from a dead one. George told me that, no, this one is educated, the son of a diplomat, and that he was more than usually useful in resolving what Kate Adie of the BBC would become fond of calling "the usual Libyan muddle".

I'd made my point. I shut up.

But what came next surprised me, even for Pat. As we hugged, she whispered a message into my ear in tones so low that even I could barely hear them. So it was fairly sure that neither George nor Kamal could.

"Terry Waite has got involved," she said.

"Who is Terry Waite?" I asked.

"He works for the Church of England," she said. "He got the British hostages out of the Iranian Hostage affair in Teheran. We've been in contact with him. But it's all got to remain secret. You can't tell anybody. Even the FCO doesn't know. George can't find out. You won't tell anyone, will you?"

"OK."

"Terry will only go public when he personally wants to do so," she finished. "That's how he operates."

We released each other and sat down again. This time, I sat next to George.

With no time to spare, I said directly, "When are we going to get another meeting."

"This is a meeting," he said tritely, but truthfully.

I just looked at him.

"I'm jumping up and down for a meeting," said George looking at me.

"George!" I exclaimed, slapping the top surface of his thigh good and hard. "George! For Christ's sake get me out of here!"

"I'm working on it," said George, slapping my thigh good and hard back.

"I'm not seeing any tangible results!" I blasted.

So he told me what really happened in HM Diplomatic Corps. The others were going to be very interested to hear this.

Then it was time to leave.

We stood up and Pat and I took a cigarette each. After we had lit them, I slid the packet of Rothmans into her hand bag.

"Here. You'll need those while you're here," I said.

"No. You need them more than I do," said Pat as she pulled them out again and thrust them into my hand.

"No, no. We've got plenty," said I, as I crushed her fingers around the pack.

She looked into my eyes as pain took hold. Uncomprehending she did as she was bid.

The following day we had another short meeting with George in attendance, before Pat returned to England.

"I'm trying to get a conjugal visit," said Pat.

"I'm afraid that's all been stopped," said George.

"Why?" I asked.

George explained. The others were going to be even more interested to hear this.

When George had finished, we shared a cigarette and she gave.me the remains of the packet of Rothmans, which I took back with me to the Italian mansion. There I found to my surprise, but no more than I had planned, that Pat had hidden a two page letter in the lining of the cigarette packet - the first letter that I had received from her during the whole of my detention.

The letter told me for the first time in her life how much she missed me - more than she thought she ever would. But then, the letter said, you probably knew that anyway. And the whole letter told me more in one reading of about five minutes than she had ever said to me in her life before.

But before we departed from the meeting, Pat said that she had smoked a cigarette or two in the hotel room the previous night, and it had taken some time for it to dawn on her that somehow the cigarette packet had seemed rather thicker than normal, and only as she was about to throw the empty packet away had it occurred to her to investigate. Then she'd found the I Love You card. And in spite of everything else that was to happen, she kept the card in her purse from that moment on - until the day she died.

After I had got back to the mansion and read the letter to myself, I told the others what had happened.

"There is something new," I said.

Malcolm looked up.

I took a deep breath. "Pat told me this in complete secrecy, and I don't know how to handle it, or even what it means," I said. "But I did say that I'd tell you what happened at my meeting with her, so here goes.

"Apparently, there's a man who sometimes does work for the Church of England - getting people out of scrapes and that sort of thing.

"Does the name Terry Waite mean anything to you?"

"Never heard of him," said Doug.

"Mm," said Michael.

"Yes," said Alan. "Didn't he do something with the embassy hostages in Iran or something?"

Malcolm, his mouth open, looked back and forth between Alan and me.

George Bush, his mouth open, looked vacant.

"Well, there's been some discreet contact between him and the women, but she swore me to secrecy because it isn't in the public domain yet," I explained.

Malcolm said, "Is this Terry Waite gonna get wor out?"

"Well, if he is involved," emphasised Alan, "then that's good news, because he has a reputation for getting things done."

"Well, let's see," I said. "It could be that it's just a propaganda exercise."

Red Head walked. He calmly ordered Doug to go to my room. Half an hour later Doug rejoined us.

Doug said nothing and looked only at the floor. He wore a clean shirt, and had combed his hair.

"What's happening?" I said.

After a few, motionless seconds, Doug replied without raising his head, "Same as you."

No one spoke.

Many seconds later, Doug blurted out, "I'm not supposed to say anything," and, with an infinitesimal turn of his head towards me, he reiterated, "Same as you."

"Ah!" said I. "Zowjetye."

"Nam," said Doug.

"What happened?" I said.

"Same as you," Doug snapped out.

"Yeah. You said that," said I. "What happened?"

"Same as you," Doug snapped out, emptying onto the table a bag that contained playing cards and a chess set. "You were right. Every bloody word of it. The FCO has done every fucking thing you said. I'm flat out, fucking astonished at the support we're getting. I never expected it in a million years. The whole fucking lot of them seem to be ganging up on these bastards to try to get us out."

But Doug's head was down. And stayed that way.

A minute passed.

"What's wrong?" I said.

Another motionless minute passed.

"What's wrong?" I soothed.

And then,

"My wife thinks I'll be out in three weeks."

All heads came up.

"Sir Adam Thompson - B-Cal - has told the Libyans that unless they let me go, they'll suspend all flights to Tripoli indefinitely."

"Well, that's no lever," asserted Alan.

"I think you'll find it is," said Doug, still without raising his head. "The Libs negotiated long and hard to get us to fly here - British Caledonian and all that - even from Gatwick. And even with all the fucking shit we have to endure to give them a service they don't fucking well deserve, they would be very embarrassed internationally if we pulled out.

"My wife thinks I'll be out in three weeks," Doug repeated.

"Fuckin' 'ell," said Malcolm.

"Mm," said Michael.

Nothing, said George Bush.

"Well, good luck to you if you can do it," said Alan.

"One out - all out?" said I.

"I don't think so on this occasion, Sport," said Doug, looking me in the eye. "Sorry."

"It would be nice if British Telecom took the same view," said I.

"I'm bloody sure it would," said Doug.

But British Telecom wouldn't and couldn't. The instant that they ever pulled out of one contract in one country to get one of their staff members out of jail, they would never get another contract anywhere. Staff members being jailed in foreign countries was just one more risk that a company such as British Telecom has to assume. Otherwise the international operation of a company such as BT would go bust.

Malcolm, Alan and I were ushered across to Doug's room by the Hajji as usual at nine o'clock in the morning. Doug and George were not there. Michael was seated at the table. Immediately upon seeing the three of us searching the room for signs of the other two, Michael diffidently but carefully announced that the other two had left.

In their place was a large, wine coloured, leather suitcase, standing beside a shiny, black brief case. Both belonged to Doug. A non-descript holdall belonged to George. The bags were to be picked up the following day, finished Michael.

I then struggled with Michael for many minutes to piece together the sequence of events, as a means of checking the veracity of what he had just said. I managed to determine that the guards had arrived early and just told George and Doug to follow them. Half an hour later the three bags had arrived. It was unclear whether or not Doug and George had packed the bags themselves in the minutes before the bags were deposited here.

Malcolm and I looked at each other without a word and proceeded to open the bags and search them to lose anything incriminating. I borrowed a leather belt. Malcolm borrowed a pair of socks.

Then we found the money. Doug's B-Cal float money.

Malcolm and I looked at each other. We were going to need cash if we were going to escape.

I seized the three inch diameter roll of bank notes.

"Give it wor," said Malcolm.

"Let me count it first," said I. And did so.

"Why?" said Malcolm.

"So that we all know how much we took, and exactly how much we have to return to Doug when this is all over."

Malcolm palmed the counted roll of banknotes - all 295 Libyan Dinars of it. Almost 900 Pounds Sterling at the official rate - and, watched by the three of us, hid it unobviously under Alan's bed.

Years later of course, I tracked down Doug to Karachi airport where he had become the country manager for British Airways, after BA had taken over British Caledonian when B-Cal went bust.

By phone from Karachi, Doug asked me if we had got into trouble over the money.

I told him that I didn't know what he was talking about.

He told me that when his suitcase was returned to him upon his release, and he had discovered the money missing, he'd jumped to the perfectly reasonable conclusion that it had been stolen by the Libyans.

He raised Cain.

Had we got into trouble?

No.

"Well, I apologise for anything that might have happened to you, Sport."

"No need, dear boy. Nothing happened."

"Well, sorry anyway."

"That's awfully kind of you to think of us. But forget it."

"I just felt so bad that I might have got you guys into trouble. Once the money was returned it was bleeding obvious what had happened. I was just terrified for months that I might have got you put back in solitary or worse."

Worse than solitary? Forget it.

At his television interview, sitting outside the British Ambassador's residence in Tripoli the following morning, with a well deserved Gin and Tonic not far away, the ITN asked Doug if any kind of deal had been struck to get him and George Bush out. Doug stated with his characteristic, Kiwi clarity that it is our way of doing things - the British way of doing things - that we would not do a trade off.

But having raised Cain about the suspected theft of the money, Doug had gone back to have one further, microscopic examination of his suitcase to see if perhaps he had missed anything.

And he had.

Down between the layers of the fabric of which the suit case was made, and tightly inserted into the seam where the layers of fabric were stitched together, Doug finally found the one inch square piece of paper that I had successfully hidden after we had taken the money, and upon which Malcolm and I had written and signed the words,

"IOU 295 Libyan Dinars"

*** *** ***

PART FOUR

1st September to 31st October, 1984

I woke. It was the 1st of September. Revolution Day.

I felt it important that we celebrate the anniversary of the coming to power of Colonel Gaddafi. He had done wonders for his country.

He had rid Libya of a weak and corrupt, puppet monarchy, at the cost of no lives; resisted manipulative influences of MI6 and the CIA; re-roaded the entire country, at a cost of five billion US dollars; put two telephones and television into every house in the country, at a cost of six hundred million US dollars; erected a supermarket and a post office in every town and village in the country; built eye hospitals for the entire population of three and a half million, each one of whom would have at least one eye defective by the time he reached the age of 40, because of the filth and squalor in which they live; written an idiotic treatise on his personal political philosophy that included the equality of women, but presided over their continued subjugation by some of the dottier precepts of Islam; raised and equipped an army and an air force with Russian equipment that they didn't know how to operate; fought a useless and pointless war against Chad, which they lost; used the Russian armaments and equipment to arm and train the IRA; built universities in Tripoli and Benghazi, in whose grounds they publicly hanged 12 and 14 year old school girls for dissent, and videoed the slow strangulation and then televised it; rounded up between twenty thousand and two hundred thousand people following the latest, biennial attempt to assassinate him, some of whom were still being detained without trial 20 years later; caused to disappear anybody who tried to organise a legitimate trade union; exported his peculiar form of Maoist "revolution" to all corners of the world; and kidnapped innocent expatriates as hostages against the release of Libyan revolutionaries caught red handed in bona fide terrorist activities in Britain.

Yes, I felt it important that we celebrate the anniversary of the coming to power of that great Revolutionary-Thinker, Teacher-Leader, Colonel Muammar Gaddafi. He had done wonders for his country.

So we were celebrating over breakfast.

I described to the others a photograph I had seen. It had been taken in Green Square on Revolution Day a couple of years previously.

In the photo, among all the other bits of propaganda in Green Square was a school blackboard surrounded by a group of Western expats. The grinning expatriates were pointing with glee at the Libyan's carefully inscribed propaganda message to the rest of the world:

"All Libyans Are Revolting"

Breakfast was interrupted. "You are leave, now!" barked a guard.

I destroyed my cryptic calendar, and threw out the unkeepable possessions. Put my changes of underwear and other clothes into a poly bag and went out to one of two waiting cars. We were going home. The Hajji was convinced of it. We shook hands with the Hajji and drove off. We drove out of the city centre and onto a newly built road, unfamiliar to me. I saw a side turning that had a temporary barrier across it, manned by a blue uniformed militia man. Then I saw another and another. At one such barrier, I saw a driver arguing with a militia man over his right to pass unimpeded by such a barrier, and the policeman's tort in trying to prevent him. The policeman moved the barrier. They had built the ring road while I had been in detention. And what an improvement! The whole, scrappy section of crumbling, Italian road had completely changed. And there were no cars on it except us. At the end of the new section of ring road, I saw the old well that presaged the coast road and all points east. It had been preserved as a piece of heritage. Hardly preserved, but heritage anyway. From there I could see the Great Al Fatah University. That was worrying. I thought we were going there. Then it dawned on me that the barriers on the side streets were there to corral our 10 minute, march route, and to ensure that no other drivers could interfere with our progress – indeed there was not another car on the whole of the new road and for a very good reason. It might have been because it was Revolution Day, but it was increasingly clear that the authorities had probably closed the road off. Then I saw the Daewoo site - that was even more worrying. It was all too close for comfort.

But instead of either the University or Deawoo on the opposite side of the road, we turned to the right. "It's another prison," said Alan, the instant the gates at the end of the short, dirt track started to open. The official looking nature of the buildings, coupled with the nature of the gates and fences, was all we needed to see. The gates and fences were the usual, ramshackle affair that looked like the boundary of a scrap yard. The useful by product of their disgraceful condition, was that they were impenetrable, forbidding, private and anonymous so that you would not suspect what lay behind them. We had seen enough prisons by now to recognise the pattern. My heart sank. It was a mixture of disappointment, heightened anxiety and fear. Disappointment and anxiety were not too bad. We'd suffered disappointment on so many occasions since our kidnapping that we were virtually immune to it by now, and anxiety had been our constant companion during waking hours for 3 ½ months. What was new was the fear and the feeling that we would have to start all over again, working on a new set of guards, acquiring new possessions, learning new weaknesses of the system, being in separate cells or possibly enduring further solitary confinement. It was just so wearing that the life we had built up for ourselves and the control that we had managed to exercise over our own lives in the last 5 weeks was about to be stripped away and we were going to have to start all over again. It was made doubly worse because we had all been entertaining some small expectation of release. The reversal was devastating. Desolation hung thick and moody in the car. Alan spoke first. "Well, we'll just have to make the best of it." I couldn't help but note an unusual feature in his voice. Alan was always assertive when he spoke, usually more than necessary, and we were used to it. But on this occasion the assertive tone had an uncomfortable edge of contrived optimism. We would have to make the best of it.

We drove down lanes between buildings. Not obviously prison buildings, they were incongruously like refugees from a modernistic, 1960s, British, university complex. That is probably how they started. However, they were doubtless co-opted by the State of the Masses when it became clear that, in order to free the socialist people of the Libyan Arab Jamahiriya from imperialist aggression, they were going to have to lock a lot of those socialist people up.

The whole complex was alarmingly quiet and peaceful. The effect was doubly disarming because it was rapidly becoming apparent that nobody would know where we were.

The cars stopped.

A fat, middle aged guard, who I had never seen before, got out of the lead car and disappeared. He reappeared after a few moments, and disappeared into a doorway recess of one of the buildings. A few uncomfortable minutes later, he was back, and we were told to get out of the cars.

We were trooped – almost frogmarched - directly through the open door of an adjacent building and thrown into the main room. The 1960s architectural style defied logic and we could not see how we'd got in there. Worse, when we turned around and there were no guards behind us, we couldn't figure out where they had gone or how they'd disappeared so quickly. They had apparently evaporated to the other side of the glass partitioning through which we had entered. The glass constituted the wall of what appeared to be the octagonally shaped room in which we were now alone. And even worse still, we could not find a door. When we eventually did find one in the glass wall, it was locked.

Abysmal dejection set in. Alan was first to recover. "Well, I'm going to make a chess set," he asserted. And, from nowhere, he produced a loaf of bread, from which he proceeded to fashion chess men, while he was seated on the carpeted floor.

When I observed truthfully that that was very clever indeed, but that it didn't help us figure out what was going on or whether we were going to be able to get out of here, Alan said that he was not interested in finding out what was going on or in getting out of here, only in making a chess set out of the bread that he had brought with him. He then added unprompted, that they had done it at Robben Island so he could do it here. My shoulders dropped. The combination of Alan not being interested in getting out of here coupled with his reference to Robben Island made it clear that further attempts at communication with him would be pointless.

Malcolm looked terrible. Michael looked unchanged as he faced the centre of our dejected group. I looked for a way out.

I combed the perimeter of the room looking high and low to see if I could find an opening that we might exploit. There were a few things to get hold of, but in the end, everything was bolt tight. We were trapped. There were no beds, no furniture, no facilities, no drinking water, no air-conditioners, no ventilation shafts, nothing – except a couple of cheap, laminated, tubular framed, Chinese made, upright dining chairs, and the low, small coffee table upon which Alan now played himself at chess. I had to admire the speed with which he had made his chessmen.

The sun came round the building. The enclosed, glass walled room became hot.

We heard the midday call.

We got hungry. "Never mind," said Alan with enthusiasm. "We can always eat my chess men." I suppressed a groan.

Malcolm and I pounded on the glass wall. If anyone heard us, they ignored us. I rattled the door violently.

"Don't do that," reprimanded Alan. "You'll just break it." I spared him any reply. Malcolm and I gave up trying to attract attention.

And then, as if it had worked after all, along came two goons. Malcolm and I mimicked the act of drinking water. Magically, they unlocked the door and asked us if we were alright.

Malcolm and I spoke at the same time. "Don't ask stupid questions," said I. And Malcolm said, "Water. You know. Aqua."

The goons re-locked the door and disappeared.

Absolute dejection returned.

But so did the goons. About 10 minutes later. With plastic cups of cold water on a tray.

And 10 minutes after that, two other guards arrived. They opened the door, barked at us to follow, threw us out, and ordered Alan to leave his chess set where it was. Alan snatched up the pieces anyway.

After two hours of being in a naturally lit room, the early afternoon light was only momentarily dazzling. And the afternoon heat was cool after the recent glass oven. We followed the goons with mounting trepidation, and deepening gloom, rounding the corner of a low building with a pitched roof. I was prowling like a hunted animal. So on the alert was I for any further turn for the worse, that I failed to comprehend what I saw as we rounded the building. There, beside the usual gaggle of useless Libyans, was a pile of broadcast TV equipment complete with sound man, lighting man and cameraman. "Fuck you," I thought. "I'm damned if I'm going to let you film our abject state for your stinking propaganda." And I started to mouth Anglo Saxon under my breath.

A big built fellow with a camera started to speak. I didn't recognise the language. "He wants us to stop," growled Alan. And I got half way through expressing which particular sexual function he could do to himself, when the Babel Fish started to work. The penny dropped. "Are you the BBC?" I enquired, incredulous.

"ITN," came back low measured voices from the motionless, three crewmembers. And I recognised Brent Sadler.

"Jesus! Am I glad to see <u>you</u>?" I respond, heading off to shake some hands. "What the fuck is going on? We've been locked up in a..." But I was cut off by a strong grab to my arm and a barked order.

I shook myself free. The heat was immediately taken out of the situation by the calm, professional direction of the cameraman. He asked us to go back to the corner of the building and simply walk towards the camera again just as we had done a minute ago. We obliged. The array of goons stood back. ITN continued to film as we were ushered into the gloom of the pitched roofed building. Once inside, we stood around between the front row of seats and the stage of a passably sized theatre as our eyes adjusted to the gloom, having no better idea of what was unfolding.

As I smoothly glided along the front row, two, engaging, Caucasian faces only a few seats from the door looked up at me. One was owned by a man who looked as though he had a thyroid condition, and the other by a distinguished looking gentleman bearing a walking stick, who looked old enough to be his father.

The first person who spoke to me was farther down and standing behind the front row. He introduced himself as one of two Members of the European Parliament present, and shook my hand. He had nothing worthwhile to say.

Behind him, seated in the third row, stood the familiar, smiling face of George Anderson.

"Hello, George," said I, trying to take it all in.

"Hello, Robin," said George, as we shook hands.

"How long have you been here?" I asked, ever more incredulous.

"Since the beginning," he said.

"Why didn't you say something?" I asked. "We've been absolutely desolate all morning, not having the first idea what's going on."

"I'm sorry. They're absolute pigs," said George. "There's nothing I could do. It's not my show. I'm only here as an observer."

"Well, whose show is it?" I enquired, scanning the entire theatre.

"Them. Those men over there," he said nodding them out. "They're here to try to get you out."

I turned to see the man with the thyroid complaint and the other with the stick who were now both smiling at George and me.

Given no time to introduce myself to them, the two proceeded to introduce themselves to the four of us hostages. We four were then ushered to a boardroom table and four chairs in the middle of the spacious stage. My initial reaction was that this was the show trial that I had been dreading since Day One. I scanned the theatre for wigs and gowns.

The Thyroid Complaint announced his name and that of his compatriot. He went on to say that they represented an organisation called Liberation. "Remember that name," he said. "Liberation." I have never forgotten it, but I have never heard of them since.

We sat down. I, uncomprehending, but ready for anything. Because if the British TV was here, then this was an opportunity not to be squandered.

Dad and Janet got married. It was a simple registry office do and afterwards everybody returned to Geoffrey's house at Orchard Way.

Dad and Janet, Barry and Andrew, assorted wives, children and close family friends were sitting in the garden at Orchard Way, taking the late evening sun at the end of the glorious summer day.

Pat was sitting in the cool of the house, glad temporarily to be away from the uncharacteristic summer heat, and from the characteristic wit of some attending the wedding reception. She was watching the telly. The theme music introduced the News at Ten, and Pat proceeded to take it in.

Without warning, an item appeared in which four, hirsute, wide eyed and strained hostages were shown seated at a large table on a stage, somewhere in Libya.

Pat dashed out into the garden and yelled, "Quick! Robin's on the News at Ten."

Everybody dashed inside.

We made our way up onto the stage, where sat Robert Maxwell. He had been done for "treating partners like wage earners". He had a foolish grin on his face like someone who had been banged to rights and knew it.

He had initially spent a number of months in the same mansion that we now occupied. Malcolm and I had seen his suitcase on an upper floor one day while cleaning. Maxwell said that things got a lot better once you had been sentenced and that his prison allowed him the use of a woodworking shop, where he spent most of his time. I thought him a fool that he should acquiesce to such blandishments so obviously easily. But you do have to keep yourself occupied. The questions on my mind were, what was he doing here? And if they were relating him to our case, what was the potential for diluting our case and clouding it in the minds of the authorities?

The Libyans had Dictaphone tape recorders and held them up to get good recordings. We were going to have to be very careful what we said.

A lot of platitudes and posturing nonsense was being talked by the representatives of Liberation and by the two MEPs. The MEPs had been followed here from the usual Revolution Day parade in Green Square, by the ITN crew who had thereby scooped the BBC and who were presented with a unique and stunning first time photo opportunity with the hostages. But I could see the squandering of an opportunity here, that could altogether too quickly be terminated by the Libyans on a whim.

However, following the recent approval of the first Libyan diplomat in London since the death of WPC Fletcher, the Libyan Justice Minister had only this day announced the release, planned several weeks previously, of Doug and George. And the Libyans - and Colonel Gaddafi in particular - were intent on using this press conference to gain the maximum of publicity. Hence the carefully engineered presence of ITN.

The presence of Liberation and that of the two MEPs, following the untimely, almost overnight ejection from Tripoli of four Labour MPs, would guarantee that publicity. Additionally, a Libyan Foreign Ministry official had, also over night, said that the Libyans had done their share in releasing Doug and George, and that it was now up to the British to reciprocate. When asked by Kate Adie of the BBC, if the official was optimistic about a reciprocal move by the British, he answered that the Libyans had no other choice. Accordingly, the press conference that we were about to deliver was going to run its full course.

The press asked some questions, which I knew would require careful answering. One journo asked were we being looked after properly. A junior administration official immediately jumped in with, "Do not ask that question. That question is not allowed." And, to us, "Do not answer that question. That question is not allowed."

I proceeded to answer the question, and was shouted down by the young official. I suspect that my answer must have been audible, at least to the most senior, bespectacled, administration official present, because he brought the young official to silence in order to hear what he predicted was going to be a propaganda victory for the Libyans.

"Our treatment has improved considerably since the first days. We are eating properly and a balanced diet. We are being well and correctly looked after by our guards."

As I spoke, I looked directly at the tall, heavily built, cameraman. He reciprocated my gaze. I held his gaze after I had finished speaking and leaned forward slightly towards him. He nodded once. We both knew. But the propaganda effect was electric.

Then the lamp bulb in the lighting man's hand held flood light blew. I immediately thought that the press conference would be over. I felt despair, as I hadn't had a chance to get half the message over yet to the ITN crew. I cautioned the others to silence and ostentatiously studied the cameraman to make him the focus of attention. An interval followed, punctuated by a bout of swearing as the cameraman unscrewed the burning hot bulb with his handkerchief and inserted a replacement. Then the camera was up and rolling again. The cameraman nodded once, professionally grateful for the pause, and the conference continued. That way the British public would get to hear everything we intended them to.

More questions followed. "Well, I know why I'm being held," said Alan with his guilty, boyish incline of the head, but got no further. However, he did skilfully steer his answer to include a statement that he knew the Libyans did not actually wish us any personal harm - a deft piece of footwork, considering how he and Malcolm had actually been treated.

And I took the opportunity to press home the advantage of the conference actually listening to what we were saying with, "We do appreciate the gesture the Libyan authorities have made in releasing the other two hostages and..."

But I was interrupted by the delegation from the floor. I felt it imperative to tell them to shut up and let me finish.

"...I would be most grateful..." I was about to ask them to be quiet. But the interruption ceased of its own accord, and I seamlessly continued, "...if we could be similarly released. Because as far as I'm concerned, there is nothing tangible for which I am being held."

"What about conjugal visits?" said Alan.

"No," I muttered under my breath and without turning my head. "We won't get that. We want out."

"We will have to see about that," said, what I took to be, a senior prison official. He certainly had the bearing and uniform of military officer.

Things broke up at a quiet order from somewhere to stage left. Without a second bidding, the Two Gentlemen of Liberation obligingly rocked themselves forward and out of their front row seats and dutifully scooted out of the theatre. "Thanks, Liberation," I called out, without a hint of sarcasm. They looked their acknowledgements over their shoulders. I never saw them again.

Without being told to do so, I made the fastest way I dared towards George. He saw me shooting down the stairs on stage right, and had the good sense to stand his ground.

"Are they going to get us out of here, George?" I said.

"What do you think?" George replied.

"What do you make of the two of them?" I asked ruefully.

"What, The Malignant Dwarf?" said George, with characteristic diplomacy. "They're only here for their own publicity."

I nodded my understanding. "When can we get another meeting?" I added.

"I'm jumping up and down for a meeting," he replied.

"You said that before," I rebuked.

"I'm always jumping up and down for a meeting," he smiled.

I mouthed a silent, "Yeah," and nodded as we shook hands.

I strode over to the tall cameraman who introduced himself as he was just finishing packing his kit away.

"Malcolm Hicks," he said, and he introduced Alan Florence, the ITN sound recordist. Alan Florence told me that he too was from Royston. This needed testing. But he mentioned details of my family, and told me which nearby village he lived in. I was astonished but elated. I instantly trusted them both.

"Tell everybody in Britain what we're going through. This is bloody awful," I said. Malcolm Hicks nodded once.

"Nobody is in any doubt about what's going on here," he said with sincerity blazing from both eyes. We stole a quick handshake. "If you can hang on for a day or two, I've got some magazines in the boot of my car. I'll try and get them to you."

"Can you get me out of here?" I tried. "In the boot of your car?"

"No," he said, and almost raced out the door to the tune of my, "Thanks, anyway."

Years later of course, I found out from Alan Florence that on this very day, the two MEPs present were offered the opportunity to take two of us four hostages home with them. Kamal even solicited opinion from Florence and Hicks as to what the British people would think of Col Gaddafi if Gaddafi were to release two of us remaining hostages there and then. Florence and Hicks laid on with a trowel how much a hero the British would think of the Colonel if he were to effect such a release. Kamal reported this straight back to the Big Green Looney himself. What takes some believing is that the two MEPs rejected the offer to take two of us home with them, on the grounds that they were too busy with important things to do so.

Back at Orchard Way, Steven sat in the sitting room with most his new step family, bewildered at the ITN news report, and facing a dawning crisis in his life. He had sat and watched the entire news broadcast on the BBC without any idea of what was going on. His eyes were wide and his mouth hung open as he tried to grapple with two questions.

First. What on earth was this predicament that Robin Plummer was in, what on earth did it all mean, and why was every body so engaged about it?

All of which presaged the second question. Who on earth was Robin Plummer?

The first question was understandable. Steven was only seven, and he could not be expected to understand the personal and geopolitical implications of a protracted hostage situation and all the potential ramifications.

But the second question was only understandable when you discover that Steven did not know who Robin was. Because nobody had ever told Steven that Robin existed.

After Anne had died, and Geoffrey and Janet had decided to get married, Geoffrey also decided that Robin's existence should be denied to Steven while Robin remained in detention because, by Geoffrey's estimation, Steven was too sensitive to handle the idea of having a step brother who was in detention in a place like Libya. Geoffrey had also laid down the law to both his other sons and to the rest of the extended family that they were, under no circumstances, to inform Steven, either.

As the reality was starkly revealed to him by ITN of the existence in Geoffrey's family of a third brother that he never knew existed, the reality was also starkly revealed to him of the enormity of the lie that had been perpetrated on him by the man that he had acquired only that day as his step father. But Steven was a bright lad and, after the way he had been treated, who knew what he was thinking ("Blimey. I've got another step brother. Any more I should know about?"). Who would be surprised if he'd felt betrayed that day.

Our new found guards ceased to exist for us. We would cheerfully have taken a beating without a flicker, for the show of insubordination that we gave them until it was time for them to relinquish us. They cannot have missed the full wattage of our disapprobation at the disgraceful way that they had treated us, now that they knew who we were. And they largely let us set our own pace until we were loaded into the cars and packed off for the wordless journey back to the Italian mansion.

I mounted the fourteen steps and, upon stepping through the open door, was presented with the Hajji, the corners of whose mouth turned roundly down at the sight of us, and who let out a genuinely sympathetic moan at our return.

I felt betrayed.

We had genuinely expected to be going home. Even the Hajji was disappointed on our behalf at the sight of our return.

For the rest of the day things were tense and angry, as we each tried to come to terms with both the exhaustion and the inevitable conclusion to be drawn at the day's events.

The place was clean and tidy, almost certainly at the hands of the Hajji, who presumably had also cleared away our chess set and playing cards.

He returned those, and made as many sympathetic noises as he could, remembering whose side he was supposed to be on, and what would happen to him if he got caught.

No-one was in the mood for bridge. And the tension and anger persisted. Violence bubbled away beneath the surface.
But that afternoon there was a cracking, late summer thunderstorm that cleared the air both metaphorically and physically so that when the door opened later, there was no longer any real danger of any of the guards getting hurt by any of us.

Just before a quarter to four that afternoon, they brought in the transistor radio, plugged it in to the socket on the wall above Doug's bed and switched it on. Restrained excitement on most faces quickly collapsed as the radio just hissed.
Seated closest to it, I played around with the tuning knob more in hope that expectation of finding the BBC. But find it I did. This was cause enough for celebration. But to my surprise and delight, I found that I had stumbled upon "The Best of Brass". I was further uplifted when about the second number played was a virtuoso rendition of Variations on a Theme of Rule Britannia on the euphonium. I was ecstatic. For fifteen blissful minutes I was on a plane far away from this madness and promising myself to learn to play brass when I got back to England, until I came crashing down at the end of the programme.
My fall was only temporary, however, as the link reader gave way to Lilliburlero, and I shivered in excitement at the familiar reminder of the impending broadcast of news in the World Service of the BBC.
Reception was terrible. Sunspot activity was at its eleven year high, and Short Wave Radio reception was correspondingly at its eleven year low. In fact, sometimes it took a practiced ear to know that there even was a radio station playing beneath the white noise. At different times of the day, it was necessary to retune the radio between the two frequencies on which this radio could receive Auntie. But this communication from the outside world was a huge psychological fillip, and for the first time ever, I realised that the people at Broadcasting House somehow managed to make you believe that they were talking to you personally in spite of whatever travail you might be undergoing at the time, in whatever stinking, mosquito blown dump you might be residing.
Years later of course, Katy and I did our Grade 3 Trumpet together. We both passed but, even at only nine years old, she scored more points than I did. Little Katy Plummer has never let me forget that.
But the radio proved to be our collective salvation that day, and continued to be so for the remainder of our detention - DLT and "Jolly Good Show", Gloria Hunniford, Sports Roundup, in depth discussions of cosmology and the Long Line Interferometer at the Cavendish Laboratory in the green fields just outside Cambridge, Best Of Brass, the News in the World Service of the BBC, Lilliburlero. "I just called to say 'I love you'," by Stevie Wonder was number one in the charts from the 8th of September until the 13th of October. 1984...

The following day, I bumped into the Hajji in the entrance hall. So far from his usual fatherly tenderness, he was circumspect and cowed. He looked away from me with his finger to his lips while muttering Arabic, and then looked up at me as he mimicked the act of being beaten across the soles of his feet.

Pat finally got the interview that she wanted.

Selina Scott gently and sympathetically asked questions, the answers to which sat at the heart of Pat's campaign to get me out.

Pat was later the most proud of this as her best interview of the whole affair. Live on BBC television, she got across very clearly her position that the British government needed to do more to get us out.

The thrust of Selina's line of questioning was clear. "Was it not Colonel Gaddafi and the Libyans with whom Pat and the other wives should be angry? They had, had they not, kidnapped me and the other hostages, murdered WPC Fletcher, and bombed and killed Libyan dissidents - stray dogs - and bombed dissident book shops in London and Manchester in March of 1984. There were four Libyan nationals awaiting trial in Britain who could be swapped for the four hostages in Libya, were there not?"

So Pat told her. "Forget the idea of a swap. That had never been what was required. The Libyan authorities had never asked for the Libyans in Britain."

Pat had no animosity towards Colonel Gaddafi or the Libyans. Robin had enjoyed working in Libya during his 13 months there.

But Gaddafi had made a gesture in releasing the two hostages on the 1st of September. The ball was now in Mrs Thatcher's court to do something, such as send a representative, anyone, to Libya to negotiate our release.

Selina Scott went around the issue again, gently, sympathetically and thoroughly for several minutes. But Pat did not deviate. Mrs Thatcher had to do something. The British government simply wasn't doing enough to get her husband out.

The FCO said that in the nature of her activities to get me out, Pat was likely to make waves, but they escorted her and kept her informed anyway. Pat went on to say in the media that Colonel Gaddafi should charge us or release us.

My dad was equally clear. Leave it to the professionals. They have a great deal of experience at resolving situations such as this. And he did exactly nothing for the duration of my detention.

Barry said, "It was difficult for us too. We were constantly bombarded by the press and the media to give interviews. We had to be very careful what we said, whilst at the same time keeping the profile as high as possible." Barry kept the profile high with regular communications to his MP and to the regional newspaper. Barry did the leg work to try to put together a private army to get me out. Barry was convinced that the phones were being bugged. Pat's father told Barry to shut up as he was making waves.

When asked what he was doing to help get me out, Andrew is said to have replied, "Praying."

Then Pat started receiving abusive phone calls - people claiming to be Colonel Gaddafi or an undertaker offering his services. At first she tried to ignore them. Then she bought a referee's whistle - the type with a pea in it. At the next two or three occurrences of heavy breathing, she simply blew a long, loud blast of the whistle straight into the handset microphone. There was a sharp decline in abusive phone calls after that.

But then, at about 3 o'clock one morning, the phone rang.

"Robert Runcie, here," said an unknown voice.

"Oh! Piss off, will you?" said Pat.

"I've got some news for you from Terry," continued the Archbishop of Canterbury.

The following day, Pat got onto the Head of Africa, Dr George Newns, at British Telconsult in London, who immediately phoned his counterpart at the regional telephone office in Cambridge. Within two hours, BT had put Service Interception on our home telephone number, free of charge. There were no more abusive phone calls after that.

Lunch arrived. We had barely started to eat when the door opened again. In walked unfamiliar footsteps. The usual guards were accompanied by a big fellow, the big, non-plussed fellow who had been at the Second Meeting with George. His eyes raked the four of us and the spread lunch, in one concerned and solicitous sweep. Instead of an admonishment, however, he appeared genuinely to be seeking an assurance that all was well. He asked, through translation, if the food was good and was there anything we needed. Politics being the art of the possible, I stood, shook his hand and said that we needed vitamin C. Could we have some lemons for the food? It was all lost in translation. Uncomprehending, they turned to go, but I raised the index finger of my left hand and Malcolm jumped in with, "Afwan?" No, the big fellow didn't mind, and he turned to face us again. So I imitated the act of cutting and squeezing a lemon, and of drinking the juice, complete with pulling a sour face. The big follow animatedly ordered the guards to get some lemons.

Capitalising on the new found cooperation, I again raised my index finger and asked for salt. This too needed dumb show. So I imitated the act of tasting bland food, followed by the act of pinching salt from a small dish, sprinkling it over an imaginary plate, and tasting it again with life in my eyes. Two words later and the word "mill'a" came out. At dinner that evening, we had our usual fare – only now accompanied by an abundance of lemons and a box of mill'a.

The following morning, we woke up to a peculiarly quiet day. There was not a breath of wind. The traffic noise was all but imperceptible. Even the usual, low cacophony of animal and insect noises was somehow absent. Ears straining for I knew not what, I proceeded the usual paces across the lobby to Doug's room - Doug's room even although it was never again going to be occupied by Doug. Lucky Fella. Breakfast came and went, and we settled down into the morning routine of puzzle books.

Barely had we let the sighs out of our bodies when the Hajji opened the doors and stepped in.

He had purpose. He walked over to the ghibli and raised it. This was surprise enough. Then he gave his familiar full handed beckon to me, interspersed with animated pointings out of the window. Cautious not to expose myself at the window, I approached to his usual stream of hissed, sympathetic and incomprehensible Arabic.

Looking along the length of his outstretched hand, I saw the tree that used to grow by the back double gates now lying on its side in the yard. I stood back into the lee of the room and lowered my head. An explanation would be forthcoming. The Hajji took on his gently animated insistence, and swept the rest of the back yard and garden with his outstretched hand. The garden looked as though a bomb had hit it. The yard was strewn with garden debris, and household rubbish; detritus, flung about and now dormant in a continuous carpet.

I frowned at the Hajji and twisted my hands, palms up.

A quaint imitation of a Macbethian witch was accompanied by a low exhalation through his teeth. Discreet glances by Alan and Michael, followed by inaudible brevity from Alan summarised the night's events. The noiseless morning had opened exhausted after a windy night. And what a wind! Malcolm was first upon the Hajji's next dumb show. "He wants us to move the tree."

This was going to require all of us. That was going to require consent. But more, the Libyans weren't going to do it without us. How strange that we were needed.

"What do you think, chaps?" I solicited.

"I'm game," droned Alan.

"Mm," intoned Michael, who tutted, raised and lowered his handkerchief into his lap for emphasis, and sighed, "If we have to."

"Malcolm?" said I.

"Are you alright, Robin?" said Malcolm.

"Dunno," said I.

The other three rose and, conducted by the Hajji, we trooped out of the room to wait circumspectly in the lobby.

I found myself starting to move sideways as the Hajji picked up a hefty, meat cleaver from the sofa. Detecting my movement, he raised his left hand and chin, lowered his eyelids and voice, and hissed soothing Arabic. I caught, "Malleish, malleish."

He led off down the back corridor, passed through the already open door, and we walked in Indian file behind him across the diagonal of the courtyard.

About fifteen feet from the tree he stopped. The rest of us shambled around him where he could clearly see us all. I looked at the tree. I looked at him. He nodded. I approached the tree.

Lying on the concrete floor of the yard was not the whole tree, but almost a half of it that had been split away from the main part of the trunk. I seized the broken part and tried to tear it free. On starting to ask the others to help, the Hajji gave a firm negative. We stopped. He raised his chin towards me. The clear solicitation was accompanied but a small twitch of the cleaver in his right hand. I looked him squarely in the eye.

We held each other's gaze for several seconds, before I started to nod my head.

"It will be alright," I was telling him.

"It will have to be," he was replying.

At fifteen feet distance, I raised my left hand to take the cleaver, and let my hand drop back to my side. A lag behind me, he raised his right hand, the weight of the cleaver forcing his hand back to his side. We bored holes into each other's eyes for many seconds before I started to approach him slowly and steadily. He stepped a pace forward, laid the cleaver cleanly on the concrete and stepped the pace back. I stopped while he did so. Then looking at the cleaver and nothing else, I stepped the remaining ten feet, stooped and cleanly picked up the cleaver. I turned as I stood up and walked back to the tree, all else a wax works.

Regarding nought but the cleft tree which I must now cleave further, I swung. The cleaver made not an impression. I swung again, and the cleaver lodged in the cleft. I depressed the cloven trunk with my left foot to open the cleft and withdrew the cleaver. I swung again. Of course the cleaver was totally the wrong tool for the job. But I started to make an impression anyway after several more cuts, and drew back for breath only after I had misjudged one cut and rammed a large splinter up underneath my thumb nail.

Malcolm, alone, saw what was wrong, and offered to take up the chopping. He stepped forward with concern in his eyes and a request in his voice. At the risk of upsetting him, I firmly uttered, "No," and shook my head once. He backed away. The Hajji's gaze had not moved from my face. I could apologize to Malcolm later.

The broken bough, separated from the trunk, I despatched into manageable pieces. All cutting done, I stood motionless for several seconds. Then I looked up at the Hajji, who still regarded me fixedly. I turned my right hand outwards to show the Hajji the flat of the cleaver's blade. The wax works resumed. Already the day was hot. I evenly paced out ten of the feet towards the Hajji, stooped and laid the cleaver cleanly on the concrete. I stood, turned and went back to the tree. The Hajji stepped one pace forward, cleanly picked up the cleaver, and stepped the pace back again.

Alan was first. "Right! Let's get it moving," his body was saying. And we did. Alan took a log, then Malcolm. Even Michael pitched in as I bent forward to grab my share. Michael turned and followed Alan. Malcolm made his own way. And as I stood up with my load, the Hajji, who hadn't moved, started to smile through his unaltered stare. Then, threatening to paddle my behind with the flat of the cleaver blade, he chivvied me off like a small child, to wherever the logs needed to be stored.

The following day the Hajji came in again after breakfast, and used his body language to show us the way out of the room. Under the supervision of several of the guards, we did a fair day's work weeding came in for lunch and rested for the afternoon.

The day after that the Hajji came in again after breakfast.

"No," I said, and no-one moved from his chair.

"No?" said the Hajji, sad and disappointed.

"No," I repeated and went back to my puzzle book.

In a split second we all agreed that we thought we were now being used.

Malcolm read the moment correctly and engaged the Hajji in broken Arabic. The Hajji's body language switched to that of telling us that we didn't have to do any work if we didn't want to. He had just thought that it might come as a welcome change from sitting around and reading all day. Would we like some tea instead? Malleish, malleish, and turned for the kitchen.

I looked up at Alan, who nodded assent.

Malcolm asked, "Are you alright, Robin?"

"Yeah," I said.

And we all followed a surprised Hajji to do another morning's supervised work.

When tea arrived, we gathered together with the guards, and drank.

Alan picked oranges off the tree with which he elected to make marmalade.

Malcolm picked an orange with which he elected to play a game of catch.

Under the watchful supervision of the guards, we stood apart and gently lobbed the orange to each other. Michael joined in. We threw it to him gently and catchably. After the initial few throws, the distances among us lengthened, and Malcolm and I took to throwing the orange at each other as hard as we could. We watched the orange disintegrate in our hands as we caught it, and as our fingers strained the paucity of juice. Upon disintegration, we would just pick another orange from the tree full of inedible oranges, and feint a top speed throw at the guards, who would duck in terror.

The magistrate went over a few details of the story. His questions and his body language seemed aimless. The translator sat attentively and gave the impression of faithfully translating whatever was said by the magistrate or me.

Then the magistrate produced a photo copy of the party invitation that I had been carrying in my bag when arrested at the university, and things got serious.

"What is this?" they said.

"It is a party invitation," I replied.

"Whose party?"

"I don't know."

"You must know you have the invitation."

I said nothing, but rolled my hand over a few degrees.

"Who was holding the party?"

"I do not know who was holding the party. All I know is who the party was for."

"Who was the party for?"

"Aka," I replied.

"Who is Aka?"
"I don't know. He is a man I met."

"Where?"
"In Tripoli."

"How did you meet him?"
"Through friends."

"You said you do not have any friends."
"Everybody has friends. You said so yourself."

"What name is this Aka? What is his other name?"
"I don't know."

"Where does he live," they asked.
"I don't know."

"You must know. The directions to the party are written on the invitation."
"That may be so. Just because the party was being held there does not mean that that is where Aka lives."

"Where was the party?" they asked.
"I don't know. I was arrested before the party took place."

In fact the villa at which the party was to be held was located next door to the compressor room in which the British Sub Aqua Club, Tripoli Branch, kept all the diving equipment and filled all the bottles for their dives. And I had been to the compressor room on an almost monthly basis for over a year before I was kidnapped.

"Why is there a gorilla on the front of the invitation?"
Whoever wrote and printed the invitation never expected his little joke to get this far.
"It was a fancy dress party."

"What is a fancy dress party?"
I told them that people went along dressed up in bizarre costumes. "It is an English joke."

They both looked at me as if I was mad.

"Why a gorilla?"
They had obviously got the point of the joke.
I told them that it was quite common for at least one person to turn up at a fancy dress

party in a gorilla costume. Most lived to regret it because the costume was so hot. Which was true.

I told them that the purpose of the gorilla on the front of the invitation was to let people know that it was a fancy dress party. Which was not true.

They both looked at each other as if I was mad.

"What is meant by 'Aka's Good Riddance Party'?"

"Oh, dear. It is an English joke. It does not translate."

"Try," said the translator, smiling.

My shoulders dropped. I figured that I was on a hiding to nothing here. But I had to say something.

"When it is time for someone to go, it is common to say, 'It was nice to know you. Now that you are going, good luck, but we are glad to be rid of you.' To be rid of someone when it is good that they have gone. Hence 'Good riddance'."

"That is a good translation. We have something similar in Arabic," said the translator, still smiling. " 'Go, in God's name. But, in God's name, go!' "

I was not going to be drawn in by his smile. So I gave an impression of a smile, a definite nod of my head and a turn away to show that all discussion of Aka was now concluded.

I didn't bother to tell them that they would be on a Wild Goose Chase looking for Aka in their files, because Aka was only a name in the respect that it was an acronym.

When it came to signing the transcript I pointed out not only the futility of signing for something I couldn't understand, but also the potential legal implications.

The translator put up a fight, and once again I had no choice but to sign.

On the way out of the court house, I met Malcolm. Together we walked to the car, with the guards in tow. Then we saw an alarming sight. It looked like an armoured personnel carrier, but for prisoners. Its bottom was high off the ground and the under surface had a 'V' section as if designed to deflect the blast of any bomb that might explode beneath it. It was dark, austere and forbidding. And it rattled Malcolm badly.

"See, look!" he said. "Wor gonna get that."

I couldn't say that he was right. But I couldn't say that he was wrong.

Alan's wife, Carole, came to Tripoli, and Alan visited her first on the 13th of September. Immediately following their meeting, the Libyans phoned Carole at her hotel and asked her if Alan was OK, and was he well.

"What happened?" I said, after Alan got back from his visit.

Alan said, "I've never seen George looking so confident."

"What did he say?" I enquired.

"It doesn't matter what he said. I have never seen him looking so confident."

"Yes," I pressed. "But what did he say?"

"It doesn't matter what he said. He just looked very confident. That's all."

"Did he actually say that Nyerere had negotiated our release with Colonel Gaddafi?"

"No. He didn't."

My shoulders dropped. "Then we are back to square one."

"What do you mean 'square one'?" queried Michael, looking up.

"I mean that we don't really know any more than we did before Alan's visit."

And in spite of a truly manful attempt to maintain its composure, Alan's gleaming face had been falling all the while that it had been dawning on him that his seemingly optimistic piece of news lacked any real substance. I felt sorry for him. Of all of us, he was the one most in need of something to hold on to. Oh, we all needed something in our different ways. But, to Alan, right now, it was this piece of "news". However, in the matter of analyzing what scant intelligence we did acquire, as with the FT, I believed that we had to be ruthless in preventing sentiment from obfuscating fact.

"I'm glad you were able to see your wife, Alan," soothed Malcolm.

"So am I," replied Alan with a warm, nostalgic smile. "And she did bring these," he added with animation.

Four Airfix construction kits, with glue, paints and brushes – one each! Half a dozen puzzle books. A load of paper backs, Master Mind, Risk, and - a pound of ground coffee! Alan was aglow at the coffee. I was ecstatic at the Airfixes.

"But I think you're right about Julius Nyerere, Robin," he conceded.

I was thankful for the twin olive branches. The tension eased.

"Who's Julius Nyerere?" enquired Malcolm.

"He's the president of Tanzania," I told him.

"Is he gonna get wor out?"

"He's probably got as good a chance as any one," I offered.

Alan growled assent.

"Why?" asked Malcolm.

I sighed, looking for a simple way to explain.

"Look. At any one time, there're probably only two percent of all the countries in this barbaric continent that are worth living in. At the present moment, it's probably the Côte d'Ivoire and Tanzania," I started.

"The coat what?" interrupted Malcolm.

"The Côte d'Ivoire," I went on. "It's capital, Abidjan, is like an African Paris - boulevards, French colonial houses - said to be beautiful, safe, welcomes expats..."

"Aye. What about that Julius?" Malcolm cut across.

"Well, Tanzania got its independence in the early sixties, I think it was, and under Nyerere it's proved to be one of the more stable countries in Africa. He's thought of as an African statesman and, as such, he probably holds more sway than anyone else that Big G is likely to listen to."

"So he's gonna get wor out?"

"Well, that's the hope, isn't it Alan," I deferred.

"That certainly is the plan," he confirmed. "At the moment he is probably our best bet, and, as I said, I have never seen George looking so confident."

"So you know him, then?" asked Malcolm.

"What, Nyerere? No, of course not!" said Alan, and added nonchalantly, "Oh, you mean George! Yes, we go way back."

"Where d'ya know 'im from?" asked Malcolm.

Alan and I looked at each, looking for a simple way to explain.

We both started to try to explain that George is the sort of person you get to know by virtue of being on the expatriate circuit.

"What do you mean, the "circuit"?" said Malcolm.

"Well, you get invited to the odd diplomatic reception, and you just get to know everybody on the circuit," finished Alan.

"Well, he doesn't seem to be doin' much to get wor out of here," averred Malcolm.

So I told him.

During my meeting with Pat at which George had been present, in response to my bitter plea that the FCO simply didn't appear to be doing enough to get us out, George sought to point out where his priorities lay.

A representative of the British Canine Defence League in London had phoned George in Tripoli enquiring with some determination about what had become of the dog left behind by one of the diplomats in the departure from Tripoli back in May.

George said to the representative, "I spend most of my time trying to get people out of prison. I currently have fourteen people that I am trying to get out. I certainly have no time to go chasing after the welfare of dogs. I hope the dog dies. Now will you kindly fuck off?"

And calmly put the phone down.

"So these, so called, diplomats are different from what they're cracked up to be?" enquired Malcolm.

"Oh, yes!" replied Alan and I together.

"How do you know?" enquired Malcolm, looking at me.

I told him of the beach party at Dead Cow, a year previously at which George and I had first met. Of how George and I had got as drunk as skunks on a bottle of indescribably foul, Cypriot brandy. Of how, once we'd got muddled and fuddled and were still trying to converse long after our mouths had ceased to function properly, we were approached by two, young Libyans who asked George if they could swap some cannabis for some of our brandy. Of how, after several pointed attempts at ignoring them had failed, George told them to fuck off.

I told Malcolm of the diplomatic receptions, at one of which I'd asked George why he was so polite to some of the Arab diplomats present, when we both knew them to be scurrilous beyond the pale.

George said, "When they come up to me at one of these receptions and ask, 'And how are you, Mr Anderson?' I kiss their hand and their arse. I even offer to wipe their arse for them - if we need their oil at the time."

"And what happens if you don't need their oil at the time?" I enquired.

"I tell them to fuck off."

Four days later, Alan saw Carole again.

Upon his return, he was as white as a sheet, and shaking as badly as he'd been doing at the first meeting back in June. In fact he looked positively grey.

He sat down and smoked a whole cigarette before trying to speak. Even then he could barely make incoherent, growling noises, through light hand gestures and disbelieving shakes of his head.

When he finally started to cohere, no one felt the need to prompt him. It would come out by itself.

He reached for another cigarette and lit it off the first.

"The Nyerere initiative has failed."

Later in the day when he had recovered some equilibrium, Alan got up out of his chair and, without warning, assertively announced, "Well, I'm going to have a cup of coffee." First to open the bag of deliciously pungent rocket fuel, Alan made his own coffee, and then scrupulously resealed the package, and replaced it in the bureau.

Later, Alan noticed that someone else had taken coffee. He welcomed anyone enjoying it. That wasn't the point. But the bag was not closed.

"You have to close the bag and seal it properly to prevent the aroma from being lost," instructed Alan.

"I'm sure that we've all had bags before that needed sealing," I heard someone say.

"Then why don't you do it?" he parented.

I traded my share of the coffee and puzzle books for construction kits.

Alan threw himself into making marmalade.

The seasonal fruit in September was grapes. Lots of grapes. More grapes for pudding than any of us could eat. So I made some wine.

I washed several pounds of grapes, bruised them and let the natural yeast get going, put them in a plastic jug with a sealable but breathable lid, that I first sterilised with bleach, hid the jug behind a pile of clothing in the body of the bureau - and waited.

After a few weeks, we decided that it was a bit risky, given Red Head's predations, so I took it out and threw it away. But before I did so, I tasted it.

Oh, my!

Malcolm's wife, Andrea, arrived. Malcolm met her on two occasions; the 13th and the 15th of October. After each meeting he was unable to report any new developments, but she had brought a Monopoly set.

Now we had lots to do. The number of books and Airfix kits was increasing. The puzzle books were sufficiently numerous that I did puzzles for half the day, every day. Malcolm made a bi-plane out of dead match sticks.

And, having seen Andrea, Malcolm was like a dog with two tails.

"Mike-al," would be the rising invocation.

"Mike-al," would be the slight imperative.

"Mike-al!" would be the hastening command.

"Tut. Oh! What is it, Malcolm?" would say Michael.

"Mike-al!" the command would continue.

"Michael," the slight imperative.

Met by silence.

"Michael! For God's sake, man!"

"Oh! What is it? What do you want, Malcolm?" would say Mike-al.

"Mike-al," would be the rising invocation. "Are you alright, Michael?"

Sigh. "Of course I'm alright!" would say Michael.

"Michael!"

"What?"

"Are ya sure?"

Sigh. "Sure of what?" would say Michael.

"Sure you're alright?"

"What do you mean 'Sure you're alright'?" would say Michael.

"I mean, are you sure you're alright, Michael?" Malcolm would say.

"Yes!"

"Yes! What?" would say Malcolm.

"Yes! I'm sure I'm alright!" would say Michael.

"Aye, OK," would say Malcolm.

Silence.

"Michael!"

"Oh! What ever is it now?" would say Michael.

"Michael!"

"Yes! What?"

"Michael! Do you want to play with my willy, Michael?"

"Oh, Malcolm! You really are the limit, Malcolm!" would say Michael.

Michael and I had been bankrupted at Monopoly. Malcolm and Alan continued.

The slow migration of hotels, houses and property had, a few minutes since, reached criticality, and the act of being no more than a spectator to the inevitable sacrifice of Malcolm upon the Altar of Mammon was not sufficient to keep me interested, however unusual the sacrifice of Malcolm might be.

Alan had the bank. He also had, with very few exceptions, every property on the board and most of the buildings to boot. It was a foregone conclusion.

I reluctantly left the table, sat in a chair and read.

The game went on longer than I expected it to. A lot longer.

Immersed in my book, I lost what remaining interest I'd had.

I was forced out of my immersion, however, by the slow rise of voices - voices of fishwives bickering over the rights and wrongs of a matter.

Alan protested. Malcolm harangued.

Alan harangued. Malcolm wheedled.

Alan capitulated. Malcolm claimed justice.

Alan's practiced look of boyishness sought, impossibly, to camouflage the increasing ruddiness in his face, as he stood disbelieving witness to the tide of fortune slowly reversing itself. The ebb turned into a rush, the rush into an accumulation, and the accumulation into an annihilation of Alan.

By Malcolm's own admission, he was a twister. But what, with his captivating eyes, his "butter wouldn't melt in his mouth" looks, and his practiced, outraged, Catholic upbringing, his plausibility soared in my esteem as, for the last half hour of the game, I watched his exquisitely light fingers rob the bank blind under Alan's very nose.

Malcolm counted his pile. Nineteen thousand pounds - plus change.

Michael could no longer resist Malcolm's enigma. "Well, why are there more eggs to eat now, even when the Hajji is on duty?" he conceded.

"Haven't ya noticed, Mike-al,?" Malcolm said.

"Noticed what?" said Michael.

"The dog's gone," said Malcolm.

"What's that got to do with anything?" said Michael.

"The guards used to steal our food and feed it to the dog," chimed in Alan, lending credibility to Malcolm's story.

"I still don't understand what that's got to do with anything?" said Michael.

"The Libyans slit the dog's throat. Ah seen them carrying its dead body away in a plastic shopping bag."

I wake at nine when the Hajji unlocks the door. I am dressed in less than thirty seconds in case somebody walks in. Malcolm is usually first out the door as he sleeps half dressed. Clutching our towels and toothbrushes, we amble across to Doug's room under the supervision of the Hajji who is seated on the sofa in the foyer. Ablutions done, and the radio, dutifully switched on by Michael, now retuned by me to the day time frequency, breakfast is sitting on the table in Doug's room. Two whole loaves of bread each, butter in airline style foil packs, two hard boiled eggs each, and two pieces of Vache Riante processed cheese each, all accompanied by hot coffee and tea which we now make ourselves. From somewhere, we have procured cheese off the round. We are scrupulous to take only our own ration, and to divide any surplus by common agreement which may include giving it to just one person if no other expresses interest. This important consideration is necessary on account of the fact that there always seems to be a shortage of eggs when the Hajji is on duty. We eat without talking, straining to hear the BBC above the effect of sun spot activity. We clear up, swab the table down and wash the dishes by turn. The skin on my hands is seriously cracked due to the heavily chlorinated water. So I do Malcolm's chores - make all the tea, swab the bathroom floor and sweep Doug's room carpet, while Malcolm does my washing up.

Doug's bed is now occupied by Michael. I occupy an easy chair facing the door, and with the air conditioner to my left. A pair of bunk beds occupies the other interior wall to my right, where the Tunisian cleric once had his world. Malcolm sits in the upright chair at the table facing into the room, and Alan occupies the remaining easy chair to the far side of the air conditioner with the table on his left. Alan and Malcolm read. I do puzzles. Michael lies on his bed appearing to reflect. His troubled hands continuously wring his, now, off white handkerchief. Silence reigns, broken only by the well oiled purr of the air conditioner on top of which are keeping fresh our packs of Lurpak butter and of cheese.

Mid morning, by common assent, we sit at the four upright chairs at the table and play Monopoly. For two and half hours it is possible to shut out reality.

Lunch arrives. Pasta with tomato sauce on it, salad covered in thin oil, and chips. Or bowls of Libyan soup each with a piece of meat in it. Bread. Butter. Seasonal fruit. We eat without talking, straining to hear the BBC...

Alan reads. Malcolm makes a model out of spent match sticks. I build an Airfix Spitfire. Michael lies on his bed wringing his handkerchief.

Mid after noon by common assent, we sit at the four upright chairs at the table and play bridge. Alan teaches. A rubber or two later, I respectfully ask Alan if I can take a nap on his bed. He never refuses. While I was still in solitary, I used to sleep for two hours each after noon. But the rush of insecurity upon waking was as a bad as when waking each morning. So I stopped sleeping afternoons to avoid the pain. I only took it up again once we were all in together. And now, I wake to the third call of the day. Alan reads. Malcolm assembles match sticks. Michael wrings his handkerchief. I read the Vets or Wilt to recover from the insecurity of waking.

Today, Alan is struggling. His firmly closed mouth and down turned eyelids are accompanied by a grey colour to face. He does not engage. He makes no sound.

Lillliburlero comes and goes and with it the news. There is no mention of us. The repeats of programmes bring as much joy as the initial transmissions did. "I just called to say, 'I love you' " is played for the fourth time in the day. The familiar, racey theme tune to Sports Roundup fills me with warmth even though I have little interest in sport especially when it is represented by football.

I get up to retune the radio to the other frequency now that the sun is setting

The fourth call presages the other hot meal of the day. Libyan soup with meat. Or Pasta with tomato sauce on it, salad covered in thin oil, and chips. Bread, butter, tea, coffee.

Variously, we read, do puzzles, hand wring, or sit and look into space.

At ten o'clock, we remind Michael to turn on the radio again as soon as he wakes up in the morning to try to persuade the guards not to take the radio away. Then Malcolm and I knock on the door, and wait to be escorted back to our room by a lone guard carrying the bulletless Kalashnikov. We kill mosquitoes by throwing a rolled up pair of socks at them and squashing them on the twelve foot high ceiling. We run on the spot for ten minutes to try to burn off some of the adrenaline. We talk about Newcastle on Tyne, where Malcolm lives and I went to university. Or about our shared love of the company of women, and how beautiful is the female form. Or about how well or badly Michael and Alan are handling the strain.

Then we turn off the light, open the casement window, settle under our respective single sheets, and get a surprisingly good night's sleep.

Laundry day was always exciting. Once I had obtained permission to wash my sheets, I seemed to walk on air. The twin prospects of clean sheets that night, and of a job whose end point was known and in sight, buoyed me up.

The mechanics of laundry day were simple. Run a bath. Add some Vim. Mix it up. Place the sheets in the bathtub to soak. Rub the grubby parts of each sheet together until they were as clean as my muscles would allow. Drain. Rinse. Twice. Three times. Wring. Knock on door. Negotiate with the guard for permission to hang sheets up. Walk with wrung out but dripping knot of sheets to outside, back staircase. Hang sheets over the banister rail in the Autumn sunlight.

Autumn. Throughout my whole life - childhood, adolescence, university - I had always felt a pang of sadness at the change of the seasons, especially that from Summer to Autumn.

It is probably because my mother used to speak of Canadian summers, long, hot and sunny - while English summers - anything but - metamorphosed into English Autumns without Summer's promises ever being fulfilled - that I always felt empty and short changed.

The beauty of the Libyan Autumn, however, left me with different feelings. The sun light through the back door of the passageway illuminated the pale wash of the hallway. The bright light, reflected off the walls into parts of the building normally in umber, cast a welcome mood of optimism.

Even when the peculiar, brown, sweat borne stain on my white sheets would remain even after the most thorough washing, the smell of fresh sheets was all the more refreshing in the beautiful, Autumn weather. God! I was beginning to sound like a television commercial!

Keep focussed, Robin. Keep focussed.

Yes.

The loss of Julius Nyerere had been a blow.

As October drew on, activity among the guards started to lose its light footedness. Visits from the officers were fewer and less bellicose. Communication with the guards was less optimistic yet now more friendly, now more tense. We were not in the throes of witnessing a massive swap off on the great chess board of life, but instead, a slow grind was limping its pendulous way towards metaphorical and literal stalemate.

Bridge playing had become a tedious routine - that of hypothermic men in a waterlogged lifeboat doggedly exercising as a means of staying alive. Chess with Malcolm had ceased to be fun - he had started to learn how to beat me. Draughts with Malcolm had ceased altogether - he had got bored with always beating everybody, and now refused to play. The nightly, late Summer tirade of celestial pyrotechnics had exhausted itself for another year, and a gloom was descending - as everybody knew what nobody could say - that we were here for the long haul, and that we were entirely and utterly alone.

"This is Hugh," said Pat. Hugh was urbane, good looking, nattily suited, well groomed, and with a penetrating, focussed countenance.

The diffident manner of Pat's introduction, and the hint of easy familiarity had me worried. Who the Hell was "Hugh"?

"Where is George?" I faked.

"He's left."

"What, is he on leave?" I continued, getting no non-verbal clues from "Hugh".

"He's left Libya. For good," continued Pat.

"Oh, so he finally got out did he?" I sallied, and, shaking hands with Hugh, I pressed my recovered initiative with, "You must be his replacement," more in hope that expectation.

"Hugh's a consul," said Pat.

Relieved, I tried conversation. "What? Are you a second consul, like George?" perhaps now "Hugh" might speak.

"I'm the first consul," he stressed, handing me his card, the Scots burr taking me by surprise.

Adopting the French pronunciation, I read, "Hugh Dunnachie."

"Dunnachie!" stamped out Hugh in the Scots, focussed eyes ablaze.

Still looking at the card, I enquired, "How the Hell did they persuade you to come to this place at a time like this?" giving regard to the Libyan guard behind me.

"I volunteered," hammered out Hugh.

So did I, I thought incredulously. I met his eyes.

"Do you have any idea what you're letting yourself in for?" I enquired.

"I volunteered!" he riveted home.

I had always liked George. He was a good man. But, after four years in Libya, he was worn out. So maybe this was what we needed - someone who ate six inch nails for breakfast and spat them out again for elevenses.

I warmed to him but didn't show it, thinking, "My countryman, but yet I know him not."

Back at the mansion, Michael identically mispronounced Hugh's surname.

But two pieces of news emerged from the visit.

"We got to see Mrs Thatcher," said Pat.

"Christ! Well done!" I said. "How did you do that?"

"Just like you," Pat replied. "Persistence."

"Come on," I said musically.

"Well, I've written to everybody," she said. "First I wrote to our MP, but that got nowhere. So I decided to write to just everybody - starting at the top - Shirley Williams, Mrs T's office.

"But then I remembered you once told me that Harold Wilson was a close friend of your Uncle Leslie. So I wrote to Harold Wilson. He wrote to Lord Ted of Edmonton, who wrote to Mrs T and we got in."

"Shame Sir Leslie's dead," said I. "Now we can't thank him. What happened at Number 10?"

"At first, I thought we were only going to get ten minutes. But in the end we got two hours."

"Jesus Christ!" I said. "What's she like?"

"Well, the first thing that surprised me is that she listened," said Pat, "to everything we said."

"Who was there?" I asked.

"Carole and me," said Pat. "Oh, and some flunkies, of course."

"Of course," said I.

"What's really funny is that we started off by addressing her by name, Mrs Thatcher," Pat went on. "But over two hours of listening to civil servants addressing her as "Prime Minister", we found ourselves increasingly doing the same so that by the end, we were all calling her "Prime Minister". It was a bit embarrassing really."

"What did she say?" I asked.

"Not much really," said Pat.

"Well, she must have said something," I pressed.

"We all went there hoping that she would help, but we didn't really know what help she could give," Pat went on. "None of us wants a deal. We just somehow wanted her to send a representative, like a minister or someone to try to negotiate for your release."

"Oh! Christ!" I uttered, knowing that that would never work.

"In the end she just looked at us and said, 'What do you want me to do?' We talked about Terry Waite even though we weren't supposed to," said Pat. "In the end she said that she would mention you to the Italian Ambassador to London, when she saw him on Friday - three days ago."

The other piece of news that emerged was that Pat had written a letter to Colonel Gaddafi. She had had it translated into Arabic, so that it ran in English down the left hand side of the page and in Arabic down the right. The letter stated a case for my innocence, and appealed to Colonel Gaddafi in carefully worded humanitarian terms, to let me go, and to let the others go as well. The letter also took the opportunity to state in plain language Pat's desire to meet Col Gaddafi.

Pat had left copies of the letter at the offices of anyone with any likely influence, in the simple hope that a copy of it would get to Colonel Gaddafi himself.

"Do you think that that will work?" I asked Hugh.

"It's cheeky. But then Colonel Gaddafi himself uses cheek," said Hugh. "If he admires cheek in other people, then who knows?"

Pat's friends on her health visitor course, which she'd duly started in October, had wished her well and success in getting me out.

"Are you going to sleep with Colonel Gaddafi?" one of them had asked.

"If that's what it takes to get my husband out," she said aristocratically. "Then, yes."

Business over, I swallowed hard and turned my attention to the children. Katy told me all about her new school - Tannewy Dwift, Mrs Bessel her teacher, and Mrs Harrison the headmistress. Ross told me all about his new pedal car. I held them and kissed them until it was time to leave.

Later at the ambassador's residence, a junior embassy man, two members of the press, Terry and Pat were sitting around in the main salon, chatting animatedly with Hugh. The door opened and in walked Ian Ridout who announced that he was going to take everybody out for dinner tonight, courtesy of British Telecom.

"I've got to go and screw Mrs Henderson," announced the junior embassy man.

"I don't!" announced a press man. "But I do have to go and develop some film."

"I have to phone the Archbishop," announced Terry.

"Look. I don't think so, Ian," announced Pat.

They all looked at Hugh, who looked straight back. Hugh caught the diplomatic ball and agreed to enjoy an evening out with Ian Ridout, courtesy of British Telecom.

"Well, toodle-oo, everybody," said Ian. "I'll see you later, Hugh." And Ian left.

Everybody breathed out.

My second day with Pat of this visit was held in the same office in which the visit in August had taken place, only this time it was just Hugh, Pat, Katy, Ross and me. The Libyans were courteous, helpful and unobtrusive. But knowing how capable the Libyans were of breaking up a meeting on a whim, I proceeded to recount at break neck speed the events since Pat and I had last met, five days previously.

All four of us had been taken before the public prosecutor on Wednesday, the 24th of October, just three days prior to this meeting, and informed of certain charges.

Alan was to be charged with practising journalism without a licence, remitting copy during a news embargo and failing to have a valid residence permit.

Michael was to be charged with inciting students to counter revolution.

Malcolm was told that he was being held for being in possession of letters which had passages criticising the Jamahiriya.

I was questioned by the public prosecutor but not informed of any charges.

All four of us were told that we were to appear before a judge "shortly". I said that I believed the Libyans could find no charges against me. I wanted to speculate on the significance of the charges laid against the others, and Hugh said that they were open to various interpretations. I said that we, the detainees, had discussed the development among ourselves.

I was anxious to know whether any new government initiative was planned, but volunteered that we all understood that there could be no concession to blackmail.

Hugh would later report all this to the FCO in London, who would escalate it to the Prime Minister in view of her recent interview with Pat and Carole. In escalating the situation to Mrs Thatcher's office, the FCO pointed out that it was encouraging that no mention had been made of espionage in the charges so far, and that if the charges were left unamended, it was possible that Alan and Malcolm could be given a light sentence or even released. Equally, Libyan courts were notoriously subject to last minute change and the charges could, therefore still be made more serious, with threatening, long sentences.

Hugh's report was also escalated to the Archbishop of Canterbury, to whom Mrs Thatcher had successfully suggested on the same day that she met Pat and Carole, that Terry Waite might undertake a mission to Libya.

"To change the mood a little," said Hugh with the suavity and twinkle that was now his recognized hallmark, "some people have been going down the pub."

The National Union of Mineworkers had been on strike in Britain. The president of the NUM, Arthur Scargill, had sent a delegation of miners' representatives to Libya, among other places, to solicit funds from Col Gaddafi to help finance the strike.

The five man delegation had gone to the British Ambassador's residence, while waiting for their audience with Big G, and had been treated to legendary, British, diplomatic hospitality. When the call came from the arriving Libyan diplomat for the Union Men to go to their audience, one of the union men was found sitting on the toilet "asleep". When the remaining four union men remonstrated through the alcoholic haze that they could not leave their brother seated on the toilet, the Libyan "diplomat" told them that if they didn't come now, right now, then The Leader would not see them.

But the best bit was at the end of the audience, when the leader of the delegation took The Leader in his arms and kissed him on both cheeks, in the full glare of the BBC cameras.

Arthur Scargill went nutty as he tried to distance himself from the actions of his errant emissary and the press were to have a field day in full Scargill-baiting flood over Libya, while the emissary, Windsor, the Chief Executive of the NUM, no less, found himself mocked mercilessly but some of the less kindly members of his staff, and developed an acute case of stress related shingles in the aftermath of the affair.

"Oh!" concluded Hugh, with his trademark smile. "They didn't take the opportunity to ask for your release, by the way." When I asked him if the antics of the NUM delegation were likely to derail anybody's efforts to get us out, Hugh looked at me and smiled and said that I shouldn't worry too much about that.

Then it was time to leave. Pat, Katy and Rossy went off to their car first, with Hugh. I had to wait in the room until they were safely away. God alone knew when I would see them again.

Then it was time for my guards and me to leave. We left the room and descended the narrow staircase. But as we stepped off the last stair, the guards were wrong footed at the sight of my family. Hugh, Pat and the children had been standing in the centre of the lobby long enough for me to be escorted down the stairs, and were presumably waiting for permission or escort to leave the building for their car.

The guards recovered almost seamlessly, and quickly steered me away from any possible encounter with my family. In turning me to the right at the foot of the stairs instead of the normal leftward, towards Pat and the children, they tried to ensure that I did not see them, and that they not see me. The combined wrong turn and guile made me feel alarmed. I tried to call Pat's name, but all I could manage to force out was a mangled squawk of concern. She heard me though, because I next heard an unintelligible mutter that, in the seconds that followed, I took to be Ross. He was asking his mummy if it was alright for him to call out "goodbye" to his daddy.

Ross put on his speaking voice and cut the air with an authoritative "Bye, Dad." The guards turned to each other to assess what all this meant. I didn't ask for permission. I elbowed my way past the guards and walked at speed to my dear Ross. Glancing acknowledgement to Pat, I lowered myself to one knee in front of the plucky, not yet four year old, little Ross, and put my arms around him. With my right hand spread across his little back, and my left around the back of his soft head, I pulled him faintly off balance and onto my chest and neck. He softened into my body, unusually for someone who was never very cuddly.

I held him gently until his body told me to let go. Leaning into him, I stood him upright again. Then, still holding him, I drew my weight back so I could see him. We looked fixedly into each others eyes for many seconds. I took in the clarity of his eyes, his round, apple cheeks, and his strawberry mouth. Then I felt a cool tickle in both my eyes as teardrops formed. I clenched my teeth hard to prevent my lower lip from trembling and, having no intention of dignifying the teardrops by acknowledging their presence, I let them fall.

Ross's eyes, lately resolute upon my pupils, shifted to the teardrops. He raised his right hand, his index finger extended, first to one eye and then the other, and wiped my tears away. His eyes returned to my pupils, and showed concern. "It's alright, Daddy," he said, meaning it. I found the muscles to fake a smile, and reached forward and kissed him on his strawberry lips.

I let slip my embrace of Ross and rose to my full height. Bastards!

"Bye, Pat," I said. And we kissed, quickly. "Ooh! Can you get me a cheap, Casio watch, next time you come out?"

"OK," she mutilated, through kissed lips.

"Bye, Kate."

Katy continued to look at me. "Bye," she mouthed, waving with the free fingers attached to a sucked thumb, and looked at Ross before lowering her eyes to her mother's feet.

The doorway and the courtyard were lit by afternoon sunlight. Having no intention of dignifying my guards by acknowledging their presence, I just started to walk towards the door with my careful, measured pace.

The guards' call for me to come back was at once both compassionate and irresolute. But back I came. Now it was the turn of Pat and the two children to be escorted to their car. I had no doubt in my mind that the guards had been given orders that strictly forbade them from letting me anywhere near Pat and the children and Hugh, while they were anywhere near the Jaguar, in case - just in case.

With Hugh the suave diplomat as usher, Pat and the children left through the door. I elbowed one of the guards aside, who had indifferently obscured my view of my beloved wife and children. And they were gone.

I walked out of the door, the guards in tow.

No more than a few feet after the doorway, I saw that the sun filled courtyard was doubly filled with a crowd of Libyan men, who had witnessed the whole valediction.

I paused, looking for a way through the crowd, and also to be seen as not wishing to offend their Libyan sensibilities by walking past them unhesitatingly. I raised my chin and proceeded, before the guards caught up with me and bade me make progress. As I proceeded, the men stopped talking and turned from their respective groups to follow me with their countenances. Half way to the gate, I turned my head back, ostensibly to let the guards catch up, but really to scan the crowd. To a man, they were looking me squarely in the eye, and most of them were shaking their heads from side to side in a gesture that said what a disgraceful treatment this was of so obviously an innocent man and his lovely family. And, having every intention of dignifying the gesture by acknowledging its presence, I gave one infinitesimal nod of my head, and turned and strode off.

Once in the street, I paused to let the guards catch up. I was once again disconcerted as the guards guided me up the street, around the back of the mansion's block, and not down the short avenue by which we had arrived. Alarm bells rang, but subsided when I realised that, coincidentally, we were bearing down upon the Jag. But the XJ6 pulled away from the kerb before we could reach it, and I was promptly disallowed from any attempt to wave to the occupants.

We walked around the block, for no reason that I could discern, except, perhaps, for the exercise, for which I was silently grateful, and went back into the mansion.

The Hajji brought me the food he had set aside for me. I ate it in silence, then I debriefed to the others who were suitably horrified that not even the trade union movement had put in a plea for us. Then I picked up my puzzle book and got on with trying to stay sane.

The game of chess fizzled out.

"The first rule of escape," I said, "is, 'Don't stand still if you can walk, and don't walk if you can run.'."

"What's the second rule?" said Malcolm.

"Like everything else in life, I suspect. 'Don't get caught.' "

"How far is it, then?" Malcolm tested.

"A hundred and seventy five kilometres," I asserted.

"How do you know?" he tested.

"I know," I asserted.

"How do you know? Ya can't know a distance like that," he tested.

"Trust me. I know," I asserted.

"How do ya know? Ya cannae kna," he tested.

"I know, Malcolm! I was in charge of the telecommunications side of the Libyan Coaxial Cable Project. It was my job to know every cable run in the country," I asserted.

"How much cable?" he tested.

"Seven thousand kilometres," I asserted.

"Howway man, Robin! Ya cannae kna every foot o' seven thousand meet'as," he said.

"Kilometres!"

"Howway!" he scoffed.

"Malcolm, I had a map on my wall that showed every cable run in the country. I had a book which showed the surveyors' hand made drawings of every kilometre of cable, every topographical feature, every hill, every rise, every molehill, every hiccough for seven thousand kilometres. And not only that, I have driven every one of those seven thousand kilometres with the exception of the run South from Marsa Brega to Murada, which is one hundred and fifty two kilometres and there's only one stop half way there, and that's not a stop, its an automatic repeater station. And the exception of the run from Tripoli to Ras Ajdir - which is a hundred and seventy five kilometres and goes through towns like Sabratha. I know this country like the back of my hand," I asserted.

"What's Murada?" Malcolm tested, changing tack.

"It's an oasis town in the middle of absolutely nowhere that nobody in their right mind goes to, far less writes home about," I asserted.

"Howway man, I've never heard of it," tested Malcolm, lying.

"Well, it's near to where you worked. Have you read "The Flight of the Phoenix"?" I demanded.

"That's a book isn't it?"

"Yes. Have you read it?" I persisted.

"Howway, man. Ya like a good book."

"Cut the shit, Malcolm. We're talking about escaping. Have you read it?" I said.

"No. But I've seen you with it."

"Exactly. The men in the book crash-landed an aircraft two hundred and fifty miles south of Murada. It's in the middle of the Sahara Desert. It's over two hundred miles from water. They're lucky not to have been as dead as dodos. Read the book. And while we're at it, it was the determination of the guy who ultimately proved to be in charge that was what finally got them through. Trust me, Malcolm, I know this country." I fought to resist pounding the table.

"Howway, Robin, ya kna, ya kna. Aye OK, so it's one hundred and seventy five kilometres from Tripoli to, what was it?"

"Ras Ajdir."

"Aye, Raj Asdair. But ya say ya've never driven that bit," he tested.

"Aye, you're right. I haven't. But I know the geography of the place. We're talking about a straight run of a hundred and seventy five kilometres along a coast road. The Mediterranean is to the right, and there's anything up to one hundred and twenty kilometres of open desert to the left before you hit the jebel. We'd be sitting ducks.

"A skilled walker, in proper boots, can only expect to make twenty five miles a day in good conditions. One hundred and seventy five klicks divided by one point six ...."

"Why one point six?" he tested.

"Malcolm, just let me do my job."

"Howway, you're not here to do your job."

"Malcolm, for fuck's sake stop pushing me, and listen, if you ever want to get out of here alive. One hundred and seventy kilometres divided by one point six is approximately one hundred and ten miles. At twenty five miles a day, that would take us almost five days along a dead straight road. We would need five day's start on them not to be missed so that they wouldn't catch up with us, and that would be lucky.

There's no way we could make it. Nobody walks that kind of distance or that kind of road. They'd be waiting for us at the border."

"Howway, we could walk along the desert behind the houses along the road," he tried.

"There aren't any houses. There are maybe half a dozen villages over the entire distance."

"So we walk on the road and then behind the houses in the villages."

"Have you any idea of what it's like walking in the desert? If you won't believe me, then at least read "The Flight of the Phoenix". You have to stop and clear the sand from your shoes every half a mile. You lose a pint of water for every half a mile you walk in temperatures above a hundred degrees Fahrenheit. We'd have to walk at night. Which means that we couldn't possibly walk in the desert behind the houses."

"Why not?"

"Because you could be walking along on the desert sand, and suddenly fall into a wadi twelve feet deep and not know what hit you. You could lie there dead or, worse, seriously injured, for days and nobody would find you. That leaves us very few alternatives."

"What are they?"

"We're not Arabs. This isn't Northern Europe in World War II. We don't outnumber our guards hundreds, or thousands, to one. We'd be missed. We don't look like our captors. We can't melt into the background. The day time temperature can rise to forty five Centigrade. My Dad needed six blankets on his bed at night in the Egyptian desert to ward off the freezing cold. We'd have to do it during May or September so that neither the daytime nor night time temperatures were too extreme. We're talking about walking a hundred and seventy five kilometres at night along a road we don't know, with no water and no food. We are not Airey Neave escaping from Colditz. They're not the Germans. We are white. They are Arabs. You're six feet three, and I limp. We stick out like a sore thumb. And then, there is no fucking way that I am escaping with those two - the game would be up before we'd gone five feet. Neither of them has the wit or competence to stay alive for five minutes without a comprehensive support system around him. One of them needs reassurance so badly he'd talk himself through the gates of Hell just to have someone listen to him, and the other needs his mother's permission to masturbate. We can't walk along the road, and we can't walk through the desert."

"So what we going to do?"

"We would have to steal a car. We've got money for petrol and food and water. But the first time we stopped at a petrol station, we'd be tumbled."

"Why?"

"Have you had a good look at your eyes lately? Mine radiate fear. I could cover myself in brown boot polish, poke out one of my own eyes, and speak what little Arabic I know, and my other eye would still give me away the moment I looked at the petrol station owner."

"Mine wouldn't."

"Aye, your right, Malcolm. You've made a career out of looking as though butter wouldn't melt in your mouth. But you're still six feet three. And while we're at it, I saw the look in your face the first time we met at the first meeting. Man, you were frightened, and there was no way of disguising that fact. On the run, we would give ourselves away the moment we spoke to anybody. That means we would have to steal a car that we were sure was full of petrol. We couldn't even change the plates, because they would have to match the papers which would be kept in the car. Then we would then have to sit for four to five hours at Ras Ajdir while the border police did checks."

"How do you know?"

"It's par for the course. Every body I know that has been through Ras Ajdir has told the same story. Four to five hours of waiting in a queue. The Libs do it deliberately to allow time for reports of people seeking to leave the country illegally to be received from Tripoli.

"Then there's at least a quarter of mile of buffer zone between the Libyan checkpoint and the Tunisian border. Our own passports would be useless even if we had them, and we don't have any other papers. If we tried to run for it we would be shot dead before we got twenty yards.

"If we're going to escape, it's going to require organization. And that means contact with someone resourceful and organized on the outside. So far we don't have that, or at least, we don't know that we have it.

"They even knocked conjugal visits on the head," I went on.

"What's 'conjugal visits'?"

I told him what George had told me at the meeting with Pat.

Another British expatriate had been in detention during 1984, in circumstances not dissimilar to ours. His wife had made representations through the Foreign Office for a conjugal visit. Surprisingly, the Libyans had complied. The Libyans made arrangements for the Brit to stay at the Grand Hotel - not half a mile from our Italian mansion. The Libyans duly and properly escorted his wife to the hotel bedroom on the 14th floor, and then left her with her husband.

During the night, the two of them slipped out of the room, down 28 flights of stairs, stole out of the hotel and into the car park where the wife had parked a Land Rover. They drove off in the direction of Ras Ajdir, and Tunisia.

One hundred and seventy four kilometres later, they could see the brilliantly illuminated border checkpoint half a mile off. The wife had her own passport with an exit re-entry visa stamped in it. She had the car's papers, which were all in order. She even had papers authorizing the temporary export of the Land Rover into Tunisia for a two week holiday - a quite remarkable achievement in itself. But there was no way through. The husband had no papers. They were in for a five hour wait and certain discovery, or in for crashing the barrier into the buffer zone, and certain death by Libyan machine gun fire.

But the wife was not finished yet. In the back of the Land Rover was her husband's diving equipment - bottle, fins, mask, demand valve, depth gauge, watch, compass -

the whole shooting match. All her husband had to do was to get into his diving gear, walk the 20 yards from the Land Rover to the sea, submerge and scuba dive for a mile on a predetermined compass bearing around the border checkpoint. He then needed only surface, walk ashore into Tunisia, and wait for his wife to pick him up. The Tunisians would need no convincing, and the husband would be free. So far so good.

He donned his equipment and spat into his masked and cleared it. She turned on his air supply and kissed him, and, with his fins in his hands, he walked to the shore line as she drove off towards the checkpoint. Once in the water he would continue to walk out to a point where the water was deep enough to submerge. Then he would be off.

As the light from the check point and the village receded behind him, he found that he needed to go farther out than he had anticipated. Quite a lot farther out actually. A quarter of a mile farther out in fact. By now the water had come up to his knees.

But he was coming into the arc of visibility from the checkpoint, and hence, the arc of machine gun fire. To keep walking or not to keep walking? That was the question.

He couldn't stay where he was and he couldn't turn back.

He went out a little farther, then, shaking his head in disbelief, turned left and, in full diving kit, with half the Libyan army less than a quarter of a mile away, he waded, ankle deep, all the way to Tunisia.

"Conjugal visits," said Malcolm, shaking his head.

"OK. There's a border crossing between Libya and Tunisia, just past Wazan."

"Where's Wazan?"

"It's about thirty five klicks past Nalut."

"Where's Nalut?"

"Three hundred klicks from here by road. No deviation. Nowhere to hide."

"Aye, OK."

"Then when we've crossed into Tunisia, we'll have to get across two hundred kilometres of a desert that I know nothing about to reach anybody's idea of civilization. We might be lucky to get a lift from somebody who wasn't Libyan. The problem is that we would first have to get across the border. They don't need to mine or patrol the border. Even assuming that we made it past the check point, the check point is half way up a precipitous edge, about a thousand feet high. The Libyans were careful to pick it. The border road runs around three sides of a canyon for twenty five kilometres before you are in the clear and in Tunisia. If we got it wrong, we'd be sewn up in the canyon by Libyan artillery fire. We'd be sitting ducks."

"How do you know?"

"The artillery I've been told about. I took photographs of the rest."

"Howway! You do know!"

"Yes, Malcolm. I do."

"There must be some way out."

"There is. But we need organization, and that means contact with the outside world."

"Aye. And we don't have it," concluded Malcolm.

"Exactly."

Discrete enquiries were made.

Was an Entebbe style raid and rescue possible?

"It could be done, but we would require information."

The success of such a raid was in doubt.

"The problem is that we don't actually know where they are. That compounds the risk of the men getting killed."

A source close to us hostages used an intermediary to give information on our whereabouts to the SAS. The information included a detailed description of each of us, and details of where we were being held. Unfortunately, the details were not sufficiently accurate.

The acceptability of such a raid was in doubt.

"The problem is that Libya is not actually a hostile regime. They make loud noises and sound offensive. But when you come to actually speak to them, they are really quite nice people."

The acceptability of collateral damage was in doubt.

"The problem is that the prison building is located on the edge of a highly populated part of Tripoli. Modern fire power is staggering in comparison with that of World War Two, and the Animals From Hereford are capable of killing an enormous number of people even when they have been told not to kill anyone unnecessarily."

Pat paid a few visits to the office of one of the major broadsheet newspaper that was covering the hostage situation. And talked the issues through with the journalist covering the case. The journalist showed her his files. The files were an extensive cardex, sorted by revolutionary groups, terrorist groups, political philosophies, political affiliations, known leaders, known contacts, known exploits etc. The files showed Pat that there were some ten thousand people being held hostage worldwide at any one time. Pat's shoulders slump as the lunacy of such kidnapping organizations became clear, and that this present brush with madness was by no means exceptional. She concluded that the chances of her husband's case being dealt with by the British government as a high priority were recessive.

Pat and the journalist got their coats and left to go to the wine bar.

My focus on the rubber was distracted as familiar words emerged from the radio.

"Something made him the way that he is
Whether he's false or true
And something gave him the things that are his
One of those things is you.

"So when he wants your kisses you must give them to the lad,
And any where he leads you, you must walk,
And any time he needs you, you go running there like mad.
He's your fella and you love him. And all the rest is talk."

199

The tears coursed silently down my face.

I bit, hard.

"Are you alright, Robin?" asked Malcolm.

I bit harder.

"Are you alright, Robin?" he asked again.

I bit even harder and nodded my head.

"Play cards, Robin," ordered Malcolm.

I nodded my head.

"Do you want to play cards, Robin?" pressed Malcolm gently.

I kept biting, raised my eyebrows and nodded my head.

"Play a card, Robin."

I dipped my hand for Malcolm to see.

Malcolm narrowed his eyes and took and played the appropriate card.

Play continued, with Malcolm playing my hand as well as his own, until we had won. As deal passed to the left, I sequestered the pack and, out of turn, proceeded to deal. No-one even thought about trying to stop me.

There were days when it was bad. There were days when it was bloody awful. Nothing in your upbringing, your education, or your experience can prepare you for this. There were times when I figured that I had about ten seconds in which to do something before I cracked. And the only way that I could escape this latest brush with madness was quite literally to count seconds out loud. So count seconds I did. And by three I was sliding. And by eight and nine I was still sliding. And by ten I was getting control - but not enough. And eleven, and twelve, and thirteen.... And Purgatory I would pluck from the jaws of Hell - mere desperate panic from the jaws of insanity. Jesus Christ, Robin, you've got to find something more than this. This is too close to the edge. Tell me all about it! What more is there? I don't know. But you've damn well got to find it!

Where is it to be found? I don't know - inside. What? Inside. What do mean? Inside. That's where the void is. What do you mean? Well, there is no support system outside so help must come from inside. What about God? God is Love. Well, He's not doing a fat lot right now, is He? So find the Void. What? Yes. The way is in the Void. Find the Void.

You don't know what the Void is. You never know what the Void is. It is a void and therefore you can't know what it is. Or what is in it. Or how much is in it. If indeed there is anything in it. You don't know how much you've got inside you. You don't know that you've even got it inside you.

The Samurai philosophy has a concept called Misogi - Training to the Point of Exhaustion. When you have trained to the point of exhaustion and all your muscles are jelly, you will be lying on the floor, incapable of raising your sword. But training to the point of exhaustion is not, in and of itself, the point.

The real point is that having trained to the point of exhaustion, you cannot stay on the floor for the rest of your life. You have to get up. How else will you deal with the next attack? And to get up - when you cannot get up - requires you to find something within you that you never knew you had.

Exactly.

So look in the void. Ok. It will take a while. Yes. Ok. One, two, three, hold on, four, five, six, seven, eight....

Alan dealt with it differently. While I was standing there counting the seconds to insanity, Alan was in the bathroom, pounding four paces in one direction and then four paces back again.

"When the going gets tough, the tough get going!

"When the going gets tough, the tough get going!"

The Greek fellow, in his leather bomber jacket, whose BMW was being washed in the yard outside by some young revolutionaries, must have heard Alan. After several minutes of pounding, the outer door to Doug's room opened and the Greek came in. He slid open the inner door to the bathroom. Without invocation, Alan ceased his dizzying, forced march and turned on the felicitations through his smile. The felicitations brought relief from the pounding. But the relief was short lived. Alan promptly did his customary trick of resorting to telling his life story to his listener, now that he'd got his listener's attention. That of itself might not have been too bad. But it came time to intervene when Alan lowered his voice and I heard our names being mentioned.

I tipped Malcolm and we separately sauntered in to the bathroom.

I went directly to the toilet and, in the presence of Alan and the Greek, started to pee. Malcolm went to the sink and started to wash his face.

Alan could be forgiven for being shocked and, quite understandably, exploded, "What the Hell do you think you're doing?"

But the real reason for his anger was elucidated by his next outburst.

"I'm having a conversation with this official!"

"Ah kna," finessed Malcolm. "That's why wor came in." The Greek's lips parted, his eyes blank.

Then the penny dropped. Furious, Alan stormed away and was heard to sit down in his usual chair.

Seeking to determine what, if anything, Alan had told them, I opened uncontroversially with, "Alan's just had a visit from his wife."

The Greek took the bait. "Yes. Special man coming to see you soon."

"No," I toyed. "Only our wives come to see us."

"Yes. Special man from House of God coming to see you."

"No," I continued. "No-one comes to see us unless they have the permission of Col. Gaddafi."

"Mr President," corrected the Greek loudly, his eyes widened.

"That's what I said. Col Gaddafi," I said.

Malcolm looked at me trying to prompt me to get it right.

The Greek's body and eyes swelled to twice their normal size as he bawled, "Mr

President!"

I read Malcolm's face and corrected myself to the received usage.

Without acknowledgement, the Greek returned to affability.

Then, spotting one of our grubby tea cups sitting on the bathroom floor, he turned to an open store cupboard at the head of the bathtub, and indifferently handed me a drinking glass, and shut and locked the door.

Making the facetious assumption that the glass was a reward for addressing the "President" correctly, I twisted the glass over in my hand as if to say, "What is this?"

Misreading me, the Greek mimicked drinking. Then he pointed at the pile of stained crockery on the floor beside the basin and asked how long we had had the cups.

"Four months," I overstated.

He explained that the cracked and broken cups harboured germs and that that could be bad for us.

I didn't believe it.

"You want more cups?"

I was reeling in disbelief.

Malcolm murmured to me that there were four of us.

I politely swept my arm to indicate this to the Greek.

Smiling, he unlocked and re-opened the cupboard, and counted out and thrust at me three more glasses. Then, on impulse, he made it a baker's three. In case we broke one, he said, relocking the cupboard.

I liked him. He knew the odds and how to maintain them, but I liked him.

"You need shoes?" he asked, regarding Malcolm's feet.

"Aye, ya can," replied Malcolm.

"OK," said the Greek, and left without another word.

Malcolm and I just looked at each other.

Then Malcolm expressed his disbelief with his usual eloquence. "Well, fuckin' 'ell!"

Then we remembered Alan.

We went in. Malcolm ostentatiously invited Alan to pick his own new glass. Alan pulled himself back from the brink, and charmingly selected one with celerity.

A couple of days later a load of new shoes arrived.

They were cheaply made with inflexible moulded soles. And they were bright blue.

We risibly selected a pair each that fitted.

Malcolm wore his to show gratitude to the Greek. Michael did not wear his, out of disdain for the colour. I did not wear mine because they were not built up. And Alan wore his for a few days.

But the going <u>was</u> tough. And poor Alan was finding it increasingly difficult to cope. He'd worked abroad to earn money for his family - more money than he could expect to earn at home. He would know that his family was suffering financially, and the burden of that suffering sat on top of all the other stresses that he, along with the rest of us, was enduring.

I was reading. Michael was handwringing. Malcolm was in the pink suite shaving. Alan was doing something that didn't involve reading. Initially, I ignored it because it was probably none of my business. But as the gusto, with which he directed himself to any project, began to take over, so did my interest. He appeared to be going to work on his pair of the ghastly, blue trainers, adjusting the insole or something. After several minutes, he put the trainers away in their normal place, under his bed, and then declared to everyone in general and no-one in particular, "There. I won't wear those again until the day we leave here."

The penny dropped.

I concluded that Alan was becoming a liability. I got up quietly, went and had a pee, and told the still shaving Malcolm what I had seen, and of my fears that Alan could jeopardize all of us if we didn't keep him on a fairly short lead.

"I think we're going to have to confront him about it," said I.

"Aye," concurred Malcolm. "How d'ya want to do it?"

"I think we need to wait for a few minutes, then walk back in together," I said. "I'll just go and sit on Michael's bed and pick up my book, you go straight over and pick up the trainers. They're under his bed. Then we'll have to tell him."

We did exactly that.

"Alan," said Malcolm with the trainers in his hands. "What's this?"

"What's what?" Alan tried to remonstrate.

But as Malcolm stood there pulling wads of Libyan Dinar notes out of the lining of Alan's trainers, there was nothing that Alan could say.

Malcolm re-rolled the banknotes, quietly inserted them into his underpants, and went back into the Pink Bathroom to finish his ablutions.

And the strain of forcing your heart and nerve and sinew for month after endless month was beginning to tell. The left hand side of my nose had been twitching more or less constantly during waking hours for a number of weeks. My chest was getting tight. My family history did not bode well. So I told them to take me to the doctor.

I was not allowed to go to the Malaysian doctor again. Instead, I was taken to see a Bulgarian. He was kindly, gentle, professional and knew exactly which way was up.

But he had been instructed that the only language that he and I were to speak was Arabic - and that in Red Head's presence. What is the Arabic for, 'Look! I'm terribly sorry, but I appear to have this awful tightness across my chest.'?

Following the usual dumb show and the writing of a few numbers, I managed to get across that my heart was never doing less than ninety beats a minute during waking hours, and that it was more like a hundred and twenty during interrogation and such. The Bulgarian took my blood pressure and pulse, nodded with satisfaction, and prescribed two sets of tablets. One was for the pain, and the other was to slow down my heart rate. "Shwear, shwear," he said gently, with a kindly look into my eyes, and making the universal hand sign for 'slowly'. Take one tablet every eight hours. Inderal. Never heard of it. There was no more chest pain after that.

A week or so later I got a minor infection in my nose. I was taken to the same hospital by the Sweet Smelling Boy, but the Bulgarian was not on duty. Instead, they took me to see a portly Egyptian.

I took one look at the shape of his face and said, "Inte mush Libyan."

He wasn't Libyan. But he was supremely arrogant. The only thing missing was the Tommy Cooper style red fez. Rocked back in his carver, and with his back to an open quadrangle to keep cool, he invited me to lean across his cluttered desk so that he could examine my nose. This he did by prising my nostrils open with a pair of flat nosed pliers that had been sitting on his desk, resting on a matchbox, much as chopsticks rest on a stand at table, and which had been up who knows how many countless other patients' noses before mine.

I grabbed the box of antibiotics offered to me, and ran.

It was the middle of the morning. The door opened. A guard came in and indicated that I was to come with him.

"Why?" I said.

"Information," he said.

I was taken to the court house, and made to sit in the waiting room. After a short while I was called and taken to the magistrate's office. But instead of being invited to sit, the magistrate took one look at me, nodded to my escort, and I was taken straight back out to the car.

In the car were men I had never seen before. And the instant we turned off the route back to the Italian mansion, I became seriously alarmed. Then the man in the passenger seat spoke to the driver, and I realised that he was holding a copy of the invitation to Aka's leaving party. He passed it to the man seated beside me in the back, who told me to point out the villa at which the party was supposed to have taken place.

My. They were being thorough.

What a dilemma.

We were close enough that the map on the invitation had plainly told the approximate location. But they couldn't pinpoint the villa itself.

Do I fake ignorance, memory loss, inability to read my own map? I'd told them that I'd not gone to the party, but they were slowly homing in on the location and it was going to be difficult to say I didn't know.

In the end I faked ignorance and gave them a number of bum steers, in the hope that they would get bored and go home.

But they didn't. They persisted with a tenacity I had never ever seen among Libyans, and eventually we found our selves cruising back and forth on the few yards of dusty road directly in front of the villa and the compressor room.

All I could do was pray that the people I knew who had lived there six months previously, had now moved or, better still, left the country.

Two of the men got out of the car. One walked to the villa and banged on the glass door.

From my seat in the rear of the car, I could see through the open gate that the ghiblis were down and the lower edges silted up with sand. I could not hear an air conditioner whirring, and there were no visible tyre marks in the sandy drive way.

After several more attempts at raising someone within, the Libyans drew the same conclusion that I did.

We drove away and back to the Italian mansion.

With summer waning and autumn on the way, the thermometer on the water heater in the bathroom had now fallen to twenty five degrees centigrade. Bathing was becoming painfully cold.

Malcolm decided to get the water heater working. I pointed out that the water heater might have been disconnected for a good reason - such as that the wiring was suspect and that it might cause a fire or that the voltage of the supply might have been changed.

"Divvent be daft, man!" rebuked Malcolm.

So I told him.

A year previously, the revolutionary committee that ran the electrical power supply in a suburb of Benghazi decided that it was time to get some new electrical generating equipment. They got the funding, commissioned the work and installed the new equipment. On handover day, the members of the committee stood around and arrogantly oversaw the switching on. The generator was run up to speed and synchronized, the field excitation was increased and the breakers were thrown. Unfortunately, between the revolutionary committee and the installers, they had forgotten to mention that the new system was delivering electricity at two hundred and twenty volts. And as the electricity came on stream, it blew every piece of domestic equipment in the suburb because all the equipment was rated at one hundred and ten volts.

Malcolm admitted the possibility but proceeded anyway with caution.

We rounded up an odd assortment of metallic tools - nail clippers, a dinner knife - that might pass for screw drivers, and proceeded to explore the wiring and the electrical outlet to which the heater had plainly once been connected.

We dried our hands, stood in our leather shoes on old copies of the FT, and avoided touching each other. Then we gingerly connected the wires to the live terminal, and the heater started to hum. I stood there for half an hour feeling the wiring, and various other parts to make sure that nothing was in danger of catching fire. When it was clear that it was in fact safe, we suddenly found that we had the luxury of hot water again.

Malcolm had been lying on Alan's bed, asleep. Now, he was lying prone, with a blanket over his back, pulled up around his head like a granny in a shawl, and he was grinning. After watching carefully for a few minutes, he started.

"Michael," said Malcolm.

"D'ya live on a farm, Michael?" asked Malcolm.

"Michael! D'ya live on a farm, Michael?" asked Malcolm.

"Yes, Malcolm. I live on a farm," answered Michael.

"How far is to town, Michael?" asked Malcolm.

"What do mean 'town'?" asked Michael.

"You know. Tripoli," said Malcolm.

"Do you go in to Tripoli, Michael?" asked Malcolm.

"When?" asked Michael.

"You know. On your night off, Michael," said Malcolm. "What do you do on your night off, Michael?"

"Oh, I don't know," replied Michael.

"Ya must know what ya do on ya night off, Michael," said Malcolm.

"Do you go out shaggin', Michael?" asked Malcolm.

"Howway, Michael!" said Malcolm. "I'll bet you go out shaggin', don't ya, Michael? I'll bet ya gan oot for a reet good shag, Michael! Don't ya Michael?"

"Oh, leave him alone. Of course he doesn't," interjected Alan.

"How do you know? Do you go out with him, Alan?" asked Malcolm.

"No, I don't. But it's obvious he doesn't. Leave him alone," said Alan.

"Well, if ya don't go out with him, ya don't know that he doesn't go out shaggin', do you, Alan?" asked Malcolm.

"No. I don't know," said Alan, following the impeccable logic.

"So he does go out shaggin' then - eh, Alan?" asked Malcolm. "You do go out shaggin', then, Michael. Don't ya Michael?"

"No, Malcolm. Oh, do stop it, Malcolm!" said Michael.

"Ok," relented Malcolm.

"So you don't go out to town shaggin', then, Michael?" said Malcolm.

"No, I don't!" said Michael.

"Oh!" said Malcolm.

"Do you stay at the farm and have a shag, then, Michael?" said Malcolm.

"Oh! Leave him alone, Malcolm!" said Alan. "Can't you see he's had enough?"

"Have ya had enough, Michael?" asked Malcolm. "Oh, sorry!"

"Do ya wear your wellies on the farm, then, Michael?" asked Malcolm.

"What do you mean?" asked Michael.

"You know. So if ya catch a sheep on the farm on your night off you can have a reet good shag, Michael," said Malcolm.

By now, Malcolm had worked himself up into a real lather of mirth, and I had to hide my own face behind my book.

Then Alan got really cross, and it was no longer fun. Malcolm pulled the blanket over his head and lay face down and quaked with silent laughter for minutes to come.

Then his impish face re-appeared - and he started on me.

"Robin. Is that a good book, Robin?" he would ask.

It was a good book. But I knew exactly where this was heading. So I smiled genially, nodded my assent, and pointedly kept reading.

"Aye, ya like a good book, don't ya Robin?" he would pursue. And I would nod.

"Is it about that - what - telephones, that telecommunications - is it, Robin?" and I would shake my head.

Seeing that he was getting nowhere, Malcolm switched. "Howway! Alan, man!"

"Mm?" mused Alan, his hearing letting him down a little.

"Can you not hear me, Alan?" asked Malcolm.

"Would it help if I spoke a little louder, Alan?" asked Malcolm.

"Do you not know that I really can't hear as well as I used to?" said Alan genuinely.

"Oh! Sorry," said Malcolm.

"Look," said Alan. "Do you really find it necessary to wind everybody up?"

"Ah divvent kna'," replied Malcolm.

"What do you mean 'divvent kna'?" castigated Alan. "There's no such word as 'divvent'. If you mean you don't know, then why don't you say 'I don't know'?"

"Ah divvent kna'," said Malcolm.

It was painful to watch. And Malcolm could keep it up for ever, all the while looking as though butter wouldn't melt in his mouth. On and on he would go, ducking and weaving, baiting and switching, just practicing his true profession.

Until it was time to start on the guards.

"Inte, shouf!" entreated Malcolm.

"Shouney?" queried Smiling Boy, looking. With circumspection, but never dropping the smile, he walked the few feet to where Malcolm stood.

"Shouf, shouf!" went on Malcolm. "Nam."

"Look, look!" he was saying. "It's OK."

Malcolm sat down opposite me. I already had a dessert spoon in my mouth.

Smiling Boy stood by for a few seconds and then turned to go.

I managed to get out the word, "Nnnhu!" from between teeth, clenched around the spoon's handle. Smiling Boy turned back and paid attention.

I went first. Malcolm, his knees interlocked with mine and a spoon now between his teeth, dipped his head towards me. I raised my head and bipped him on the top of his cranium as hard as I could with the dish end of the spoon. He winced.

Now it was his turn. I dipped my head. He bipped me. I winced.

My turn. I bipped him. He winced.

His turn. He bipped me back. I winced.

I bipped him. He rubbed his head.

His turn. I hurt, and rubbed my head.

My turn. He rubbed.

His turn. I hurt again, pulled a face and rubbed my head harder this time.

Malcolm turned to Smiling Boy. The usual cardboard smile had turned into one of fascinated delight.

"Inte!" instructed Malcolm. "Fi. Nam," he encouraged in his limited Arabic.

Smiling Boy took up station opposite me. I went first. I bipped as hard as I could.

Smiling Boy dropped his spoon. I retrieved it.

His turn. I winced.

My turn.

His turn. I rubbed my head.

My turn. I summoned up all the momentum I could. Whack! He winced.

His turn. I rubbed.

My turn. He rubbed.

His turn. I let out a low moan.

My turn. He let out a serious cry.

His turn. I started to smile.

My turn. He looked around at Malcolm.

Behind him stood Malcolm with the catering sized ladle held high waiting to bop Smiling Boy again as I motioned to do so.

Smiling Boy let out a quick laugh and got up to leave the room. "Oh dear," said I. Malcolm said, "It's OK," as Smiling Boy turned at the door, half raised an index finger, and pursed his lips to indicate quiet. And he was gone.

Doors opened, doors shut. And then opened and shut again as Smiling Boy ushered in Laughing Boy. Smiling Boy twinkled at Malcolm and me, seated Laughing Boy opposite Malcolm, and picked up the ladle.

It took the half-wit longer and many painful blows to the head to realise what was going on. But when he did, he and Smiling Boy grinned and giggled together in Arabic. Then Laughing Boy suggested something. Smiling Boy let out a low moan and both of them disappeared. A minute later they were back with the Black Kid.

I had trouble suppressing a smile. "This should get things going," I thought to myself, and whispered, "Oh, Christ."

Malcolm looked at me smiling broadly.

Laughing Boy twinkled at Malcolm and me, seated the Black Kid opposite Smiling Boy, and picked up the ladle.

It took the moron a great deal longer and many more painful blows to the head to realise what was going on. But when he did, the Black Kid, Smiling Boy and Laughing Boy laughed out loud in Arabic. Meanwhile, Malcolm and I were having difficulty containing ourselves. Then the Black Kid grunted something, Laughing Boy and Smiling Boy let out unsuppressed hoots, and all three of them disappeared. A minute later they were back with the plaster casted Gigolo, on crutches.

The Black Kid twinkled at Malcolm and me, seated the Gigolo opposite Laughing Boy, and picked up the ladle.

It took the Gigolo very much longer and many, many painful blows to realise what was going on. And when he did, he was not amused. "We're all going to die," I ventured to Malcolm without moving my lips. The Gigolo looked up at me. I ignored him. Smiling Boy, Laughing Boy and the Black Kid were dancing a tarantella with laughter. The Gigolo was clench jawed. Malcolm wore his butter-wouldn't-melt-in-his-mouth look. I was catatonic with silent laughter. The humiliation was complete.

Summoning what little dignity he could, the Gigolo raised his broken body and broken ego, and shuffled painfully to the door. The Maleishes flew from the guards in choruses, but forgiveness was unlikely. And so it proved. Any shred of dignity still possessed by the Gigolo evaporated as he bawled a stream of Arabic. The commands sent the guards into silence and us to our respective beds. An early night for naughty children. But, oh, my God, it would have been worth taking a beating for, just to see the look on his face. We never saw the Gigolo again.

I wasn't sorry, but the next few days were tense as we anticipated retribution. It never came, and our routine resumed as if nothing had ever happened. Nothing, that is, except a new light in the eye of Smiling Boy whenever we saw him.

A week or so later, I was in the downstairs kitchen cleaning lunch plates, when Smiling Boy stopped by. He saw me finishing, and amicably pointed out the drudgery of being dishman. I nodded assent. He opened the refrigerator door and reached for a can of pear juice. In one movement, he closed the door, turned to me and passed me the drink. With two hands clasped around the pile of dishes, I was in no position to take the pear juice even if I had wanted to. I turned down the corners of my mouth and shook my head. He offered again. Still I refused. He prodded my chest in a friendly manner with the hand clenched can, and tried to catch my eye. OK, so lets be friends. No, Robin. OK. So let's just play the game. Yes. I put down the dishes, took the ice cold can and placed in inside my shirt next to my skin so that no other guard would see it. I looked him in the eye. My Arabic "thank you" was met with lowered eyes and broadened smile. I picked up the dishes and measured my way upstairs to the room. Laying the dishes aside, I produced the can and offered it to the first comer. All declined, but within two minutes it was clear that the spoons incident was over, and that some of the Libs, at least, had seen the funny side of it.

The cockroach died under the heel of my built up shoe. I had to hit it six times.

I'd heard it one night while we were all in bed, rattling its way around the skirting board. But, while Malcolm was dozing off, his face acted as a runway as the cockroach glided off the dado rail and gathered pace for flight. Malcolm let out a strange assortment of sounds at the intrusion. I rolled out of bed, Alan flicked on the lights, and I set about the act of murder with zeal, energized by imagining that I was stoveing in the skull of the Black Kid. The cockroach was not going to escape this. But I was surprised at how resilient it was. I took no joy in thinking that I might have to hit the Black Kid this many times with the iron bar before he stopped moving.

Tweedle Dee had just returned, tired and hungry, from a six week tour of duty at a prison in Benghazi. I was in the ground floor kitchen making tea, and it took me little more than a couple of attempts at offering him food, and then cutting and filling a cheese roll and thrusting it into his hands, for him to get suckered in. Only minutes afterwards the entire mansion reverberated to the sound of the telling off that he received. I was sure that he would tell that I had given him the food, and then I would be for it as well. Inside, I shook as mightily as did the building. But it was worth it just to hear one of the guards getting into trouble at my instigation.

I finished making the tea, stacked a number of whisky glasses onto a tray beside the tea pot and sugar, and picked the tray up. I walked up the marble floored corridor all the way to the guards' day room.

I had finally done it. I'd walked all the way from the kitchen to the day room on a marble floor, wearing leather soled shoes without making a sound that I could hear.

Now I was ready to escape.

I put the tray down on the carpet, and proceeded to pour tea.

A new guard was there - a slight man in a cheap suit. The others deferred to him.

But a chorus of negatives and waves of hands from all the guards told me that I was instantly to cease serving the tea. I assumed that there was some rule in Libya about who was allowed to serve whom. But in didn't matter. I'd made my point. There was no more tea serving after that.

But I was allowed in to watch television. An astonishing occurrence, until I found that the permission came from the newcomer. His shock of frizzy black hair shrouded his eyes. The eyelids were permanently half closed. The eyes hunted hither and yon. His mouth never closed and his lips moved as if he were rehearsing lines for the stage. He silently fingered the Browning automatic that lay between the cushions on the sofa on which I now sat a respectable foot or two away from him.

Five or six guards and I watched a video in which a large number of blue uniformed, and knee booted, white policemen, in black Sam Browne belts, were seen to be beating a large number of blacks in the street with large batons.

The slender man raised his hand in the direction of the screen and said, "You see. This is England. This is how they treat black people in England."

I couldn't let that go.

"No," I said. "This is not England."

"This is England," he repeated.

"No," I said, and paused for effect. "Look at the uniforms."

And he shut up.

Over the next few days, the slender fellow took it upon himself to visit us in Doug's room whenever he felt the need.

After a couple of half hearted attempts to ensure that we had everything we needed, he slid out of pastoral mode and started to induct us into the way of the Third Universal Theory. The distortions of reality written in Colonel Gaddafi's political treatise, sat at the heart of the Big Green Looney's revolutionary thinking. It also gave authority to the revolutionary committees that ran the country, one of which boasted this fellow as a member.

After a day or two of silently listening to his revolutionary ramblings, a number of things became clear. Firstly, the man in front of us was a student at the Agricultural Department of the Great Al Fatah University in Tripoli. So was the Gigolo. It also became clear that all the most ambitious revolutionaries in Libya joined the Agricultural Department. Further, this Italian mansion was, what the Americans would call, the "Frat House" of the Revolutionary Committee than ran the Agricultural Department - the most fervent of all Revolutionary Committees in Libya. And finally, that it was the Agricultural Department Revolutionary Committee that was holding us as hostages.

Accordingly, we had in front of us a self confessed, key player in our kidnap and detention, who walked around the Italian mansion carrying a fourteen shot, Browning automatic pistol loaded with dum-dum bullets, to whom everybody paid deference and who, it was entirely possible, had links to the murder of WPC Fletcher.

He talked in exalted terms about the revolution that The Leader was exporting to various parts of the world, and talked in functionally neurotic terms about how the rest of the world worked.

He said that he would shortly be going to Canada to help a local community of oppressed Sikhs in their revolution against the Canadian government.

The Revolutionary was additionally interested to know why the big man from the church was so interested in us.

"Why are you so important that he comes to Jamahiriya?" he said.

When The Revolutionary had gone back to his day room, Malcolm turned to me, worried at the implication of the question.

I told Malcolm my thoughts that, in the midst of all this half baked, self deluding, ideological claptrap, The Revolutionary was just trying to put the frighteners on us.

"I hope so," said Malcolm.

Now that we had got the water heater working, I spent several days fine tuning the thermostat until the water temperature was just under boiling point.

Now we had water hot enough for two baths in succession if you were careful about how much hot water you drew. You also had to be very careful not to scald yourself.

Now we had water hot enough to wash our dishes properly, an important precaution against food poisoning which, I suspect, we had been lucky to avoid until now.

Now we had water hot enough to make our own tea. Luxury! All we had to do was to persuade the guards to give us periodic supplies of tea leaves and we were away.

Now we had water hot enough to make - rice pudding. Every lunch time, our meal included a generous quantity of boiled rice. After lunch, we would place the serving dish of surplus rice next to the left-over butter on the top of the air conditioning unit. After dinner in the evenings, I would wash the rice through at the bathroom sink with the nearly boiling water until the rice was hot and salt free. Then I would drain it, add sugar and a little milk to make a perfectly acceptable rice pudding for all who wanted it. It was surprisingly good in spite of starting out as long grained and savoury.

But once the guards realised that the water heater also fed the sink in the basement in which Michael and the Sudanese had originally been held, they decided to clear the basement and use it as their new kitchen.

"Oh, brilliant!" I thought. "Now they have another green field site to litter with putrefying household waste." And that's exactly what they did.

"He's not a full shillin', man," said Malcolm. Laughing Boy discharged his orders with a little more bark than the other guards, but a lot less bite.

Laughing Boy subjected us to the occasional pantomime of someone who has just learned karate. He launched spirited attacks on everything in sight.

"Hi, cha!" he would scream as he launched himself through an open door.

On the 1st of September, when the rest of us had left the mansion in one vehicle, Malcolm was waiting for another to take him to the Revolution Day news conference, Laughing Boy unlocked and opened the outer door and insinuated himself through the inner door as Malcolm lay on Doug's bed. As quietly as he could move, Malcolm heard him anyway. Laughing Boy screamed while throwing his arms and legs around in all directions. Malcolm kept his gaze resolutely fixed on the ceiling.

Things came to a head one day while we were exercising in the garden. "You, James Bond!" he ventured.

"No, me not James Bond," I assured him.

"No, no," he argued. "You James Bond. You - me. Same - same." And he adopted a fighting posture, only he was lot closer than usual. I spread my feet a little.

Malcolm interjected "No, Robin. That's exactly what he wants you to do."

Even as I tried to ignore Laughing Boy, he started to try to land blows upon my chest. The first few missed because I stepped backwards. The next few missed because I stepped to the side. Then Laughing Boy's face changed from the usual, stupid, playful look to one of annoyance that he hadn't landed a single blow. The kicks and punches started in earnest. I sought to avoid him but he came after me with a will.

Even as I tried to ignore him and merely sidestep his blows, he became increasingly agitated. His mood hardened and so did his blows. I had managed to sidestep everything up until now, but it was only a matter of seconds before he actually landed one. I was going to get hurt, and nobody was seeking to stop this nonsense. I was going to get a beating from Laughing Boy if I just stood there, or a different beating from the other guards if I retaliated. Damned if I win. Damned if I lose. So win and be damned. It was left to me to stop this nonsense, and a fight began.

In the two or three assaults that followed, I let him touch me two or three times. As the next assault started, I stepped forward and blocked his punch. Twin reactions of surprise and delight greeted my involvement, and the battery continued.

In quick succession I blocked kicks and punches. But he was not deterred. I blocked harder until his wrists, ankles and feelings were all hurt. It was all to no avail. On the next assault, he landed a painful blow on my chest. That was it. I attacked.

Now, he was doing the blocking. But his blocks were not as good as mine. Of course I had nothing to gain by doing him any real damage. So I stung him several times with straight fingers to the ribs. His offensive blows were now transmuted into blocks, which weren't working. And to rub the point in, I entered deeply and caressed the line of his jaw with the tips of my fingers and withdrew before he could block me.

Then, following one large stride, I raised my left leg to kick him. But there was no need. He faltered. He backed away. He cowered. It was all over.

I did not hear or see Laughing Boy for some time. When I did, he approached me with a supplication bordering on apology. I saw it as good politics to give and receive a saluting kiss on each cheek, praying that I would not catch his eye affliction. And the deed was done. There was no more karate after that.

There was no more James Bond after that.

*** *** ***

PART FIVE

1st November to 25th Dec, 1984

It had taken five months. But we had done it. We had won the psychological war against the guards.

Additionally, with the exception of Michael, we had, by mid October, all had visits from our wives. Michael's sister, Mary Berdinner, eventually came to Tripoli and met Michael on the 15th of November.

But what little contact we had had with Hugh elicited nothing of substance which might inspire hope. In fact it did the opposite.

There had been virtually nothing about us in the FT or on the World Service since we first had access to them at the beginning of September. But we were beginning to hear on the BBC that Anglo-Libyan trade that had been all but suspended in the months following the cessation of diplomatic relations between the UK and Libya had started to resume by companies that could not afford not to do business.

I was getting better at holding on. Poor Alan was getting worse.

There was no indication from the moribund Michael. And, except for the odd and very welcome outburst of mischief from Malcolm, he also had become increasingly dejected.

We felt abandoned and alone.

What we were unaware of, and were never going to be told - because it is not in keeping that the FCO should tell everybody what they do - was the staggering amount of effort being expending on our case by various offices of the government, Her Majesty's Diplomatic Service and the FCO - up to and including the House of Commons, the Foreign Secretary and the Prime Minister. Even Buckingham Palace was on the circulation list for certain correspondence.

In all correspondence, we were always called hostages or detainees, and consistent reference was made to an illegal U-turn.

The British government in all its guises adopted a consistent and all pervasive position of no negotiation or bargaining with the Libyans.

There would not under any circumstances be a swap of the hostages for the four Libyan bombers awaiting trial in Britain, as that would jeopardise the other five thousand Brits who worked in Libya, and the five or six million other Brits who live around the world. It would just lead to more hostage taking.

There was, however, no wish to escalate or complicate the issues. The British Government simply wanted the Libyans to let us go before there could be any suggestion of even considering the resumption of normal relations.

Under any circumstances the Rule of Law must prevail.

There was a great deal of diplomatic activity, even if any progress being achieved was slow. The FCO was, in fact, doing exactly the job they're paid for.

8 Oct NENAD minute of a phone call by the Moroccan Ambassador to the Under Secretary of State at the FCO. The Moroccan Ambassador had accompanied King Hassan's special envoy, when he called on the Prime Minister on Friday, 5th October.

Mr Luce is grateful for the Moroccan Ambassador's offer of help with the Libyans to try to secure the release of the remaining four hostages, when you saw him on the 19th of September.

17 Oct Mr Cambridge to Rabat.

At the request of Mrs Thatcher, King Hassan the Second sent an emissary to Colonel Gaddafi to examine the fate of the four, and to obtain their release.

Colonel Gaddafi showed a sincere willingness to resume good relations with Great Britain and an equal willingness to endeavour to improve them.

Colonel Gaddafi accepts the principle of their liberation.

However, he puts forward certain conditions which would constitute in his eyes Mrs Thatcher's contribution to the improvement of British-Libyan links.

The conditions are the following:

Col Gaddafi would wish that some Libyans presently detained in Britain and facing charges before British courts be set free and handed over to Libyan authorities.

If by reason of separation of powers Mrs Thatcher could not have them freed, she should ask the British judicial system to have them tried as soon as possible, but once sentenced, Mrs Thatcher should authorise them to serve their prison term in Libya.

The British authorities should follow up and order the expulsion of certain Libyans presently the subject of an Interpol investigation.

Additionally, King Hassan indicated that if it were judicially or legally impossible to respond favourably to Colonel Gaddafi's conditions, then the tried and sentenced Libyans in Britain could benefit from the prerogative of a pardon.

King Hassan offered to broker a meeting in Rabat between three Libyan ministers, including the Minister of Foreign Affairs and the Minister of Oil, and the British Ambassador to engage in direct talks.

20 Oct FCO to Downing St with a draft of a letter from the PM to King Hassan.

20 Oct The letter, now from Sir Geoffrey Howe, thanked the King for his efforts and pointed out at diplomatic length the importance of his ambassador stressing to the Libyan Foreign Minister, Dr Treiki, that the Rule of Law must prevail, and that there could be no exchange. Buckingham Palace was now on the circulation list.

23 Oct FCO to Rabat. Gaddafi's offer did not change the Libyan position and our reply was based firmly on our existing policy. No mention of the offer of a meeting between Dr Treiki and Mr Cambridge.

24 Oct ICRC, Mr Renton to the Under Secretary of State at the FCO, mentioned the problems of the Libyan detainees in Geneva, when he had a long meeting with the International Committee of the Red Cross. The ICRC said that to intervene at the request of the UK was extremely difficult as the standing of the ICRC is dependent on its impartiality. But if one or more of the wives asked, they might be able to help.

Mr Renton wondered whether the FCO might write to one of the wives suggesting such action.

Mrs Thatcher did not specifically endorse the idea when she was notified on the twenty second of October, but nor did she raise any objection to it.

25 Oct NENAD to the United Nations copying Mr Renton's note of above to the UN, stating the attractions in involving the ICRC, and requesting the UN's view on the ICRC angle.

30 Oct UN to NENAD, in reply to the above. The ICRC do not intervene on behalf of hostages at the request of governments until all possible avenues open to those governments have been completely exhausted.

Even at the behest of families concerned, this is not usually done. The ICRC would be prepared in the Libyan case to consider a request from the families on humanitarian grounds. But it was by no means clear that the ICRC envisaged itself responding positively to such requests on anything other than a very occasional basis.

The issue was the likelihood of Libya being favourably influenced against the improbability of the ICRC getting involved.

30 Oct UN to NENAD, re-iterating ICRC policy, and not raising false hopes or expectations.

30 Oct Consular Dept notifying No 10 that we, the hostages, had been to the Public Prosecutor. Alan was to be charged with practising journalism without a licence, remitting copy during a news embargo, and failing to have a valid residence permit. Michael was to be charged with inciting students to counter revolution. Malcolm was being held for being in possession of letters which had passages criticising the Jamahiriya. I was not informed of any charges.

There was agreement with news department, that the line should be taken that we understand that no charges have yet been made against the men, but acknowledges that Alan made phone calls and Malcolm was carrying letters

The note also stated that I volunteered that we knew that there could be no concessions to blackmail.

1 Nov NENAD to Mr Egerton, Under Secretary at the FCO. Reiterates the ICRC position, but recognises that in concert with others it adds to the pressure on Libya.

2 Nov Far East Dept to Mr Luce. ICRC position reiterated but it might add publicity.

2 Nov NENAD to Egerton, chasing progress on Terry Waite's intervention, to say that before going to Libya, Terry is waiting for the fuss to die down following the NUM debacle.

5 Nov Renton to Luce, bemoaning the firm position of the ICRC as stated by the UN.

5 Nov FCO to Downing St, listing the charges, but noting that espionage was not amongst them. Terry still waiting for the NUM fuss to die down before he goes to Tripoli. The FCO learnt on the 5th of November, that Alan and Malcolm were to appear in court later during week commencing November the fifth. Relatives of the two men were to be notified.

6 Nov Luce to Elliott. Luce was grateful for minute of the second of November, and agreed that is does not sound appropriate to explore the possibility of ICRC intervention in these cases for the time being, but would like this option to be kept in mind for the longer term.

6 Nov. Hugh was summoned to Civil Affairs Bureau, Tripoli. Alan and Malcolm were now in the custody of the Public Prosecutor. Hugh was taken to see the Public Prosecutor's secretary very briefly and told to submit a written request for consular access to Alan and Malcolm. Hugh said that no reply had been received to a note verbale of the 4th of November asking for consular access to all four prisoners. Hugh asked for certain questions to be asked of the Public Prosecutor.

Where were Anderson and Russell being held?

Were all four detainees being kept together?

Were Plummer and Berdinner to be charged?

What were the charges against Anderson and Russell?

How were Anderson and Russell to be defended?

When would consular access be granted?

Hugh was told that a visit might be allowed on the 7th of November. The time and place would be notified later today, the sixth or tomorrow. No answers could be given to the other five questions.

Hugh's reception at the Civil Affairs Bureau was very cool. Likelihood of Hugh being allowed to see Russell and Anderson on the seventh is not good.

7 Nov British Interests Section Tripoli to London via Rome. Hugh was again summoned to the Civil Affairs Bureau, and saw Alan and Malcolm. The charges were stated. Russell asked the prosecutor about legal representation. He was given no details about how to arrange defence counsel but was told that Dunnachie would be allowed in court. The prosecutor told Anderson that he would be contacting Dunnachie regarding the charges. Russell said that the information that he had passed back to the BBC was innocuous and mainly concerned with the day-to-day contacts between Libyans and expatriates citizens which he had reported as being friendly. He said that he wanted to ask Alex Kirby of the BBC to appear in his defence. Both Russell and Anderson want to engage defence counsel. All four detainees are being held together. Alan and Malcolm are in good spirits and, though worried, are hopeful of early release. They reported Plummer's condition as nervous and Berdinner as unstable. They said that they were being well treated.

Hugh asked the Head of the Civil Affairs Bureau for information on the trial date, defence arrangements and whether Michael and I were shortly to be charged. He was told that these questions would be answered soon.

9 Nov Luce to Downing St, stating that the charges against Messrs Russell and Anderson were ominously reminiscent of those recently levelled against a Brit in Iraq, and that HMG should in due course make clear to the Libyan authorities that HMG expects Messrs Russell and Anderson to be given a fair trial.

9 Nov Howe to Cairo. Terry Waite is to do a church and pastoral visit to Libya on the 10th of November.

Sir Geoffrey asked for the message to be passed on to Bishop Malik, who had tried, unsuccessfully to visit Libya recently.

9 Nov Dr Runcie, Archbishop of Canterbury, to Muammar El Gaddafi, Leader of the Revolution.

Dear Colonel Qadhafi,

May I express to you my gratitude for so kindly responding to my personal letter written on 1st August 1984, and also for inviting my personal representative, Mr Terry Waite, to visit the Socialist People's Libya Arab Jamahiriya.

I have asked Mr Waite to convey to you my personal greetings. Mr Waite is authorised by me to discuss issues which have concerned me for some considerable time. I am anxious that he should discuss these matters in a spirit of religious fraternity. He will make my appeal to you, which is based on humanitarian and religious grounds, and I know you will receive him in that spirit.

I am looking forward to receiving your message through Mr Waite, and I am sure the relationship between us will do much to promote peace and understanding between our peoples.

In the name of the one God whom we jointly worship,

I remain,

Yours sincerely,

Archbishop of Canterbury

12 Nov Luce to NENAD. In response to a request to put down a Private Notice Question in the House of Commons on the fate of Alan, Luce indicated that there should be no parliamentary activity this afternoon please as it might jeopardize the prospects for Mr Waite's visit.

Terry's first visit was delayed by his contacts in Libya. His contacts remained cordial, but they too were awaiting a diminution in the UK media over the NUM affair. Terry had told the Russell family and Malcolm's wife, Andrea, that a possible explanation was a delay in getting a Libyan visa, an explanation which they appeared to accept.

A briefing note at the FCO was ready, awaiting Terry's visa. Terry would pop along as soon as the visa was confirmed. He would then travel B-Cal and pick up the visa at Tripoli Airport. If the visa was not there, then he would come back on the same plane.

Terry met the Libyans. Terry met a lot of Libyans. At various levels in the administration. There was no discussion of policy, no discussion of hostages or of the international situation whatsoever. The discussions were purely interlocutory to clear the air and to make it unequivocal that Terry did not in any respect represent the British government. This was purely a pastoral visit organised by the Anglican Church for the spiritual benefit of the detainees.

The guards came for us and took us one at a time to the building at the top of the road. As I entered the familiar room at the top of the stairs, two things became clear to me.

One was the unskilled, diplomatic diffidence of a well groomed, dark, straight haired Libyan, who wore a good suit, a white shirt with cuff links and a tie, and who stood, demure and conciliatory, half facing the door.

The other was the immensity of a man, who towered head, shoulders and a bronze bust above the Libyan stood next to him. My initial reaction, as my eyes adjusted to the gloom, was that the Libyan security service had brought along another, professional neck snapper. And then I saw the watch chain, the pin stripes and an immense hand extended for me to shake, surmounted by a warm smile, a twinkle in the eyes and an inclination of the head. And then it all fell into place.

"Hello, Robin," he said. "Terry Waite."

We shook hands. It was a warm and gentle handshake, firm and feeling, and not indifferent to any signal my hand might be communicating. This was a man who had shaken hands with an awful lot of people. He did not let go until I wanted to. Even then his hand offered to remain around mine if I had wanted it.

And I did.

"I rather figured," said I, gripping a little more tightly.

"Oh, what made you think that?" he said, and made a noise mid way between a giggle and a chuckle, that was intended to invite me to laugh.

Instead of laughing, I wondered if he knew what he was dealing with. I looked deep into his eyes for a sign of the character that was going to be needed if he was going to get us out.

I couldn't find it.

"Am I glad to meet you?" I said enigmatically.

We remained standing.

Terry brought greetings from Pat. He proceeded to ask me why I had been detained and what if anything I had done wrong. I started to fluff the answer and took the opportunity of the Libyan momentarily dipping his head to indicate with my own that I didn't want to talk about this in front of the Libyan. Terry eased his weight from one foot to the other, and for a split second unsighted the Libyan to me. Reluctantly, I proceeded. The Libyan appeared not to understand a word I was saying.

I told Terry about the university, the maps, the interrogations, and then I told him that none of this mattered anyway.

"Because they're holding me as a hostage," I said. "I can't account for the others."

"Oh, don't worry about them," said Terry.

Terry probed individual points that I recounted to him about my personal situation.

Then I said that his line of questioning tended to imply that I had done something wrong, which I resented, and I momentarily clammed up.

Terry told me that when he's in a situation where he is here to help, he has to satisfy himself that the people he's here to help have indeed not done anything wrong for which they might legitimately be arraigned.

And, as I searched his dark eyes, he finished the remainder of his own sentence, saying that he could not find a shred of evidence in anything that I had said to suggest that I had in any way acted against the law.

My shoulders dropped.

"Why did you come out here?" I asked.

Never taking his eyes off me, Terry cocked his head and said, "Because I wanted to let you know that you are not forgotten, and because I heard that you and Malcolm were going to try to escape and I didn't want you getting shot."

My. He was well informed.

"Alright," I said. "What are you going to do?"

He told me that he had been authorised by the Archbishop, Robert Runcie, to make a pastoral visit, and that his first concern was to see each and then all of us, to ensure that we were OK. And while he was here, he went on, he would naturally take every opportunity available to speak to the Libyan authorities to see what could be done to create an understanding in order to ease the present circumstances and that he would, when the time was right, see what he could do to get us home.

"How long is that going to take," I asked. "Three days, three weeks, three months, three years?"

At each increase in timescale, Terry's eyes widened a little more. As I finished speaking, Terry extended his massive right paw again to shake my hand. And, shifting his weight from one foot to the other, to unsight the Libyan to me once again, he opened his eyelids to the limit of their travel and blazed his smiling eyes at me. As he did so, he put his left arm around me, my shoulder tucked neatly against his lower ribs, and tenderly clamped my upper body to him. It was the most reassuring moment of my life.

I looked deep into his eyes for a sign of the character that was going to be needed if he was going to get us out.

And I found it.

The following day, the four of us were amassed and trooped up the road to the building. There was Terry. A different, suited Libyan was in attendance. Terry took charge the instant we were seated.

He talked in general terms about the pastoral nature of his visit, of the meetings with the Libyan authorities, and said that he was seeking to get a better understanding that would ease the position. He said that it was his intention to get us out if it was at all possible but, raising his head as he said so, that he didn't know what our individual futures are going to be. And, looking past Alan, he looked at me.

Terry phoned NENAD at the FCO to say that, relenting to strong pressure from the relatives of the four, he had taken them out to lunch on the 19th of November to de-brief to them on his Libya visit. The meeting had lasted nearly three hours

Terry had told the relatives details of his visit to the men, but had not gone into detail of the visit to Libyan officials, merely describing the atmosphere as cordial. Terry told the relatives that he had left the Libyans in no doubt that the Church regarded the detainees as hostages and that an exchange for Libyan prisoners in the UK was out of the question and the Church could not in any way be party to such a deal.

There would be further meetings with the Libyans, Terry went on, and he was working closely with HMG, with whom he would be discussing the next steps. In his view it was right to keep pressing forward one step at a time even if there was only a glimmer of hope. He had tried to avoid arousing the hopes of the relatives of an early solution and had specifically undertaken to go back to Libya to see the detainees if they are still being held at Christmas.

The relatives asked Terry for his opinion of the usefulness of a meeting with Richard Balfe, MEP, planned for the twenty third of November. Terry told them to make their own decision, but that they should not disclose anything that he had told them in confidence about his own meeting. He encouraged them to avoid making a fuss in public and to think carefully about when and for what purpose publicity should be employed. He judged that the relatives would call off the Balfe meeting. Only Mrs Walters (Alan's mother-in-law, Carole Russell's mother) and Carole Russell herself appeared keen to go ahead.

20 Nov Consular Dept, to Barrington. Malcolm and Alan may now be brought to trial on the12th and 13th of December respectively. A draft telegram to the Italians was prepared.

23 Nov Via Rome, Sir Geoffrey sent a telegram in which the Italian Ambassador, Mr Quaroni in Libya, was requested to seek early consular access, so that Hugh can discuss preparedness to pay for legal representation. If consular access were not quickly granted the Italian Ambassador should also be asked to urge the Libyans to arrange for the early appointment of defence counsel gratis. NENAD concurred.

Seven hundred dinars, about nineteen hundred pounds was necessary for each defendant. Carole and Andrea said that they were unable to put up such a sum. Andrea went on to say that it was in any case pointless as the trials are essentially political anyway. The men themselves were getting paid and they may not be without funds, and if possible Hugh should see them to find out their views about whether or not they wish to pay for their own legal representation. However on Libyan form to date, it may not be possible for Hugh to see the men, and therefore the main requirement was to avoid any unnecessary delay in holding the trials solely on account of uncertainty over the appointing of lawyers. In the opinion of the former consul, George Anderson, in which NENAD concur, the quality of defence counsel made available was not likely to vary greatly whether paid for or provided free.

HMG does not pay for legal defence of British nationals overseas, but in certain circumstance they, or their next of kin, may sign undertakings to repay the cost of legal fees which can be lent from official funds.

23 Nov Fleur Fraser to Mr Atkinson. Mr Renton had raised with the ICRC in Geneva the question of the detainees in Tripoli. Mr Renton had been told that if one or more of the wives were to ask the ICRC to intervene, they might well be able to help. Mr Renton suggested that individual members contact ICRC, and the suggestion was taken up by NENAD. The ICRC had left themselves the option of refusing such a request. The suggestion of an approach to the families was endorsed by Mr Luce.

Fleur Fraser had informed the six members of the families, on the 9th and 12th of November. All showed interest; although Mrs Walters observed that it was far too late to make an approach to the ICRC.

The families had felt confident in Terry's visit.

No approach to the ICRC was made. Miss Berdinner had discussed it already with the other families, and Mrs Walters told Fleur that she had approach ICRC early in the situation but they had not been able to help.

If the others were not interested, then Mary Berdinner would write to Mr Convers (ICRC, Assistant Director of Operational Activities).

27 Nov. Egerton to Renton. The families decided to delay any approach to the ICRC until the outcome of Terry's visit to Tripoli was known.

But not so much as a whiff of this diplomatic activity filtered through to us, and from hereon the situation appeared to get worse.

The Liberation initiative had come to nothing.

The Julius Nyerere initiative had come to nothing.

The Moroccan initiative had come to nothing.

The Greek initiative had come to nothing.

The ICRC initiative had come to nothing.

The Church of England initiative, while not finished, had so far come to nothing.

Amnesty International refused even to get involved.

Visiting Labour MPs had been peremptorily kicked out of the country.

The NUM had not even mentioned us to Col Gaddafi.

Alan and Malcolm were set to go to trial.

Michael and I were still under investigation.

And no diplomatic relations were expected for the foreseeable future.

27 Nov to 12 Dec   *Nothing*

We turned up the heat from the air conditioner. Malcolm dressed in his wine coloured, V-necked sweater. He walked around the room and the Pink Bathroom. He had the far away look in his eye. Then, as he heard the key turn in the lock, he walked straight up to me, and shook hands.

"Bye, Robin," he said.

"What?" said I, looking up. "Are you going home?"

Malcolm was convinced that he was going to jail and he had been steeling himself for it for two days. And now it was the 12th of December. Malcolm was a twister, but he didn't deserve that.

"I'll see you when you get back," I said, not knowing whether I believed it or not.

"See you in ten years," he said, looking me in the eye.

The guards came. Without a backward glance, Malcolm turned and went.

I completed four puzzles, sitting on Alan's bed. Michael lay on his. Alan growled incomprehensibly. His lips and body twitching beneath a face of ashen grey.

The doors opened.

Leading the guards was all six feet four of Malcolm in his shoes, walking lightly on his tip toes and raising his knees at each pace, his hands in front of him like Jenny Woodentop. His tongue was hanging out of his slack lips, and his head and eyes were turned up and to the side.

I was momentarily alarmed. Several callings of his name made no impression on him whatsoever. I thought of 'One Flew Over the Cuckoo's Nest'. Malcolm was a twister, but he didn't deserve that.

He turned into the room, totally failing to acknowledge me.

He walked unseeing towards Doug's bed.

"Are ya a'reet, Michael?" he volubly enquired. "Howway!"

"It's adjourned 'til the 12th of January," he said, eating a loaf of bread stuffed with cheese. "What's "adjourn", Robin?"

I just looked at him. But I couldn't resist a smile.

Malcolm had met Hugh at court as promised. Hugh had turned up with a briefcase. Full of money. A lot of money. Nine thousand Libyan dinars to be precise, he'd told Malcolm, all the cash in the Diplomatic Corps, Tripoli bank account. Twenty five thousand pounds in real money. Just in case there was the possibility of hiring a defence lawyer.

And now it was the 13th Dec. Alan was ready in his cardigan and open necked shirt,

224

almost champing to get the court appearance over with. But I was called too. I pulled on a thin, grey, V-necked sweater, over a thin, poly cotton shirt and my Marks and Spencer summer weight suit trousers. I turned up my shirt collar and headed, by car, for my six-weekly interrogation.

The vast, soulless, concrete court house whose ill fitting or non-existent doors now admitted the rather colder draught of winter, was no place to sit and wait for the beak.

Sitting on a bare, wooden bench in an unfurnished concrete alcove, without any food inside us, Alan and I were constrained to sit hard up against each other with our arms folded across our respective chests, in order to conserve what little heat we had. We smoked. We shivered.

Then Alan was called to his hearing. He smoked and shivered all the more. With Alan's body warmth gone, so did I.

Striding out of my earshot, and into the company of Hugh, Alan turned one way then another, then, shown into a courtroom, sat down and then stood up again.

It was quite unprecedented for the television cameras to be allowed into a courtroom. Kate Adie said that the Libyans were highly sensitive about how their country is reported. So the Libyans were taking this opportunity to show the world what their idea of due process looked like. As the machinations wore on, overseen by a triumvirate, unprecedentedly gowned and mortar boarded, and translated by the translator of all my recent interrogations, Kate Adie, Brent Sadler and the crews were given the historically unique opportunity to interview a defendant, Alan, even as he sat there in the dock.

Never one to miss an opportunity, and though his propaganda was obvious, you had to admire Alan's courage considering that he was surrounded by militia men who bore the Kalashnikov, and court officials who had just charged him with five serious offences, adjourned his case until a sentencing hearing during the last week in December, and who were entirely capable of sending him down for a very long time

"You know that we are allowed a radio?" he said with a self re-assuring look straight at Kate. "Well, the problem is that we don't hear very much protest being made by our own government."

Asked by Kate Adie if he had a message for his wife, Alan rolled his head from side to side, batted his eyelids up and down, smiled broadly and ran his hands through his limited hair, as he delivered a few jovial words to Carole.

In the same building, I sat down in my usual chair across from the magistrate. I hunched forward, legs and arms crossed, and ignored both the translator and the magistrate. Both the magistrate and the translator looked up at me without a word.

At the behest of the magistrate, the translator asked me what was wrong. I shook my head without looking up and, referring to the pointless repetition of questioning that was about to follow, I simply said, "Get on with it!"

The translator told me that His Honour would ask me questions when he was ready to. But for the moment, His Honour wanted to know what was wrong.

"We are freezing cold. We have not eaten."

"Did you have no breakfast?" enquired the translator.

"We had to leave to come here this morning before our breakfast arrived," I said.

"Have you no winter clothes?" the translator asked, with genuine surprise and concern in both his face and voice.

I looked at him. A cold, filthy and incredulous stare. Then I enlightened him as to the sum total of my accoutrements on the day that I was arrested.

I understood only one word of the magistrate's next question, "gowa". After a few seconds I nodded briefly without looking up.

The magistrate turned his head towards the door and barked a loud order. Instantly, an old hajji, wearing a hooded, blanket cape over the black fez, desert whites and black waistcoat, opened the door and poked his head in. His sandaled feet bore socks. The magistrate spoke tersely and the hajji looked me quickly up and down, and disappeared. A minute later he was back. In his left hand was half a loaf of bread, mercifully wrapped in a piece of clean photocopier paper. In his right, a handled, bakelite cup of hot rocket fuel, and a couple of disintegrating, Libyan cigarettes.

I ate the bread, which was fresh. I sipped the hot, sugary gowa to play for time.

The interrogation, meanwhile, was on the back burner, so I took my time over smoking one of the cigarettes in order to keep thinking about where to go from here.

They had nothing on me. All they had done for the previous two or three, six-weekly interrogations was to go over and over the same story again and again, to try to trip me up on some significant detail. I figured that these return visits were their idea of habeas corpus - that a detained man must appear before an investigating magistrate at regular intervals - six weeks! - for the magistrate to show why the man should be detained further. But given the circumstances, I dismissed it as fanciful and a charade. Nevertheless, there was something about the progress of all the interrogations, something about the demeanour of the magistrate and the translator that gave me the impression that they were presently drawing a conclusion.

The tedious question and answer session began.

This time it was about cars and registration plates.

But in the midst of grinding routine, of slow and patient question and answer - question to tease out an inconsistency, and answer to give them nothing to go on, nothing on which to base a supplementary question, nothing that wasn't either true or uncheckable - they still read my body language correctly.

"Is something wrong?" asked the translator, leaning forward slightly.

My first instinct was to rail on both of them that - after seven months of detention on no authentic pretext, and having undergone the apoplectic stress of solitary confinement followed by interrogation about things that it hadn't even occurred to me to do or that I had done, and now to be sitting here again, without the benefit of proper breakfast while inadequately dressed for the weather - they should have the temerity to ask if something was wrong.

But to rail on them would be to squander my opportunity. Instead, it was time to capitalise on their newly manifest compassion.

After a long silence, I told the magistrate that we were afraid that we were going to go jail for something that we had not done.

The magistrate clasped his fingers, and laid his forearms and hands upon the writing pad on the desk in front of him. He lowered his head and became motionless.

The translator found a fixed point on the ceiling, looked up at it and also became motionless.

For a moment I thought that the hajji usher was going to bring in a black cap and place it on the magistrate's head.

After an even longer silence, the magistrate spoke.

Without moving anything but his lips, he said direct to me, "You will be acquitted."

Outside in the car park was the BBC listening to Hugh about Alan's court hearing.

When Hugh had finished speaking, he politely disengaged from Kate Adie as I moved over to shake hands with him.

I asked the BBC to stop rolling while I debriefed to Hugh what I had just undergone. Kate said that I was not to worry; she would do a voice over for that bit. And she did.

Then I took what I held to be a God sent opportunity. I turned to the camera and said, "I've done nothing wrong. Let's get this absolutely straight. I've done nothing wrong. Tell my wife, tell my company, tell the whole world, I've done nothing wrong. And if I go to jail, it's a stick up.

"Oh, and by the way, if there is anybody out there listening..." I went on.

And under his breath, Hugh intoned, "There are lots of people out there listening..."

"Do you think you could let us have some winter sweaters please, because it's frightfully difficult to be British when you're standing there trembling with cold."

Then we were interrupted by leather soled footsteps coming across the car park.

The translator was walking to his car. Upon seeing me talking to the camera, he shot me a look, warning me not to breach a confidence and, waving us away with the back of his hand, he shouted, "Adjourn! Adjourn!"

That night, on the BBC News, Pat appeared with Katy, Ross and Christopher at Lambeth Palace. Pat had brought to Terry, in preparation for his next visit to Libya, a cake, jumpers, chocolates, books.

She also gave to Terry a letter for me. It was the first I was to receive, outside of the one in the cigarette packet. And following my broadcast request for sweaters, she had written on the sealed envelope, "Well done, Plumsie. British. We loved it."

That night, Hugh briefed the FCO in London that at Malcolm's court hearing, on the 12th, Malcolm had said that Michael and I had been questioned several times over the previous days at the Public Prosecutor's office. And that Alan and Malcolm had been similarly questioned immediately before being charged.

That night, Malcolm's mother, Kathleen, was reported on the BBC News as having said that the Government had abandoned us.

The following day, the guards walked in and placed a polythene wrapped package on the desk. The contents were squashy and coloured. I tore the package open and found, to everyone's astonishment, two woollies. The close and resilient knit brought a smile to my face. The roll necked sweater was not for me. But the cardigan was. Bold in its Argyll check, I warmed up within seconds of putting it on. And wore it every day.

18 Dec Atkinson, Consular Dept, to Parliamentary Unit. Atkinson attached a briefing for the Leader of the House, in response to a question by Tim Yeo, proposed in the Christmas Adjournment Debate on 19 Dec.
The response said that there would be no bargain or response to blackmail.
The response said that the Libyans were being legalistic.
The response said that free legal representation had been provided for both men.
The response said that many channels have been kept open. But that there was no indication that a high level meeting would be useful at this present time.
There would be no relaxation of the British position on visas until the Libyans make a positive gesture. The release of Doug and George could not be regarded as such, while the other four remained.
19 Dec. Sir Geoffrey Howe to the Italian Ambassador in Rome, sent the text of interviews given by Luce to the BBC and to independent radio on 19 Dec, for transmission to British Interests Section, Tripoli, ASAP.
Luce had re-iterated the principle. There could be no diplomatic relations for the foreseeable future.

Terry arrived in Tripoli. On the 23rd of December, the BBC reported that the British government was maintaining the position that the four were quite definitively hostages against the four Libyan bombers being held in Britain.
Dressed in a Burberry raincoat to show the extent of his understanding of western culture, Col Gaddafi announced to the assembled British TV, being Kate Adie and Brent Sadler and their crews, his own opinion of the four which was that he too considered them definitively to be hostages.

Terry had to choke back his shock as he announced that we were not now going to be released by Christmas as he had hoped, but he went on to say that while we're talking there's hope. "You only run out of hope when communication breaks down completely," he stated.
But he would, he said, "try to organise a carol service for the detainees, as some measure of celebration, and to let them know that they're not forgotten."

Under Libyan scrutiny and an air of great tension, a carol service was held.

The BBC and Hugh had asked if members of the British Interests Section and the local British community could be present, but both requests were denied. And so it fell to Kate Adie and Brent Sadler and the camera crews of both the BBC and ITN to give support. The three or four Libyan guards in attendance knew instinctively that they were in the presence of something to be respected and kept their uncomprehending peace throughout.

The four us had been marched from the Italian mansion to the house up the road, and into the room where Pat and I had had some of our visits. There, to our astonishment, we saw the assembled news crews instead of the older Libyan officials, and Terry Waite in a winter weight, woollen cassock instead of the usual pin stripes.

"I've organised a Carol Service for you," he pitched in, shaking each of us by the hand. "I hope you don't mind," he chuckled, starting with Michael.

"How are you Michael?" he went on, genuinely concerned, and spent several moments in conversation with Michael.

"What's happening?" I said.

"Don't worry about that for the moment," he confided to me, looking straight into my eyes. "Let's do the service first," he finished, and momentarily flicked his own eyes towards the guards, who stood by the door.

"Hello, Kate," said I. And, "Hi," to Brent Sadler, who stood next to her. I nodded to Alan Florence and Malcolm Hicks.

Kate mouthed to Michael, "Are you alright?" and, "talk later."

Terry handed out presents to the four of us. It felt great to have this piece of contact from home - my wife had handled this package only days before - handwritten messages from Katy and Ross on misspelled Christmas cards. But even amidst the jovial and sympathetic patter of Terry as a bizarre and incongruously dressed Father Christmas, it also meant once again that we would not be going home anytime soon.

An unspoken gloom descended over the four of us. It was only possible to describe the four of us as extremely pissed off. And I was going to get that message across to the cameras if there was anything I could do about it.

Terry undid another box and produced a Christmas cake. He passed it to me. It weighed a ton. Gripping it tightly, I stepped forward to show it to the camera. It was white with stippled icing, and decorated with deer, tiny Christmas trees, and the words "Merry Christmas".

Terry called upon each of us in turn to deliver a greeting to our respective families.

Alan said, "I'm sure that with the help of God, everything will turn out right, and that opinions will come together."

Malcolm waved his hands about a lot and managed through a charming smile, "I send me love to everyone at home, and hope things are resolved soon, God willing." He looked to Heaven and then to me.

Michael said, "I send my Christmas greetings to all my family and I hope that they will have a very happy Christmas."

But I was in defiant mood. I put my hands on my hips.

"Things are very difficult," I began. "We're on our own. It's wonderful to know that we have got the support of Terry here," looking at Terry. "It's wonderful to have you chaps along," looking at the press corps. "It gives us a lot of support.

"I hope my wife and children have a good time at Christmas. I'm sorry I can't be there. But, as you can see, the Libyans have been kind enough to allow us some measure of celebration - the normal, traditional gifts," I said, indicating the suitcase full of presents. "We're very grateful for this."

And looking directly into the camera, I said, "I'd like the people of Great Britain to appreciate," pointedly lowering and then raising my eyelids, "the magnanimous gesture the Libyans have put forward, and let's say I hope this situation is resolved soon."

Terry gave it a suitable moment to allow the impact to sink in, before saying, "Don't forget me! I don't know if I'm going to be home for Christmas yet!" And we laughed.

"Bless me, Father," said Malcolm, the good Catholic.

"Bless me, Father," said Alan, the good churchgoer.

"Thank you," said Michael, the diffident agnostic.

Then the sartorial penny dropped, and I moved over a foot to place Terry between the guards and me.

"You're not wearing a dog collar!" I quietly intoned.

"I know," said Terry. "I'm not ordained."

"Then you can't give the Blessing," said I, with a smile.

"That's right," said Terry, smiling and looking directly into my eyes. "But the Libyans don't know that."

I shook his outstretched hand, and we grinned genuine, naughty school boy grins and ducked our heads towards each other almost to the point of touching. Our eyes blazed. "Bless me! Father," said I.

Terry placed the hand of peace upon the crown of my head and smiled, saying, "Go in peace, my son."

I stifled a laugh.

"Let us pray."

The four of them knelt on the floor and folded their hands. I sat in a chair and folded my arms.

With all of our heads bowed, Terry proceeded to pray.

"The spirit in which we meet today is very much the spirit of the first Christmas when our Lord was born, vulnerable and uncertain as to the future. But let us not forget those at home who are thinking of us on a daily ..."

That night, Kate in her BBC News broadcast said that individual appeals for our release had come to nothing and that we were helplessly stuck between two governments.

Brent in his ITN broadcast gave a suitable, narrative commentary on the day's proceedings, with a fine piece of editing that brought out the words of The Lord's Prayer when it came time to "deliver us from evil."

And then, there came the time, pre-arranged as it would appear, that all save Terry and us would leave the room for Terry to provide private, pastoral words and spiritual guidance, and for us to give private messages to our families.

As the guards, camera crews, Brent Sadler and Kate Adie were filtering out at Kate's prompting, Terry delivered the Blessing.

"In the name of the Father," he uttered.

The guards left.

"and of the Son," in ecclesiastical tones.

The crews left.

"and of the Holy Spi..."

The door shut.

"Right. Listen carefully," he commanded, from his knees. "I don't know how long we've got. This is what's been happening.

"I have been invited to see The Leader tomorrow," he continued. And at machine gun speed, Terry spelt out what had been going on and what, in broad terms, he was planning to do. He finished up with, "There's no guarantee of course."

"How likely do you think it is," I said, still at prayer.

"I'm cautiously optimistic," he said cautiously.

Terry handed a copy of the Bible and some photocopies of the lessons and carols to Alan. Michael and Alan started to leave the room.

But Terry was not finished yet.

Alan had written a letter to Col Gaddafi.

In the letter, Alan had attempted to justify his actions in seeking to inform the BBC about the events at the time of the assassination attempt on Gaddafi in May, for which he had been tried, convicted and sentenced. In the letter, Alan had said something to the effect that, "I want you to understand that my actions have been because of my love for my wife." In the letter, Alan was talking, and all the while you are talking, you are giving things away.

As Michael and Alan left the room, Malcolm pattered on in his transparently harmlessly way where Terry was concerned.

I knowingly assisted in spinning out the pleasantries and valedictions, because Terry was looking at me with that smile that said there was more to come.

Amid Malcolm's faintly ingratiating inanities, Terry was not making a point of trying to speak his peace, not wishing to attract the attention of the Libyans.

Yet time was fleeting, and I was concerned that it was beginning to look obvious to the Libs that we were conspiring.

So I started towards the door, hoping to quiet Malcolm, and precipitate a now tense Terry into speech.

Malcolm was stationary, with his back to the yellowing, white emulsioned wall, beside the door, waiting for a last exchange with Terry.

Terry led with, "Robin..." but I had already brushed Malcolm's hanging arm with my own, and commenced to lead the way down the staircase.

Using the seamless, inscrutable flow that I had developed to give the Libyans no hint of my thoughts or spoken asides, I was already under way, and had inadvertently caught Terry, who had been waiting for just this moment when Malcolm and I would be left alone with him, on the hop. But I could not now go back into the room to listen without giving the game away. I just took a Biblical eternity to negotiate the two top stairs, and listened, while Terry caught Malcolm instead.

Terry, almost whirling like a spinning top in his agitation to get his message out, as good as pinned a surprised Malcolm to the wall.

Then, to my surprise, astonishment, delight and disappointment, I heard Terry expostulate, "Robin..." and in desperation, "Malcolm! For God's sake, tell that man to shut his fucking mouth!"

And, while I was recovering, "He's going to get everyone into trouble if he keeps talking like that. He has got to learn to keep his mouth shut."

Malcolm's array of emotions evidently matched mine, for I heard him turn to Terry and barely force out a neutral, "Aye, OK."

I was relieved that it wasn't just me who was despairing of Alan's behaviour. I was doubly relieved to hear the self evident candour of Terry's outburst.

"Why did he have to write to Col. Gaddafi in the first place? Couldn't you have stopped him, Robin?"

I started a whispered relay of Alan's own explanation of his motives, and the fact that I hadn't even seen him write the letter, but footsteps below silenced me.

"Next time," I said.

"OK," nodded a disbelieving Terry, and I measured my way down the staircase.

Obeying instructions to stay in the room until we had departed, Terry took the opportunity to tidy up his stuff, and the rest of us left for the mansion.

As we walked, I realised that it was approaching crunch time, and decided to talk to Alan at the first reasonable opportunity.

We went back, made and drank tea, and sat down into routine.

Alan, you have to stop talking to the Libyans.

Alan, you have to shut up.

Alan, Terry asked us to convey to you that you have to be less garrulous in the presence of the Libyans.

Alan, let me tell you what the man, who, by your own admission, is the person in all the world that you hold in the highest regard and esteem, just told us to do. He just said to Malcolm, "Malcolm! For God's sake, tell that man to shut his fucking mouth!"

But at every attempt to get my point across, Alan simply kept up his well practiced ability to blot out unwelcome news with a barrage of perfectly reasonable sounding verbal fog.

Malcolm tried. Alan cut in with a masterpiece of manipulation by instantly and pointedly engaging Malcolm's discourse in complete distinction to his fogging of mine. He was visibly taking pride in snubbing me.

He smugly acquiesced to Malcolm's faltering appeal to watch what he said in front of the Libyans. And, following a respectful pause after Malcolm had finished, he turned to put the boot in on me, with, "Robin, you may be the most intelligent person in here, but I'm afraid you are a long way from best when it comes to dealing with people."

He was quite right, of course. I didn't have the touch. He had got me annoyed. I hadn't handled it very well. I had shot my bolt.

But it was getting to the point where the possibility of killing him while he slept was not an unconscionable idea, if that was what it would take to prevent him from talking the rest of us into an early grave.

Instead, Alan said, "Look, I know I talk too much. So if in future you hear me starting to talk too much, would one of you just start talking about the weather, and I'll take that as a signal to stop talking. Just talk about the weather. That will shut me up."

We did. It didn't.

I went to bed that night a sadder, wiser and very worried man.

The following day, Malcolm and I had the first of our discussions about excluding Alan from further deliberations. We certainly agreed that from hereon in it would be unwise to tell him any further prejudicial information, although we were forced to admit that it was probably too late by now, because we had all mostly shared our secrets with each other anyway.

"I don't think he'd knowingly tell incriminating stuff to the Libyans," said Malcolm.

"He doesn't have too," I said. "Intelligence isn't always about one person spilling their guts all in one go. It's about gathering information in dribs and drabs. All the Libs have to do is go home each night and write down each snippet of information as they get it from him, or any other of us for that matter," I continued, "and over time they build up a pattern of information which is perfectly adequate to hang the lot of us. That's why I simply won't talk to any of them.. Not Smiling Boy, not even the Hajji."

"Aye, you're right," said Malcolm. "When they first had him they didn't have a thing on him. And he told them everything they needed to lock him up for over three years."

"After today's carry on, we've got to stop including him in our discussions. And while we're at it, I think we're going to have to keep Michael out of it as well."

"Why?"

Shaking my head, I observed that Michael's preparedness to challenge comments made by others had increased of late, particularly where such comments indicated a marring of our position.

"He's getting percipient after all these months and, in an anxious moment, he might blab stuff to Alan that you and I don't want Alan to hear."

"Aye, OK," concluded Malcolm. "So it's just you and me from here on then?"

"I regret to say, I think it's going to have to be."

"It's just you and me then?"

"Yes."

On Christmas Day, lunch arrived. It was almost the same as usual, with the difference that we were served an additional course, fish. I refused to eat it on principle. If they were going to bang us up like this, it was no compensation to be shown recognition of our religious festivals. I didn't give a twopenny damn what they did at Hari Riya.

The others said that it was probably just the hotel workers who catered for the prison service offering a gesture on a purely human level - not one officially sanctioned. It was just possible, they said, that the hotel staff are as disgusted with our treatment as we are, and just wanted to show solidarity. I admitted the possibility. "Notwithstanding..." I said. My fish went to Malcolm.

Then it was time for Christmas cake. We looked at it, studied it, tried to decide who had made it, tried to decide how to cut it, while also ensuring that it stayed fresh. I suggested that while it might be nice to eat our fill of it now, we could consider the idea of having just a square inch each, after each meal until it was all gone. That way we would have some enjoyment every day, and would continue the enjoyment for several days to come.

Everybody nodded assent.

"Shall I do it then?" solicited Malcolm, already holding a knife.

Everybody nodded assent.

Malcolm took a skilled approach to cutting through the icing - and failed. The icing was concrete hard.

"Well, that's good," said I. "Because it means that the icing can be used to keep the cake fresh. Just lift the icing off like a hat, and replace it after you've cut some slices."

Malcolm eased the entire icing cover off in one piece, and there sat a magnificent, nut brown, fruit laden, Christmas cake that I instantly recognized as Pat's handiwork.

Malcolm eased the knife through the cake all the way to the foil wrapped, wooden board on which it sat, and carefully cut off the first, inch square piece of cake. He passed it to Michael. Then Alan, then me, then himself.

We looked at our portions and salivated.

"Well, you cut it. You try it," said Alan.

Malcolm picked up his slice and bit heartily.

The next second, all our faces fell, as Malcolm recoiled with a mixture of shock and surprise.

"What's the matter," I asked, fearing that the cake was rotten, after all the expectation.

"It's soused!" he exclaimed. Then, after several seconds when he politely cleared his mouth, "Rum or brandy or something."

And it was true. Pat had made her usual, exemplary Christmas cake, with the usual dose of brandy. But on the day that she had taken all the presents and the cake to Lambeth Palace for Terry to bring to us, she'd got the cake out again, along with a bottle of brandy and a syringe, and proceeded to pump the one into the other, before icing it.

"Well, I don't suppose you'd had a drink for months," she later said to me.

"This is a bloody good cake," said I.

Everybody nodded assent.

That afternoon, we sang carols as agreed. There was no real motivation except that we said that we would do it. The door opened and two guards could be heard shuffling in through the outer door. They stood motionless, silent and unseen as they tried to figure out what they were listening to. And then, exactly as at the carol service of the previous day, they quietly, discreetly and enduringly locked the door and left us to it.

"Do you think we should read a lesson from the Bible," somebody said.

Everybody nodded assent.

I read a lesson. Isaiah, chapter nine, verse six. "For unto us a Child is born...And His name shall be called..."

We sat for a few minutes in a peaceful silence.

Then Alan suggested that we might be able to get Carols from King's on the radio. Alan politely solicited if I would mind switching on and tuning in.

I found the BBC World Service and we listened for a long while, hoping to get the traditional Carol Service from King's College, Cambridge.

We didn't get it. And there wasn't even an announcement as to when or even whether it might be broadcast.

"Oh, well," said Alan, disappointed. "It was worth a try."

Everybody nodded assent.

What we got instead was Lilliburlero.

What we got next riveted us to the radio for the next several hours, and made the hair stand up on the backs of our arms.

The BBC World Service News stated that the Archbishop of Canterbury's Special Envoy, Terry Waite had had a meeting with Colonel Gaddafi in Tripoli and, that after two hours of discussions, Terry had made the following announcement.

"The Colonel said to me," said Terry, "that out of respect for the Archbishop of Canterbury and the efforts of the church and his envoy, he will ask the people's congress, when they meet in January, to authorise the release of the four detainees."

Malcolm and I just looked at each other with our mouths open.

Then I started to smile but not for the obvious reason of the good news. I had known Terry for just long enough to know how he delivered a line. On this occasion his delivery was different from anything I had heard before.

Usually, he was measured, pointed, articulate and careful in his choice of words, in order to avoid saying something he might later regret.

No. What was different is that amidst the apparently unhurried delivery of this wonderful piece of news at his normal, measured pace, I could hear Terry choking back the jubilation in his voice at such a result, particularly in view of the disappointment that he had had to choke back following Col Gaddafi's announcement only two days previously that we were formally acknowledged as hostages against the four Libyan bombers awaiting trial in Britain.

Back in England, Carole said that it was a wonderful piece of news, and agreed that it was the best Christmas present she had ever had.

Pat told the BBC, "He's not free until he steps off the plane at Gatwick. I'll believe it when he arrives at Gatwick."

When the BBC asked Pat, at her parents' home in Norfolk, if it should have been left to the church to do something, or should it have been the FCO, Pat stated very clearly that it should have been the FCO.

"They should have done something a long time ago."

When the BBC asked about our condition when we last appeared on the news, Pat said, "They looked pretty rough at the carol service - very tense - my husband looked very pissed off."

Her biggest fear, said the BBC, was that I would be jailed for twenty years or get shot trying to escape.

Dr Runcie and Terry had been on the phone, and Dr Runcie had called the wives - the famous call at 3 o'clock in the morning.

There had been confirmation on the 26th of December of the agreement by Col Gaddafi to recommend a release. Terry returned to Britain on the 27th, and planned to return to Libya during the first week of January to attend a Basic People's Congress.

Pat went on say that the Libyans had so far honoured every agreement that they had made.

On the 28th of December, back in England and at Lambeth Palace, Dr Runcie was seen on the television with Terry, who had brought back from Libya a copy of the Koran as a personal gift from Col Gaddafi to the Archbishop. Dr Runcie read Col Gaddafi's personal greeting to the cameras, and then replied quoting his own passage also from the Koran.

"It is not God's way to have your trust be disappointed."

*** *** ***

PART SIX

28th December, 1984, to 7th February, 1985

Rumour being of the nature that it is I did, as always, set about piecing together as much as I could from all sources. I had to consider the possibility that several sources had each heard the whisper from the same original source. If this were true, it would discredit the whisper.

Colonel Gaddafi had some weeks previously indicated his willingness to see us released. He had even given his commitment that he would so advise the forthcoming Basic People's Congresses - advice which under the circumstances would almost certainly be heeded.

Terry was indicating a new optimism, and the journalists were suddenly of the opinion that something was afoot.

Even the demeanour of the Libyan guards was subtly altered as, upon our return from new meetings, they looked into our faces with a new inquisitiveness seeking reassurance for some new intelligence.

As the 15th of January drew closer, the diplomats became increasingly tense with optimism. Even Hugh's face looked lined.

Taken by and large, I felt that there was something abroad of a substance greater than anything heard to date, even the involvement of Julius Nyerere during the summer.

In fact, when Terry had come out at Christmas, he had brought with him, amid some publicity, a letter which, it was claimed, he carried from the British government to the Libyans with the offer of a deal.

If the claim were true, it would be quite extraordinary.

If the claim was to be believed, it left me with mixed feelings and the four of us with opinion sharply divided.

I personally felt some relief that, if the claim was true, HMG had finally done something of substance.

But I also felt that I did not want to go home to a country that was prepared to do deals with terrorists in order to get me home.

Alan didn't give a twopenny damn how they did it, just as long as HMG got us home. Under any circumstances we would just have to wait and see.

Terry claimed not to know what was in the letter, and said, quite characteristically, that he was not going to speculate. He did, however, let on that he was very confident that the letter could be the answer to our predicament.

This, therefore, was probably real.

When, on the 2nd of January, the four of us met Hugh for the third time, Hugh said that the purported deal promised the Libyans that if they released us on or before the 15th of January, the British government would commence talks about resuming diplomatic relations.

"That's giving in to terrorism," I said to Hugh.

"What do you mean," he smiled.

"Offering anything to get us out is to negotiate with terrorists," I clarified.

"We're not offering them anything," he went on enigmatically.

"Yes you are," I asserted. "You are offering them the commencement of talks about the resumption of diplomatic relations."

"Yes," he said simply. And, smiling his winning smile, he added, "We're offering to hold talks about the resumption of diplomatic relations. That doesn't mean the talks will ever come to anything."

"That's better," said I, catching his eye and, as we both smiled, I asked, "Are you lot always so Machiavellian?"

"There is a time for straight talking," he replied, who famously once called a senior Libyan official to his face a Barbarian.

Over the remainder of the 90 minutes of our meeting with Hugh, each of us spent a few minutes with him to get personal aspects up to date.

Michael opened up and talked calmly and lucidly.

Malcolm talked about the cake that we had started on Christmas Day, and that we had listened repeatedly to World Service reports of Terry's visit to Colonel Gaddafi, which had plainly heartened Malcolm considerably.

Malcolm and Hugh discussed with uncertainty whether or not Malcolm would appear in court on the 6th of January to hear verdict and sentence. Hugh said that both the lawyer and he would attend the court unless they had been told in the interim that Malcolm would not be appearing.

I told Hugh that we had discussed among ourselves how to deal with the press and television journalists once we were released. I had proposed to act as spokesman, thereby keeping Alan from the press, to which, to my surprise, Alan had agreed. I then put forward to Hugh the idea that a press conference might be held at the Ambassador's Residence. The plan was that I would ask the journalists to turn off their tape recorders and listen, and appeal to them for restrained and truthful reports. And I solicited all of the others to tell Hugh that we had all agreed that none of us would sell our story to the press. I had also asked Michael to stick to the party line - not to refer to being frightened but to just being very insecure; and to Malcolm to say nothing of substance, so not to invite unwanted supplementary questions.

"What about you?" asked Hugh.

"I will be pure obfuscation."

Hugh sought to point out that his relationship with the Libyans represented an encouraging improvement, which must be regarded as the result of Terry's visit which was having a beneficial effect on the situation.

After we had given personal messages to Hugh for passage to our dear ones, we indicated that we were all cautiously optimistic that we would be released, possibly during the course of the following week.

When we got back to the Mansion, I told the others my conclusions regarding the letter carried by Terry.

Michael registered distinct, if unspoken, interest in the possibility, by a passable imitation of the Royal Incline.

Alan latched onto the perceived certainty that if Col. Gaddafi were to advise the Basic People's Congresses of his desire, then it would be tantamount to a fait accompli.

I reminded Alan that in January of nineteen eighty four, the Congresses had rejected Col. Gaddafi's advice on the subject of women eschewing housewifery in favour of going out to work.

Alan supported his own argument by saying that that had been a domestic issue, whereas this was geopolitical.

He had a point to which I indicated agreement, and let the rest go.

Malcolm gave a passable imitation of a Wimbledon spectator, looking back and forth between Alan and me, with his eyebrows fixed high, and his mouth an orifice of just the size to receive a small glass marble.

But it was impossible to ignore the fact that Alan, alone amongst us so far, had been sentenced a few days previously to three years and three months in prison, and a fine of fifteen hundred pounds. He put a brave face on it in court when he sat there awaiting sentence with his fingers crossed on the rail of the dock so that the BBC camera could see. When asked by Kate Adie for his reaction, he said, "I might really learn some Arabic, but I'll definitely teach a few English," and laughed as he sought the eye of the camera. When Kate asked him if he had a message for his wife, Alan said that three years and three months wasn't a long time, that Carole wasn't ever to give up hope, and that he thought that in contacting the BBC he had done something worthwhile, and that sometimes when you do something worthwhile you have to pay for it.

Alan was now in the bizarre position of being dealt with by the courts and by the people's congresses simultaneously.

Although I was now not used to sleeping during the afternoons, I was equally not used to any kind of commotion by the guards, especially during siesta hours.

The pounding of several sets of feet towards the outer door to Doug's room alerted me, although I tried to dismiss it.

What I could not dismiss was an uncharacteristically noisy turning of the key and the bursting open of the outer door.

Next, the inner door burst open and in stormed about four guards, their eyes wild. Resistance would have been useless, but I was up off Alan's bed, seated and rising anyway as they came in.

The guard holding the radio wheeled right and quickly plugged it in. The others stood pregnant but motionless. The anticipation was palpable. The radio's silence during warm up was followed by a long burst of deliberate and courteous Libyan Arabic, the reason for listening to which understandably eluded all four of us. Any expression of surprise or any request for explanation was silenced by unusually helpful waves of the guards' hands accompanied by several, short, sharp, "shush"es. The atmosphere was electric.

The Arabic reached a full stop. There was a decent pause. Then, in Oxford English I was at once surprised and delighted to hear projecting over Jamahiriya Radio, the unmistakable tones of Terry Waite.

Daring not to give anything away, I stood transfixed, trying not to look at the others for needless confirmation of the self evident fact of Terry talking to a Basic People's Congress.

And the bastards had brought us the radio to hear him!

I was elated. He'd done it. What a coup! Now let's see if he puts his money where his mouth is.

As Terry started to talk, the guards intimated their exit. But Alan ventured forward slightly to ask if it was alright to listen to the broadcast. The guards paused for a while to give us reassuring looks that it was alright to listen to Jamahiriya Radio. Try and stop us!

One waved at me to be seated again. I ignored him and sat down. The four of us were now totally focussed on the radio, as if our fixation would prevent the guards from removing it. Anyway, it worked and they left the radio alone.

Then the guards' pause proved lucky for us.

Terry finished his point and the translator took up his own task with surprisingly good mimicry of Terry's vocal inflections as if he were keen to assist Terry to make his points.

Then the translation was finished and, during another decent pause, Terry was preparing to embark on his next point.

Not a voice murmured, not a car moved, not a bird tweeted. The whole city was listening in silence.

"The Libyan people have expressed concern to me about their loved ones held in prisons in Great Britain," he carefully intoned in his mellifluous and refined Mancunian accent.

"You're breaking my fucking heart," I thought to myself while the translator was speaking, but I showed nothing.

"Especially, the Libyan people have been concerned to know that their sons are not being mistreated in any way by the British authorities," he continued.

"That's right Terry. Get to the point," I thought during the translation, and invisibly focussed all the more to keep the radio set just where it was.

"I can tell you that I have been to visit them in prison."

Translation.

"I have seen them," he said.

Translation.

"I have spoken to them," he built.

Translation.

"I have shaken hands with them," he peaked.

Translation.

He paused...

Don't stop there, Terry!

...for effect.

"They are not being tortured!" he thundered.

Sensation!

It was like winning the pools.

Every corpuscle of my body screamed in silent ecstasy at every other corpuscle, and kept screaming and screaming for seconds to come.

Out of the corner of my eye, I saw the guards eye up our motionless and cueless bodies as they took in the translation. Then I saw their shoulders drop as the implication sunk in.

We were going home.

There came a time in the present address when I thought that Terry was beginning to lose his way and that he should shut up and get off before we all got our heads handed to us in a basket. And it is certain that he never again touched the magnificent and important height of oratory that he did on the subject of torture, which, I am grateful to say, was heard by all of our guards as they stood there in their lucky pause.

At another congress, Terry made other similarly effective orations. "Laws are made by men. Mercy, compassion and justice are made in Heaven..."

And at another meeting where he addressed the tearful relatives of the Libyan bombers held in Britain who, the relatives were afraid, were being tortured, he intoned with consummate integrity, "I intend to discuss these allegations firstly with the Archbishop of Canterbury who has the authority and power to take these matters up at the highest levels of government, and any abuse of right, if found, will be properly and thoroughly investigated."

Years later, of course, Terry told me that he hadn't had the faintest idea of what he was going to say when he got up in front of his first Congress, and that he just said what came into his head as he went along.

Kate Adie, commentating for the Beeb, remarked on "the style of his address going down very well with the members of the congress." Well, Kate, it went down pretty well with us too.

Nothing was guaranteed though. The Libyans being what they were, anything was possible. A different speaker at a different congress was broadcast speaking in English. He indicated by his own speech the extent of his grasp of world affairs.

"We want some gold," he said. "The Americans have gold. The British have gold. Why can't we have some gold?"

Whoever was chairing the congress just let the matter silently fall.

I was allowed to watch television again. The Revolutionary was now back from Canada.

"How did your trip go," I asked him, smiling.

"OK," he said, rolling his head.

"You were only there for a short time," I said, encouraging. "You must have been very effective with the Sikhs."

"Yes, yes, well..." he replied, looking away.

"It must have been very cold in Canada," I said warmly. "How deep was the snow?"

"Oh er, about er half a metre," he replied.

I didn't bother to tell him that the BBC World Service had just reported the remarkable fact that for the first time in twenty five years there had been no snow in Canada so far this winter.

"I'm going to ask the Libyan authorities if I can move in there with you for the rest of the time you're in Libya," said Terry with his usual generosity.

I wasn't sure about this. We had order. The four of us got on as a stable unit. Well, we limped along with a degree of cohesion, but we got on as a stable unit.

I foresaw instability, the reordering of relationships, the need to establish a new status quo in a new place, with the dubious benefit of well practiced survival tools modified by this very considerable influence. And all at a time when I was tired, becoming disinterested and, deep down inside, reasonably sure that we were going to be going home. All in all, I think that I simply didn't have the energy to make the adjustment to another influence - especially one with Terry's presence, but one who had not ever actually been through our experience.

"What are you seeking to achieve by moving in with us?" I enquired.

"Oh, I don't want to interfere," he was quick to point out. "My-my purpose is really purely pastoral. To give you some support."

I still didn't like it.

"I-I won't come if you don't want me to."

Well, there's no answer to that.

But we were not going home.

Terry was genuinely disappointed. So was Hugh. So was an obscure column inch buried deep in the FT. It was uncertain, said the FT, whether or not Col. Gaddafi's advice had been heeded by the Congresses.

What was certain was that we were still in Libya, and that we were by now totally inured to disappointment.

We had shrugged our shoulders again and got on with our board games.

But the failure of the Libyans to take up the offer of talks was also perplexing. It just didn't make sense in the light of Col. Gaddafi's commitment to advise the Congresses to release us, and that the whole of the Libyan regime was now smarting under the effects of international isolation.

Then again we were so used to the spurious nature of Libyan decision making that we just passed it off as another aberrant piece of single mindedness.

The deal had not failed completely, however.

The news that Terry had just brought to us, during an hour and a half that we all got together on the morning of the fourteenth, was that we were to be moved to a different prison. The new prison was said to be of lesser security, for low category prisoners, where we would have a lot more freedom to come and go. Oh! We'd still be in prison, but there'd be fewer locks and keys, and we would be out of the hands of the revolutionary committee that had been holding us.

That, at least, was good news.

The place was more like a collection of villas, where you lived an existence more of your own device than one that was imposed upon you.

The place sounded like the prison in which the now released George Bush had been held. That, judging from George's account, was somewhat re-assuring.

I visualised a verandahed go-down, with Terry sitting on a cane chair, his feet up on the front balustrade. No, this was too much.

All in all, though, the news sounded better than what we had been used to, and if Terry had negotiated this much, it was almost certainly an improvement. Above all, it would have been foolish of us to be seen by the Libyans to disagree with Terry.

But the real reason that we weren't going home is that the letter that Terry had been carrying and that he had handed to Colonel Gaddafi on Christmas Day was not in fact from the British government at all. It was from the Archbishop of Canterbury. Terry had been briefed by the FCO before leaving, but he carried no Government message as such.

When it came, there was no other warning of the move. Just up and leave, with little more time than enough to grab those artefacts with which we had arrived, and to have a pee. Malcolm expressed a preference for all the Christmas cards, and I took all the books. But we weren't allowed the poor clothing that they had given us, and certainly not the lurid blue trainers.

So much for Alan stuffing the money into his trainers.

We were ordered to our respective rooms. Red Head was in charge. There was no doubting that. But for all my earlier fear of him, I was beginning to see him as a loveable buggerlugs who was doing his job very well, and to whom you simply didn't show that you're frightened.

We were assembled in the entrance hall, supermarket bags in hand.

The guards were calmly ordered by Red Head to search us. When Red Head was not satisfied with their frisking technique, he described, sotto voce, what he wanted. With a few patient minutes of practice by the guards, he got it.

Immobile 'til the last, and firmly and unrelentingly patted down over every square millimetre of our bodies we were found to be concealing nothing.

A cruciform and indifferent Malcolm, in Tee shirt and tracksuit bottoms did winch and buckle slightly as the zealous hand of the newly confident Tweedle Dum exceeded requirement and found one of his testicles. A brief exchange of "Malleish"es and shakes of the hand restored honour and dignity, and Malcolm was clean.

Red Head's next instruction to the guards, on how a detainee should be escorted, was conveyed by illustration. A disconcerted Malcolm, half a head taller than Red Head, found himself being half dragged by Red Head in the vice like grip which was so familiar to me, out of the side door.

Upon Red Head's lone return, the Intelligent One was bid to follow his master's example. He made a passable attempt at immobilising me, but one that would not have withstood a determined effort to break free. The thought crossed my mind but died right there. Red Head's scrutiny was persuasive alright, but there was more. I quickly found myself enjoying once again the spectacle of a discomfitted guard, his head lolling from side to side in obvious embarrassment at Red Head's overtly draconian tutelage.

I smiled inwardly as I imperceptibly caused the Intelligent One to lose his footing on the way down the marble steps. He looked at me unsure, tightened his grip nevertheless, and walked me out of the large double gates at the back of the garden to a row of waiting cars. To my faint relief, the back seat of one car was occupied by a stationary and only slightly less disconcerted Malcolm.

Through unlooking eyes, I took in about half a dozen wary faces. I recognized but few of them - Laughing Boy and The One With Fat.

My guard stopped me and we paused, and only upon a signal was I funnelled into the back of a car. Having been given no time to articulate my damaged leg, I just fell into the back seat, and onto the seated Malcolm. We just lay there for a few seconds gently cuddling each other, my head half in his lap, both humorously whispering comments about the marital status of the guards' parents.

In the minutes that followed, lesser built guards were similarly drilled in detainee escort procedure with, successively, Michael and Alan as fodder.

We sat in pairs in our respective cars, our small bundles of worldly possessions on our laps.

Following another pause, Red Head imperceptibly indicated his satisfaction with security. And we were to be off.

The One With Fat proceeded to walk the length of the column of vehicles towards its head. As he passed in to my field of view, the display of authority of this slightly comic figure walking was faintly risible. But he was now in charge, and he was damn sure that nothing was going to go wrong, and everybody knew it.

The column drove at a sedate and disciplined pace. The cars became widely separated in the traffic until they were out of sight of each other.

We drove roads quite familiar to me which made me feel at ease, but which took our car Eastward along a part of the coast road that only goes to Wheelus Air Base. I started to choke, but began to breath again when we left the airbase behind us.

The car cleared the traffic. The suburbs fell away. The level of population diminished. There was nothing and nobody around. In fact there was nothing really but open road in between us and Benghazi six hundred miles away. I drew to mind that one or two of our earliest guards had been to Benghazi to do their six week tours of duty at a prison there. Is that where we were going? Perish the thought. We'd be completely out of contact with our families, the diplomats, the press and the journalists. In any case the car was totally inadequate for a drive of that demand. There was nothing out here but open space.

The driver dipped the right hand indicator switch and we slewed off with no further warning into a country lane.

The driver didn't bother to accelerate again, and more or less rolled the car to a halt by the road side. On the opposite side of the road was a very high, poorly constructed, breeze block wall. This was all wrong. This is how I had envisaged it in the earliest days of captivity. This is how they were going to murder us. This is the point at which I would fight.

But one honk of the car horn had two, enormous, rusty, steel gates in the high wall opened inwards, and I instantly saw three armed guards.

The new prison was typical in the characteristic of obfuscation. The entrance was exactly similar to that of the prison to which we had been taken on Revolution Day, in that it looked for all the world like a scrap yard. You would need to know that there was something behind the gates worth discussing to want to take any interest. From the road it did not invite a second look.

The driver nosed his way in to a hard standing set between the outer and some inner gates.

The driver got out. Unbid, I started to follow, and was promptly told to stay put. They were waiting for the others to arrive.

When they arrived, we were all assembled in a tight huddle, which protected us from neither the One With Fat, who stood aloof, nor the newly falling drizzle, which didn't.

When hostages, revolutionary guards and soldiers had all been assembled, the inner gates were opened and we trooped in en masse.

The sight that met us was of an orderly layout of slightly austere, single storied, breeze block villas set in a high-walled, spacious, grassy compound, more or less exactly as George and Terry had described it.

We were walked without hurry or threat to the nearest of the villas, and were ushered directly into an interior room.

The One With Fat stood around with the dubious authority of a passed over manager attempting to radiate signals that he continued to be promotable.

The definite feeling in the room was that the revolutionary zealots were handing over control of us to professional prison minders. And both sides knew it. We, pawns in the game, were ignored by both while the power and status games were played out.

The other revolutionaries sidled out, leaving The One With Fat who bid us a farewell. One by one we shook hands with him - God alone knew why - and when it was my turn, I even thanked him! God himself would have trouble explaining that.

Finally, to our intense relief, The One With Fat shook hands with someone obviously in charge and, without a backward glance, walked out with his promotable walk. It cost me nothing never to see him again.

The atmosphere lightened considerably. Unencumbered, the professionals were now free to get on with their job.

Two men held the room, an officer, and a gentleman. I sensed rather than saw other professionals in a small adjoining anteroom, to which there was easy access through a doorway in the corner diagonally opposite that through which we had entered the room.

The officer had the familiar, slightly stiff, confident and professional manner and bearing that distinguished him from the common throng. The gentleman wore an expensive and well fitting suit, white shirt and tie, and had groomed, curly black hair, and a moustachioed, amiable, but impassive round face. I was sure that I had seen him before but I couldn't place when or where. He said nothing throughout, but neither did he look at anybody nor did he catch anybody's eye. I was going to say nothing to him and nor, if they were wise, should any of the others.

The officer spoke for the first time. The rules of the prison were quickly, efficiently and unemotionally stated in simple English. Our questions were answered clinically but with an assured grace. He told us that if we obeyed the few, simple rules that we would be free to do more or less as we pleased while we were there. We were told that we could talk to anyone we pleased, but that we were not to talk to prisoners in certain cells which the officer clearly identified to us. He told us very clearly that we were not under any circumstances to try to escape. If we tried to escape, the punishment was very severe. And finally, he reiterated that the prison regime was really quite liberal, but that we would be severely punished if we broke the rules.

And to reinforce what was allowed and what was not allowed, the officer outlined with some generosity and a pointed arm, where we were free to roam and, with some slight animation what we were free to do.

So the rules were set and surprisingly generous.

But, as if to remind us who was really in charge, we were each in turn ordered into the corridor where we had our photos taken. The photographer would snap his fingers in front of his glaring face, and demand in Arabic that you look into the lens of his Nikon. The good news is that in the state I was in, I thought that I looked nothing like the real me, which might be useful at some time in the future. As it happened, Malcolm would cut my hair in the course of the next few days and I would look rather better than just presentable again. They also took our finger prints.

In the few minutes following our briefing, we were left alone and sat with guarded demeanour, silent and disconsolate. I took stock.

The building was solidly constructed of breeze blocks, and rendered with grey cement inside and out. Our room was probably twelve by fifteen feet. The door to the villa through which we had entered had just been locked from the outside.

Immediately inside the main door, and to the right of it, was the entrance to the room in which we now sat. I had already bagged the only bed in the room; the rest was chairs of doubtful integrity. At a height that required an elevated eye to regard it, was a window sill and glassless, window set, very similar to that in my first basement cell, only this one was high enough that I could see only the sky. Cool, damp air rolled in through the open facade. A bakelite bulb holder hung forlornly in the middle of the room from the end of a length of scruffy, woven, fabric insulated, flexible lighting cord suspended from a ceiling rose. There was no bulb. It gave scant prospect of cheer during hours of darkness.

Even as I conducted my survey, the grey afternoon light of cool, late winter gave way to a dull, chilly evening. The humidity, not reduced one wit by the light English rain, turned into penetrating dampness. It reminded me of Newcastle-on-Tyne. None of it boded well for comfortable sleep. Especially since there was only one bed.

The clatter of busy workmen broke my reverie.

In a trice all was activity. Standing upon the doubtful chairs, two of them, neither in uniform, proceeded to build out the window set with shutters. Gloom descended both metaphorically and physically, as the green, wooden, slatted shutters, intended for this precise location, were insinuated into place with a surprising degree of competence.

The cold and damp would be to some extent assuaged as we eventually managed to work up a fug. To assist the build up of any fug, it would be necessary to keep closed the inner door by which we had entered, but the almost complete absence of light was so redolent of my first cell, that I was forced to the conclusion that our circumstances had indeed regressed to those of our first incarceration. I felt both bitter and a lump in my throat.

But the men had not finished their working day.

Upon their almost immediate return, they brought a forty watt bulb and screwed it in to the bulb holder. Far from illuminating the place, it produced no more than a lurid glow. All I needed now was some Leonard Cohen records and a packet of razor blades and I would have been all set.

Next they struggled in three collapsible, barrack room beds. It was only at this point that I noticed that not one of us had said a word since the end of our initial briefing. No-one said anything now, but glances were exchanged that conveyed less than any optimism that we might have felt up until now.

Three mattresses and then blankets, but only four. That did little more than thaw some of the sullenness. But then a big cardboard box was thrust in through the door, which, once opened disgorged a copious supply of regular, army blankets. I silently cheered up a lot. Alan was on his feet assisting the assembly of all - his assistance being met by the workmen with co-operation. We all began to feel better.

Construction complete, we asked for some cigarettes and were obligingly passed a half empty and slightly crushed pack of grisly, Libyan smokes. Three of us took a cigarette, each of which was lit, to our surprise, by the Libyan workmen themselves. They then left us in peace.

No-one could find anything useful to say. So we smoked in silence. But not for long. More footsteps were succeeded by a clattering in the anteroom on the other side of the wall behind the head of my bed. A head poked itself around the door frame and spoke a single word of Arabic. I neither saw the head nor acknowledged the word. Michael translated. "Oh, food," he said with some surprise.

We slowly rose for the occasion, and ate what proved to be among the worst meals of our entire captivity.

Automatically, we trooped back to our respective beds, and agreed that we would do well to get some sleep; at least in bed we would be warm.

Some stripped, others bedded down fully clothed. With the combined effects of ample, if heavy blankets to go round, food, however poor, in our stomachs, and four of us in the same room, we soon warmed up. A desultory conversation began, and petered out as we dozed off, until there was only Alan talking in the mistaken belief that someone was still listening.

The fact that the previous night's food had been terrible did nothing to allay my fears that we were about to start all over again - new prison, new routine, new guards to have to go to work on.

We woke the following morning to the woofling sound of the biggest German Shepherd in creation.

What little I knew about dogs had been conveyed to me by my father.

"Remain absolutely still, and the dog will ignore you," he had said.

I lay absolutely still. At my back, I could feel something bestial attempting to get into my bed with me.

"At least it can't make me pregnant," I thought.

I heard the clack of the Kalashnikov against the uniform of the guard.

"Spare me!" I thought. "You need a gun when you have two hundred and fifty pounds of dog on a chain in front of you?"

"Malleish, malleish," I croaked from under the covers.

In reply, I heard the Arabic for, "Remain absolutely still and the dog will ignore you."

I lay absolutely still.

Finished examining me, the dog continued its rounds and checked the other, still sleeping bodies.

Satisfied that none of us had acquired the means of escape during the night, the dog's demeanour changed while still woofling Malcolm, its front paws on his bed.

Through my usual invisible peep hole in my covers, I could see the look of a manic jester in the eyes of the dog. With what little I knew about dogs I was now totally out of my depth. So I left this one to Malcolm.

In one swift move, Malcolm flipped over onto his right hand side to face the dog, pulled the covers down from over his head, and filled the room with a convincing bark, while nearly head butting the animal.

I'd heard this before, of course, but the German Shepherd hadn't. The dog lost his footing on the bed as it recoiled in astonishment.

The guard hesitated. Malcolm didn't.

His arms, now unencumbered by bed clothes, wrapped themselves around the dog's neck and shoulders. He scrubbed the dog's coat and made commanding lovey-dovey noises into the dog's neck.

The dog must have been as confused as I was. The guard certainly was, as he fought, at first vainly, to withdraw the now whimpering German Shepherd from this worrying frot.

Dog and guard gone, there was just Malcolm and me awake. Me, still motionless to stare at him. Him, now re-ensconced with covers up to his ears, to stare his seductive stare at me.

I looked at him as if he were mad. He looked at me as if I was missing something.

"Howway, Robin, man!" he led off. "Did ya sleep well?" and laughed his seductive laugh.

"You must be fucking crazy!" I muffled. "That dog'll tear you to shreds."

"What d'ya mean?" he played. "It's only a dog. Howway, man!"

"Yeah? Dog? Fucking dog? Hate the bloody things. I just hope they keep it away from me."

"Can't man," he said, and pointed out, "Routine. They'll be in here every mornin', you watch. Aye, you'll be alright. Just leave the dog to me."

"I still think you're fucking crazy. Aye, but then you had two like that, didn't you?"

"You really don't like 'em then?" he solicited.

"No, I bloody don't!"

"Aye, well they can tell ya know. Howway! Whenever it comes in, just don't show anything, especially don't show ya scared," he said sagely.

"I'll try and remember that," I said dryly.

I rolled over and dozed. I was surprised that I was warm, but six blankets had sufficed for my Dad in a tent during the Egyptian winter, so I shrugged and pulled my six blankets up over my ears. But the air was cold and damp and no-one seemed to have any inclination to get up, so we whiled away the morning in our respective beds, and dozed.

We woke again to the turning of a key. Then a non-committal voice announced the single word of Arabic that food had arrived, and a metallic clank could be heard.

As ever, Malcolm was first to investigate.

"Robin, man!" he commanded. "Come and get ya scran!"

"Oh, piss off, Malcolm," I thought.

Then, after several seconds, he added, "It's your favourite, man - cauliflower!"

Bullshit, I thought. The stuff is unobtainable in Libya. But I was alerted by the unmistakeable sound of cling film being torn away and, as ever, Malcolm's casuality was absorbing. So I rolled off my bed, and joined him in the "kitchen".

His matter-of-factness was all the more surprising when I saw what he was unwrapping.

The meal - no, the repast - was so extensive in both type and quantity of food, that, look as I might, I could not see the food for the meal.

The cauliflower was instantly recognizable and conspicuous by its very presence, to say nothing of quantity. The rest was just a sea of colours.

My interest focussed on one particular plate.

I took a fork to prod the contents. An incredulous frown spread involuntarily across my face as, rather than prodding a dollop of brownish clag, I found myself separating one from another the skillfully carved slices of lean topside of beef. I developed tunnel vision. I heard not a word of Malcolm's enthusiastic patter as I weighed up the quantity of still-hot meat. I had just finished estimating the weight when Malcolm's words finally cut through my disbelief.

I was arguing to myself that the carver had run out of patience by the time he had delicately carved the last of the four whole pounds of topside, and had resorted to hacking thick slices off the now rare joint, when Malcolm joined my incredulity with a querulous, "It's steak, man!"

Eight, half pound slices of medium rare, sirloin steak. We looked at each other, wide eyed and slack jawed.

I don't know who was quickest to recover, but Malcolm's gape sublimed into a laugh of innocent delight as he reached out and gently tore a thimble-sized piece away from the oozing sirloin, and popped it into his appreciative mouth.

The seamless pantomime had him direct his salacious eyes at me as he lingeringly chewed, swallowed and laughed his seductive laugh.

In spite of myself, I smiled warmly. Well bred manners momentarily forgot, he urged, through half chewed sirloin, that I should "get in there".

I followed his lead and took a sample. Moaning, I took a whole half pound.

Malcolm waited long enough to finish his mouthful and then rent the air to call the other two in.

Alan came first and preyed like an animated black widow.

Michael lurked in disdainfully and, on eating, vocalised a surprising utterance of genuine appreciation.

That the food was good was unquestionable, but I wasn't sure. This was too easy. I ate my fill from the array of vegetables, nevertheless.

Michael uncrackled the Clingfilm from another dish, which appeared to contain rice - and boiled potatoes. The third dish contained fruit - fresh fruit - no maggots.

Malcolm piled a dinner plate high, and went and sat on his bed. The others ate, first in the kitchen, then on their respective beds.

When we had finished our first helping, we rested. The pull of medium rare sirloin was too much, however, and back I went to satiate one of my great weaknesses. But eight months of weight loss diet had taken their toll, and my eyes were easily bigger than my belly. The insecurity cut in as well, now that the pangs of hunger had been initially assuaged. I could eat no more.

Regarding the copious quantity of food, I found myself becoming appalled at the potential waste. We had barely dented the mound - Malcolm's capacity notwithstanding.

We slept.

The call to prayer woke us. It was cool and humid.

The end of siesta was accompanied by the entrance into the cell block of a guard. Malcolm was first onto his feet to greet the "Salaam Aleikum".

New orders were calmly issued about work-a-day matters. Malcolm discerned the requirement. The guard wanted the serving dishes, and Malcolm said so.

"Tell him to get stuffed," I thought to myself.

But Malcolm read it correctly.

He scooped the generous remaining mound off each of the three metal serving dishes and into the rubbish bin, rinsed off each serving dish under the tap, and placed all three dishes in the cardboard box from whence they had emerged upon delivery.

The guard took the box, hissed a thank you and left as quietly as he had arrived.

We slept.

The call to prayer woke us. It was chilly and damp.

The good news was a three hundred watt bulb and, for the moment at least, that we were allowed to be together. But the three hundred watt bulb was very good news. A workman had come in and replaced the feeble forty watter. My biggest concern was for the antique, electrical wiring which I fully expected to start smouldering under the strain of this veritable Hiroshima.

They'd also brought an oil filled, electrically powered, mobile radiator. I had little faith that it would work because it was of some antiquity and even if it did work, judging by its mass and the unreliability of the Libyan power system, it would probably take all night to heat up.

The door to the cell block opened. The relaxed clatter of one set of footsteps up the concrete hallway, by now a familiar and unintimidating feature of our new abode, heralded we knew not what. The footsteps faltered in the kitchen, and a cardboard box was slid onto the marble draining board.

Malcolm was first.

"Food," he said, as much in disbelief as expectation.

"No," said Alan, sceptically.

"It's time," said Michael, nodding. And he was right.

Malcolm stood there watching the guard unload the three metal plates.

On one was four pounds of slices of topside of beef, and eight, half pound slices of medium rare sirloin steak, all surrounded by cauliflower, carrots .... . On another was a mound of steaming white rice, a mound of boiled potatoes and a mound of chips.

The other plate was laid out with seasonal fruit - fresh fruit - no maggots.

Without a word, the guard turned and sauntered out.

My shoulders dropped. That for the first two and a half months of our captivity we had been kept close to starvation by this same bunch of shits, stealing our food and feeding it to the dog, only to be confronted with this scandalous excess which was mostly destined for the waste bin, was difficult to take.

But Malcolm was thinking with his stomach. He piled a dinner plate high, and went and sat on his bed.

Somebody said that they were fattening us up for departure.

"Yes, well, I'm damned if I'm walking out of here looking in the peak of health just to satisfy their propaganda needs," I grumbled.

"Howway, man! Gerrit down ya neck!" articulated Malcolm from his bed.

We ate.

We slept.

The cellblock door opened. Several sets of footsteps alerted us.

Then the room was filled with large, business-like men, who ignored us and chatted animatedly in Arabic. Their discourse was warm and energetic, and the earnest enthusiasm from each, as he tried to be in charge, was at worst only mildly disarming, and at best faintly amusing.

Frankly, it was like Fred Carno's Army. But they slit the massive cardboard box that they had brought with them, and it had disgorged its polystyrene encased contents. When they had finished their observable ineptitude with electrical wires and aerial, we found ourselves staring at twenty seven inches of glorious Technicolor, and Fawlty Towers to boot!

The mutually congratulatory backslapping among the workmen at the success of their handiwork had Malcolm and me marvelling. But our thoughts were quickly subordinated to uncontrollable mirth as we cracked up at John Cleese.

The guards just left. We couldn't believe our luck!

In our seclusion, we laughed out loud at Basil Fawlty searching for the duck. It couldn't last of course. And it didn't. Malcolm's questions about how we got the BBC on Libyan television, coupled with Alan's genuinely cathartic laughter, gave way to Lena Zavaroni. Gloom descended. Lena Zavaroni in turn gave way to the televised call to prayer which effectively signalled lights out. Minutes later the light and television failed as the power was switched off.

The door was locked.

We slept.

We woke to the turning of the key. The German Shepard woofled its morning way around us again and departed, after Malcolm had given the dog another serious petting.

Unheard during the dog's second visit, breakfast had arrived. As ever, Malcolm was first to figure it out.

"Robin! Howway, man!" he cried.

I dug into a cardboard box full of the familiar, baton shaped loaves of bread, the butter, the airline packs of strawberry jam, and the Vache Riante processed cheese. The others woke and joined us. Alan poured coffee and he and Michael drank.

Ten minutes later, the gentleman from the day of our arrival appeared. He told us in halting English that the outer entrance door would no longer be locked during the day and that we were free to go outside when we wished, provided that we were back in the villa before night fall.

"Howway, man!" led Malcolm. "Let's go and have a look."

"No," I said. "I don't trust that bloke."

"Why not?" said Malcolm.

"I don't know," I started. "He's too good just to be a goon. He's too busy not saying or looking at anything. He's just waiting."

"What for?" said Malcolm.

"Someone to say something," I said.

"So he's secret police, then?" said Malcolm.

"That's not a bad way of putting it," I concluded.

"Howway!" he said, and started off to go outside.

Then I realised where I had seen Secret Police Man before - at my first interrogation on about the fourth day of my captivity.

And preferring to be with Malcolm than without him, I jumped off my bed and followed.

We went out of the main entrance door and stood still for a minute to see if anyone was observing us. Then, on turning to the right, I nearly knocked my teeth out on a wrought iron projection that protruded from the wall.

"Did it get ya?" solicited Malcolm.

"No, just missed," I said, as I took in the elaborately curved, wrought iron bars whose shape accommodated the geometry of casement windows in the breeze block wall, that swung upwards and outwards from a horizontal hinge along their top edge.

We walked around the villa. As we rounded the first corner, there was a bare, flat patch of sand under the shade of a palm frond about ten feet high. The patch was punctuated by a long, slack chain and a bowl of water. As we moved to the end of the short wall of the villa, we encountered a track with tyre marks. To the left were the forbidding entrance gates, no more than thirty feet away. To the right, the track disappeared up the full length of the compound. Before us, and surmounted by the plain, green, flag of Libya, was the office. We followed around and saw for the first time, a straight line of three or four villas running beside the track for perhaps a hundred yards up a slight gradient.

We walked up the length of the villas, on the side away from the track, which boasted a green verge and a kerb, stopping to pass the time of day very briefly with one or two other inmates, and scrupulously avoiding the gaze of those prisoners whom we had been warned not to talk to. In the third villa, we got talking to a well fed and professionally amiable Libyan of about thirty five and with a black goatee beard who, it transpired was such a successful business man that he was being locked up while his affairs were being investigated to see how he had acquired his wealth. In the mean time his BMW had been confiscated and his wife brought him food each day.

He was totally unconcerned, he told us. He would be let go in a few days when the authorities found that, although his wealth ran counter to every socialist principle of the Jamahiriya, he was in fact squeaky clean.

I saw a shady man lurking in the shade of the locked door from behind which he was not allowed to talk to us. I kept walking.

We walked back to our villa and went into the room.

"Are you alright, Michael," said Malcolm.

"Yes, thank you, Malcolm," replied Michael.

We climbed onto our beds.

A few minutes later, an officer came in.

"Blummen," he said. He then re-read a small piece of paper, and carefully articulated the name, "Plummer."

Something gripped my heart. We had done exactly what we had been told to do, and scrupulously avoided what we had been told to avoid.

I walked behind the officer to the building across the track and, after only a brief pause for a guard to check my identity, was ushered into the main office.

There, on the right sat Secret Police Man and a well suited subordinate, busy at work on a huge, ornate, wooden desk in front of them.

And there, directly in front of me and sitting on a black leather sectional sofa, was Pat.

Hugh stepped forward on cue and shook my hand.

"What's happening?" I said.

But he offered me the opportunity to talk to Pat first.

I sat on the sofa between Pat and the desk. I put my left hand on her flat tummy and kissed her. Secret Police Man and his subordinate raised their left hands to shield their eyes, and squirmed in embarrassment, looking ever more deeply into their papers.

"What's happening?" I said.

"Terry's going to come to spend a day with you," she said.

"When?" I asked.

"Tomorrow, isn't it Hugh?" she said, turning.

Hugh silently nodded, and smiled.

"They wouldn't let him come out here and live with you," she said, "so he's coming for a day instead. We're waiting for the results of the General People's Congress."

And, referring to January, "It's going to be held at the end of the month."

Secret Police Man decided that enough was enough. He looked up slightly and uttered the guttural, "Kalass."

I was outraged and disappointed that the visit was all over so quickly.

But Hugh loaded a Scottish mouthful of six inch nails. "This lady has just flown two and half thousand miles for this interview with her husband. She is not leaving after twenty minutes," he spat out.

Secret Police Man indicated that he did not understand.

Hugh stood up. "This lady has just flown two and half thousand miles for this interview with her husband. She is not leaving after twenty minutes," he riveted home.

Secret Police Man still did not understand.

So I stood up and translated Hugh into BBC English. "This lady has just flown two and half thousand miles for this interview with her husband. She is not leaving after twenty minutes."

An hour and half later, I emerged from the office with a less energized Hugh, and a less worried Pat, but also with five pounds worth of black, plastic, Casio, digital watch. I also smelt of Pat, and I didn't wash or change clothes again until the smell had worn off.

Pat said that she would be back the following day. She would get as long as she could with me tomorrow, but she had to dash for her plane back to England.

I kissed her, hoping to see her the following day.

The following day, the 17th of January, was a wet Thursday. Pat and Hugh duly turned up early in the morning. But they were not allowed in. The soldiers that formed an informal little huddle in the rain between the inner and outer gates were perfectly civil, but adamant in the execution of their instructions. So Pat and Hugh stood there in the drizzle, Hugh with a rain coat draped over his nattily suited shoulders, Pat with an umbrella over her impeccable Burberry, and waited.

A while later, Terry arrived and proceeded to engage everybody standing there, while one of the soldiers went off to announce Terry's arrival.

Terry greeted Pat and Hugh and then proceeded to tower at six feet seven inches over the four hapless Libyan soldiers, whose Kalashnikovs were now spoiling in the rain. Making great play out of the weather, Terry helped himself to Hugh's raincoat, and draped it around the shoulders of one of the soaking wet soldiers.

Terry laughed. Hugh smiled. Pat demurred.

Then the soldier found himself the beneficiary of an incomprehensible charm offensive, and then of a gentle cuddle around his raincoated shoulders that saw him lifted a clear foot off the ground. Terry just stood there and held the helpless individual in space while continuing to tell him in smiling English what a great job he was doing.

Pat explained to Terry that they would not allow Hugh to enter.

Terry explained to the soldiers.

"Hugh can come in can't he?" he chuckled. "I-I think Hugh ought to come in," he advised. "Yes, Hugh can come in!" he decided. "Hugh is coming in with us!" he commanded.

The inner gates opened again, and Terry, Pat and Hugh were admitted into the compound. Hugh took back his rain coat from the sodden soldier.

Again I was summoned to the office.

Terry shook my hand and went directly to the villa, to spend the day with us as promised.

Hugh said that they only had about ten minutes, on account of being kept waiting for nearly an hour when they first arrived.

I kissed Pat and she filled me in on the fun and games at the gates. I asked if she would like to see where we were living.

I took her and showed her quickly were we lived and where the food came.

She walked right up to Malcolm and kissed him a big, firm smacker on the lips. "That's from Andrea," she said with a twinkling smile.

The shock and desire had Malcolm open mouthed and wide eyed.

Then I called her out into the hall way and told her that I had something to tell her. She looked worried.

We snogged. Her soft, feminine body, lean through months of no real appetite, and her thick luscious lips, turgid for the very opposite reason, yielded beneath my embrace.

When we surfaced, I said to her that we had to get one thing absolutely straight.

"What's that?" she said, worried - afraid that I was going to tell her that she and I were finished.

"You have to be absolutely clear about one thing," I said. And, looking at her straight in the eyes, I said, "We're not out of Libya until we're sitting on the tarmac at Gatwick. We're not out of Libya until we're sitting on the tarmac at Gatwick. Have you got that?"

"Yes," she replied. And looking straight back at me, "You're not out of Libya until you're sitting on the tarmac at Gatwick."

"Right," I said, finally. "Don't forget that."

Then it really was time to leave.

We all shook hands quickly with Hugh, and the other men shook hands quickly with Pat. Then Pat and Hugh stepped out the door and off to the airport. Pat narrowly avoided braining herself on the projecting, wrought iron bars.

"Remember, Pat," I called. "Gatwick!"

"Gatwick! Don't worry, Plumsie," she called back. "I won't forget."

I sat down on my bed.

Malcolm asked, "What's 'Gatwick'?"

I told him.

Malcolm asked, "What's 'Plumsie'?"

"Fuck off."

We all sat down, Malcolm on his bed, and Michael and Alan on chairs facing Terry.

Secret Police Man was also in the room, so conversation was light and inoffensive.

Beneath his apparent nonchalance Terry was concentrating on everything that was being said, and measuring anything he said with great care.

Then Secret Police Man was called away as Terry was in mid sentence and careful flow. As the doors shut, we were finally alone. Malcolm instantly leaned forward and looked straight at Terry.

"Terry," he interrupted.

But Terry took no notice and, offering no signs of bridling at the interruption, just continued talking.

"Terry!" urged Malcolm.

"I'm sorry Malcolm, I-I-I'm talking," said Terry, but starting to sense something.

"Terry!" I cut in. "Listen to Malcolm!"

A deep frown came across Terry's face and he flashed back and forth between Malcolm and me. I saw the word "No" silently cross his lips.

Malcolm didn't wait for a space. "Terry. I've got Doug Ledingham's float money. It's three hundred dinars. Can you get it back to him?"

Terry simply wasn't ready for this.

"Terry!" I jumped in. "We took it out of Doug's briefcase on the day he was released in case we needed it for escaping. I put an IOU in Doug's suitcase. Ask Doug. He'll verify it. You've got to take the money. It belongs to B-Cal. Can you get it to them?"

It was now Terry's turn to play Wimbledon. But it was very clear to him from the looks in the eyes of Malcolm and me that we were deadly serious.

"Where is it?" said Terry.

And from within the folds of his underpants, Malcolm produced the roll of banknotes.

Terry palmed the roll of notes and put them into his pocket.

A split second later, the door opened and in walked Secret Police Man to a motionless and silent tableau.

Leaning forward in his chair and giving a vibrating thumbs up sign, Alan said, "Nice one with the money, Malcolm!"

Satisfied that there was no conspiracy afoot, Secret Police Man stood up, shook hands with Terry, and left without a backward glance.

As soon as the door had shut, Alan leaned forward in his chair and asked Terry, "What do you think of Colonel Gaddafi?"

"I think he is a very charming and wise man," said Terry.

"Yes, but what do you think of him personally?" said Alan, at the point of a wagging finger.

"I think he is a very charming and wise man," said Terry.

And as Alan drew breath again, Terry said jovially, "Alan, why don't you sit down and write about your life? Start with the first two weeks that should keep you going for about four months."

Alan responded with boyish embarrassment at being too much in the spotlight.

Lunch arrived. I ate my desultory amount. Malcolm ate his usual mountain, and Terry made a lot of appreciative noises at the food.

Then it was time for pudding. To be gracious, I asked Terry if he would like to split one of the chocolate dessert bars with me, as I had not the capacity for a whole one to myself.

He smiled at me admonishingly. "At seventeen stone, don't you think I need a whole one to myself?" he said.

OK.

After lunch Terry slipped off his navy blazer, slackened his tie, and lay down on Malcolm's bed. His immense frame overhung the bed at both ends.

"Ah, this is the life," he said, smiling and looking at the ceiling, redolent of Ratty and Mole.

Malcolm looked at his occupied bed, waiting for the next verbal cue - which didn't come.

The rest of the day fizzled out. There was only one issue to talk about. And you can only go over the essential issue once. In fact even once is too much because we all knew what the issue was. There was nothing else to talk about. And there was nothing useful that anyone could say.

I had been right, I thought to myself as Terry left at about ten o'clock that night. It would have meant a very considerable re-ordering of relationships if Terry had come and lived with us for the remainder of our detention.

I helped Malcolm clear up the kitchen. Malcolm worked while loading a loaf of bread stuffed with cheese into his face.

"How did you do it?"

"Ah just made it out of left overs,"

"No," I said. "The money."

"D'ya really want ta know?" he said, starting to laugh. "Howway!"

"I know you're a twister," I said. "But that was a good one. How did you do it?"

Malcolm finished his mouthful.

"I stuck it in the bidet," he started.

"I never saw it," I said.

" Round the back, in the pipin'," he continued.

"So that's where it went," I concluded.

"Aye, when ya gave it wor after Alan was playin' with them trainers, li'e."

"Well, how did you get it out?" I said.

"Aye. When they came and got wor to bring us here, I went to the toilet and stuffed it inside wor underpants - wearing them tracksuit bottoms - so it wouldn't notice. I mean, Ah'm big enough down there anyway..." We both grinned.

"Yes," I said. "But they patted us down - Red Head and all that."

"Ah kna," he said. "When they got to that bit, the guard found it. But I just went "Ow!" as if he'd hit one of me, what's that?, them testicles."

I smiled.

Malcolm finished, "He said that "Malleish" and I shook his hand and smiled and walked out to the car."

The following day, Malcolm and I were lounging around on our beds. Stress was already giving way to boredom. Board games had no appeal, reading did not inspire, and television of any interest would not come on until early evening.

I got up and went to the lavatory.

I was conscious of Alan sitting on the grass outside the main entrance door holding forth to someone, who I took, without looking, to be a silent Michael. Rather than be obvious, I presented my back to them and kept moving. I continued down the long corridor, past Alan's room and Michael's room, and beyond to a large void, on the right hand side of which was situated a hole in the floor toilet and an unscreened shower cubicle. Having walked past the two men without distracting them, my presence would be expected as I made my return.

As I came within earshot of the conversation, I saw that Alan was not talking to Michael, but to Secret Police Man. My worst fears were about to be realised, as Secret Police Man raised his eyes towards me momentarily before returning his concentration to Alan.

In that split second, I heard the words, "...Robin lives in Royston..." I was horrified, as I seamlessly completed my journey to join Malcolm.

"We've got to say something," said Malcolm.

"We'll have to pick our time," said I. "This is past the point of careful handling."

"What ya gonna do?" said Malcolm.

"Ah divvent kna," I lied.

The nightly Fawlty Towers gave its hysterical way to an inane variety show.

All four of us persevered with the dreadful numbers since there was nothing else to do.

Then the crummy television editing cut to an English pop singer of a late 1970s genre, to judge by the outfit he was wearing, against a bland backdrop, skillfully lit, well miked, and with a professional band off.

The song was humbly and reverently hagiographic, extolling the virtues of some saintly leader or other, who gave the impression of being able to walk on water.

Then the chorus cut in.

> "For he joined the army as a cadet...
> Got rid of false governments...
> And rose to build the Jamahiriya...
> Blah, blah...
> In a nutshell - Colonel Gaddafi."

...eyes turned respectfully to the floor.

All four of us in the room reacted.

"Do ya think them expatriates think that?" asked Malcolm.

"I'm bloody sure they do," I assured him sarcastically.

"Do ya think they'll make us say anything like that?" he continued.

"Not if I have anything to do with it," I assured him.

"Aye, but do ya think we'll ever say anything like that?" asked Malcolm.

"Aye!" said I. "Next time the nightingale sings in Berkeley Square."

Alan chuckled. Michael snorted.

"What's 'Barclay Square'?" asked Malcolm.

"Hell freezing over," growled Alan.

Malcolm looked quizzical. Michael demurred. I smiled. Malcolm took the moment.

"If I ever meet the bastard that sings that song," averred Malcolm, shaking his head. "I break 'is bloody neck."

We all sat back feeling somehow warmer.

Later that night, Malcolm and I were chatting again about what I had heard Alan say to Secret Police Man, when we became aware of a repeated thrashing noise. My first instinct was that it was just that - a thrashing - and was gripped by the fear of a return to the early weeks of my detention.

"That's water," said Malcolm. And after a few seconds, "That's Alan."

"What's he doing?" he said.

"Having a shower," said Malcolm. "He did the same last night. He's pushing the water out of the shower stand and into the drain beside the shower."

Malcolm went to investigate. Better Malcolm than me.

"Howway man, Alan! Howway, man woman man!" he harangued.

"What do you want, Malcolm?" said Alan.

"You're just attracting attention," said Malcolm truthfully.

"If I want to get the water out of the shower, then I'll do it, and I'll do it my way," insisted Alan.

"No. I mean talking to that secret policeman," said Malcolm, bait and switch.

"If I want to have a conversation with an official," Alan parried, "I am perfectly entitled to do so."

"Robin thinks you mentioned him," went on Malcolm levelly.

"I don't care what Robin thinks," Alan said. "If I want to have a conversation with an official I am perfectly entitled to do so."

Kalass. Enough was enough. It was time. There are some people who understand only one language.

I rose from my bed and calmly walked the score or so of yards to the shower, leaving, what I judged to be enough time for Alan to get decent. He was. I passed Malcolm on his way back to our room. We shook our heads at each other.

I told Alan that we had all tried - Terry, Malcolm, me - to bring to his attention the need to curtail his garrulousness where the Libyans were concerned. That we had tried every argument we knew in order to get him to stop talking, because all the while he was talking he was giving things away. He had even acknowledged it himself, invoking the fanciful idea of someone else talking about the weather.

I then went on to tell Alan what I had heard him saying to Secret Police Man earlier in the day.

Alan refuted it point blank.

I told him in so many words that he was lying.

At such a grave and accurate accusation, Alan's defences collapsed, and I pressed my advantage home.

"So I am going to make myself absolutely clear," I said. "Because you have had all the warnings you're going to get."

And without a hint of malice, I told Alan that in my view I had done everything in my power for the previous eight months to make sure that the Libyans did not get to hear a single thing that might jeopardize or incriminate me or anybody else and, now that the end was in sight, if anything happened to me on account of what he was telling Secret Police Man, I would beat him to a pulp.

"You will be lucky ever to walk again. Stop talking to the Libyans."

"I'm quite sure you could do it, Robin," said Alan, shaking like a leaf, pale grey, and looking at the floor.

The following day, Alan moved rooms.

Without his usual declaration of intent, he just upped stumps and moved. Lock, stock and whatever little barrel he possessed. That little included the radio, which, he pointed out, it was fair that he took, on the grounds that the rest of us had the television.

Nobody questioned or commented on what he was doing. And nobody went to visit him either. In silent and sullen tension, he packed up and left for the large room across the corridor, where he proceeded to immerse himself in a world of his own.

The temperature dropped.

Breakfast came and went.

Lunch came and went.

Malcolm set about cleaning the metal dishes.

"They look like silver," he said.

Over three days, he polished off what had once been a coal black deposit on all three of the plates until they were shining - like silver.

"Here Robin," he came in one day. "Come and look at this. It's that Russian or something?"

I went into the kitchen and saw the plates.

"Jesus Christ!" I said. "Where the Hell did you get those from?"

"Them's wor plates," he said, elated.

"How the Hell did you do that?" I followed up.

"Newspaper," and he laughed his dirty laugh.

"Bloody Hell!" I exclaimed. "Where's this Russian?"

Malcolm turned the first plate over and handed it to me. It weighed a ton.

And there, beautifully engraved in the centre of the back of the plate, and picked out by the ingrained tarnish, was an array of unintelligible letters and symbols.

Upon close examination, it wasn't Russian, but Gothic Script and what I took to be hallmarks.

It all meant that the three plates were German, 1920 to 1937 and, to judge by the weight and markings, solid silver.

"Solitary confinement to solid silver!" laughed Malcolm. I smiled

I hefted the longer of the two oval ones. If you were to hit someone over the head with it, it would crush their skull.

The following day, my tie and my old Casio watch appeared along with breakfast. The watch had lost two whole minutes in the eight months since it had been confiscated. I was outraged.

Malcolm was taken for questioning. Before he left he borrowed my tie. He thought it best to look as good as possible. I also gave him the five pounds worth of Casio that Pat had just brought me. When he came back he told me that the Libyans had tried a different tactic. They'd told him that he had to regard his lawyer as a doctor. If the doctor is to help him, Malcolm would have to tell him everything that is wrong with him. Similarly, Malcolm would need to tell the lawyer everything he knew. Malcolm's instinct appeared to me to be right. It sounded like a trap.

"I don't think they've got anything on wor," he said. He'd refused to tell them anything.

The following morning when I walked back into our room after showering, Malcolm was lying on his bed, propped up on one elbow, reading.

"What's that?" I asked.

"I've gorri' back," he replied.

"Got what back?" I said.

"They've give it back to wor," he continued. "Wor suitcase. What's this, Robin?"

I sat next to him. We leaned against each other, shoulders, arms and thighs, and read the bits of printed, A4 paper together.

"Bit technical, isn't it?" I said.

"I were studyin' for me weldin' inspectors when I got lifted," he said.

"So you're taking up where you left off eight months ago," I concluded.

"Nam," he confirmed. "I've got to get me weldin' inspectors. You don't see any welders over forty. Only inspectors. Unless they so piss poor the only thing they can burn is their fingers."

I suggested that he form his own company. "Jama or Juma Welding or something."

"What's this, Robin?"

And he showed me graphs and tables used in the X-raying and interpreting of industrial welds. We spent the day together while I explained some of the more mathematical bits. He only needed telling once.

Pat and Carole met Sir Geoffrey Howe. In fact Pat met Sir Geoffrey twice.

The first meeting was how Sir Geoffrey planned it. When they met for the first time, in Sir Geoffrey's Whitehall office, the substance of their discussion was that Pat wanted visas for the relatives of the Libyans being held in Britain issued much more quickly. At present, Pat pointed out, Libyans first had to go to neutral country, wait a few weeks and then get their visas before they could come to England, if indeed the visas were granted at all.

Pat and Carole then went on to the BBC shortly after the meeting and recounted in interview the points that they had made to Sir Geoffrey.

But Sir Geoffrey also went to the BBC for a related but unconnected interview.

There was the feeling out there, said the interviewer to Sir Geoffrey, that the British Government had thrown in the towel and left the release of the hostages up to the church.

That, replied Sir Geoffrey, was a wholly false impression. The government had brought a lot of pressure to bear on the Libyans, not least through the Italians who were the protecting power in Libya since diplomatic relations had been broken off over a year previously, in a very difficult and delicate situation; and to do it in a fashion that wouldn't jeopardize the position of thousands of other British people both in Libya and all over the world.

Sir Geoffrey went on with a delivery, sincere in every respect, that was soft, level and devoid of passion, but which was in fact a masterpiece of British understatement. "I can understand why the families of the detainees feel that way," he went on. "But I'm afraid that the criticism is not justified. We are naturally working very closely with the church and with Mr Waite, but it is not something I can easily talk about on a programme like this."

But the second meeting was not how Sir Geoffrey planned it.

The horror stricken look on his face at the sight of Pat was born of the fact the he, the Foreign Secretary, Her Britannic Majesty's Principle Secretary of State for Foreign and Commonwealth Affairs, had been cornered by the wife of one of the hostages as they both exited from their respective, subterranean lavatories at Broadcasting House. Sir Geoffrey was convinced that Pat was now bearing down on him to personally excoriate and eviscerate him for not doing enough to get her husband out and that, in a basement corridor of the BBC with no-one around to bail him out and nothing that he could actually say, he was helpless to defend himself.

"Oh, hello, Sir Geoffrey," Pat bubbled as Sir Geoffrey recoiled in horror. "Do you think I could have a cigarette?"

Sir Geoffrey fluffed and fumbled a packet of Silk Cut in Pat's direction, and together the two of them smoked a well deserved cigarette.

We hadn't heard from Alan for a couple of days. He didn't eat with us, or join us for Fawlty Towers. In fact we never saw him. We only knew where he was by the trail of cigarette smoke, or the World Service at high volume so that he could hear it.

At different times, each of Malcolm and me had stuck our heads around the door of his vast room when we judged that he was asleep or indeed elsewhere in the villa or the compound.

And we agreed that we had both seen the same thing.

Alan's bed was placed along side the inner wall a few feet from the door, with the head end away from the door. A large cotton sheet hung as a canopy over the bed, suspended from a number of points - the wall, a couple of chairs, a couple of erect poles that were, themselves wedged in an upright position by heavy objects or, in one case a bucket of sand. A gas heater supported a tea pot. And another bucket of sand supported a large palm frond.

The whole ensemble was fronted by a free standing, two bar electric heater that ran, quite necessarily, 24 hours a day. Alan could on occasions be seen sitting motionless on the bed, wearing a further cotton sheet wrapped around his lower body, and his greyish cardigan worn back to front on his upper body. Some times he was naked from the waist down except for his sandals. A plate and a cup were situated on a low stool nearby.

The radio sat on a shelf, head height and integral to an outer wall in Alan's room. It was the only place high enough off the ground to make reception even passable on account of sun spot activity.

It was the end of January and the General People's Congress that was supposed to have ratified the decision made by the Basic People's Congresses to release us had not sat. The fact of being charged therefore appeared terminal.

On the Monday, the 28th of January, I was taken to see the magistrate. As he stood in an office, not that in which I had previously been interrogated, his body language was highly restive - almost violent - for such an otherwise austere, grave and authoritative man. He spluttered angry and frustrated Arabic to those around him, and used his authority to avoid my gaze. A number of 'Baden's, followed by a few 'Bukra's, amidst some genuine and vocal annoyance on my part at being more or less ordered out of the office, told me that today's business would be deferred not simply until later, but until tomorrow.

I was returned to the prison.

The following day, they came and got me again.

The body language of my escort looked very serious, so I took a beta blocker, squared my shoulders and got into the car.

I soon found myself in the same corridor that I had been on the previous day. I recognized the office of the investigating magistrate. After being made to wait for an interval, I was brusquely ordered across the corridor and through a door which gave onto a rather more substantial office. This housed a grand, high desk against the left hand wall and, elsewhere, the tasteless and gaudy furnishings beloved of all Libyans.

To the right of the grand desk as I faced it, were about a dozen chairs in an incongruous L-shaped array that jutted out into the room so that all chairs essentially faced the desk.

Almost without exception the various occupants of the chairs ignored me - some older and dignified, others affecting authority or status, some sycophants. I spotted the magistrate in the wallward arm of the "L".

If it takes this many to put me in my place, then I've already won. Regarding this assembled mass of self importance, I felt sorry for the genuinely dignified elders in the room for whom this gathering was obviously as much of an embarrassment as it was for me. For the remainder, I let out a low breath as I resisted the temptation to shake my head from side to side.

I turned my head away from them all and awaited the commencement of whatever proceedings awaited me.

The alpha dog, seated at the grand desk, bawled at me in Arabic to pay attention. I slowly turned my head to face him. He bawled again at me to stand to attention. I was already standing up straight, so there was nothing further I could do. I knew this gambit. I'd seen magistrates do it to the disrespectful accused in courts in England. "Alright, you overblown little shit," I thought. "You want a show? Your pathetic little revolution is only fifteen years old. We, by contrast have over three hundred years of officer training behind us. Do your worst."

Quite usefully, he resorted to English.

"You are Robin Blummen," he faltered, and corrected himself. "Plummer."

I ignored the statement.

He bawled my name at me again. Some one passed him my pink card. He knew who I was so I answered him.

"Have you been investigated?" he rapped out.

"I have been asked some questions," I replied levelly.

"Have you...," he broke off, confused, and ran his eye up the line of "dignitaries" until he caught the eye of the investigating magistrate.

I didn't bother to look, but following the receipt of an obvious affirmative, Alpha Dog returned to me.

"You have been investigated," he stated.

This idiotic pursuit of ridiculous procedure was risible. I fought successfully to keep a straight face. His statement had in fact been intended as a question. I chose not to take it as such and therefore felt no obligation to say anything.

This made him cross.

He bawled at me, "Have you been investigated?"

"I have been asked some questions," I carefully repeated.

Now he could barely contain his own authority.

"You have been investigated, then?"

Now it _was_ a question. But before I could answer he had started making notes to record his own conclusion.

But answer I did. My "Yes" caught him off stride. My timing was perfect. Now he was spluttering.

Laughable procedure all spent, he could now ignore me. He got a grip on himself now that he was approaching the apotheosis of his purpose in the room.

"You are to be charged," he lorded.

"Oh? What with?" I enquired, innocently and knowingly daring him.

I knew exactly what was coming, although somehow I expected it to be a little less bald when it was eventually said.

"You have been in contact with persons inside Jamahiriya and outside Jamahiriya for purposes connected with espionage."

The word resonated inside my head.

I lowered my eyes and looked indifferently away.

While the four syllables were still rattling around inside my cranium, insult was added to injury. Alpha Dog added, "What is your plea? How do you plead? Guilty or not guilty."

There was no litany, no catalogue of detail, no dates, times, persons, contacts. The charge would not withstand scrutiny anywhere in the civilised world. But I <u>had</u> just been charged with spying.

I wasn't going to dignify this farce by selecting an answer from the choice offered.

Although it welled up inside me to do so, I managed to squeeze out, "I have <u>not</u> been in contact with persons inside Jamahiriya and outside Jamahiriya for purposes connected with espionage."

My voice tailed off as I reached the last word. And as it did so, I could not prevent my head from turning to seek out the eyes of the investigating magistrate who had so solemnly assured me that I would be acquitted.

To his credit, or more probably his salvation, he had already turned his head away from me and to the wall. It did not prevent me however from relegating him in my mind, to the level of the other scum that floated around the room.

Without another word, I was herded out. And the last thing I heard as I was shepherded down the corridor and out of earshot was the sound of kangaroos hopping around.

Not a word was spoken on the return journey to the prison. In fact the guards were almost polite.

When we got out of the car, the solicitude was undiminished. And I was conducted very courteously through the gates.

I was a spy.

They had known it all along, of course, but now it was official. And given that convicted spies are usually executed, I appeared to be conducting myself with a remarkable degree of calm.

But dead men have authority. And so the guards left me alone to make my own progress.

From that moment on, no-one really interfered with me. And on the few remaining occasions that I was confronted by Secret Police Man, even he looked up to catch my eye.

As the huge, steel, prison gates closed behind me and I was ordered, unaccompanied, off to my billet, I was shaken to see what could only have been the death throes of a prisoner being savaged to death by the guard dog.

Initially, I was appalled, but also impressed at the fight that the prisoner appeared to be putting up. As the dog's teeth closed once again around an arm, I expected to see arterial blood gouting into the air, then, upon falling, meld with the dry desert sand. And, predictably, after a few seconds, all motion ceased.

"Are you alright, Robin?" called Malcolm cheerily, without unwrapping his legs from the dog.

So now Malcolm's relationship with the dog had progressed to the sexual.

"How does he do it?" I thought.

I kept walking as ordered by the guard still watching me for signs of disobedience.

I kept walking between this disgusting bout of dusty dog wangling and the end of the cell block. I kept my distance from the dog.

Malcolm read me correctly.

"Aye, it's OK, Robin. The dog's on a chain."

Best foot forward then.

Remain absolutely still, and the dog will ignore you.

Well, I'd had that, because I was under orders from a guard at my back with a gun in his hand.

Let's try, "Just keep looking ahead of you, and the dog will ignore you."

Yes, let's try that.

I heard the dog leap to its feet.

I heard Malcolm shout, "Look out, Robin!"

If you are moving in one direction, it is easier to accelerate in that direction that to turn and go back the other way. But such knowledge of mechanics was useless in the face of a dog that had long ago learnt his arc of fire.

The dog's claws beat out the tattoo on the dry ground of a fast dash as he faultlessly covered the distance between us.

Chain? Bloody chain?

Hit the kick down!

I accelerated like the six million dollar man. All I had to do was to outdistance the length of the chain. But the dog had done this before, and trying to accelerate away from him was as frustrating as running the hundred metres without spikes. This was a bad dream.

I gave it everything I had, but it wasn't enough.

Out of the corner of my eye I could see the manic jester in the dog. With what little I knew about dogs, I was now totally out of my depth.

Everything went into slow motion.

I shortened my stride and kicked harder, but it wasn't enough.

My right leg was half way through a stride. I was just about to lift my left leg, when I felt the dog's teeth close around the muscle of my left calf. "No, please, no!" I heard myself say. "Don't rip the calf muscle out of my leg."

"Kick, Robin! Kick!" I heard inside my head.

I lifted my left leg.

I felt the dog's lips close over his teeth and around the muscle of my left calf.

I heard a musical note rise by octaves as the dog's chain went tight.

I felt the dog guide his own teeth exactly to avoid ripping my calf muscle out.

I felt the teeth close on the linen fabric of my Marks and Spencer suit trousers and, as I kicked my left leg forward, tear out about a square foot of material.

The tight chain stopped the dog's head stone dead.

The momentum of its body, however, produced unplanned acrobatics, and two hundred and fifty pounds of bisexual menace spent the next while spinning around in the air at the end of its taut chain.

Then dog and chain fell to earth with a sickening thud. The ensuing silence would have been complete had it not been for Malcolm writhing on the ground in uncontrollable laughter.

"I told ya not to show them you're scared, Robin," he said.

"You're crazy!" I lambasted. "You're totally fucking crazy!" And, narrowly avoiding braining myself on the projecting window cages, I disappeared around the corner of the cell block to the sound of hysterical laughter. To this day I could not tell you who was laughing the louder, Malcolm or the dog.

I never went around that end of the building again.

A simple, modest, white, stone memorial carries a plaque that bears the words

HERE FELL
WPC
YVONNE FLETCHER
17th APRIL 1984

The memorial was unveiled by the Prime Minister, Mrs Thatcher, on Friday, 1st February, 1985, in front of hundreds of people who attended the dedication, which was widely publicised in the media.

It was Saturday, the second of February. I came back from my shower to the cardboard box of breakfast, and took a loaf of bread and some butter. I drank a cup of rocket fuel as I stood there in the kitchen, failing to see the brown, leather object sitting out of sight behind the box on the marble worktop.

Malcolm had decided to dismantle something mechanical. As I sat down on my bed to eat my loaf and butter, I couldn't find Malcolm on his bed. So I called out for him.

The sun was up far enough that it shone its South Eastern, wintry yellow, from over the top of the high wall that separated us from the women's prison next door, and onto the South facing wall of the villa, against which Malcolm now leaned, seated on the ground. I joined him to finish my loaf.

"Howway, Robin," he greeted me, concentrating on his mechanical strip down. But the concentration wasn't enough and he changed posture onto his knees, kowtowing before the device that now lay on the ground.

"You've not gorri' then?" he said.

"Not got what?" I enquired.

"Aye, it's in the kitchen," he went on.

"No?"

He rose, and returned a few seconds later with my hand bag.

"Fuck me," I said.

"We're going home," he said.

"Nah," I said. "We're not out of Libya 'til we're sitting on the tarmac at Gatwick."

"Howway, man," he said. "Wor gannen away hyem! Think of all that hairy pie we can have when we get there!"

I checked my handbag. My pink card, my ball point pen, my dark glasses, my cash, my cigarettes. It was all there! With my watch on my wrist and my handbag clipped to my belt loop, I began to feel almost normal again.

But while I was checking the contents of my bag, something went 'ping' and Malcolm swore. Over the next hour and a half, Malcolm quartered many square yards of the grassy verge in front of him until he found the tiny piece of springy metal that had flicked away. I admired him for his persistence and said so.

That afternoon, Alan's Bedouin tent was empty. Alan was in talking to Michael. Malcolm and I had got bored and wanted to listen to the radio. So we crept into Alan's room.

"Go on, then," said Malcolm, and I sought to retune the radio to find the World Service.

But the interference was desperate, and I couldn't even register a station on the usual late afternoon frequency - far less hear anything. I sighed.

"Don't give up," said Malcolm encouraging me with his deep, dark eyes.

I found Moscow Radio and moved on. I found Voice of America and moved on.

Then I found a channel I had never heard before. It certainly wasn't the BBC - the break frequency was different - so was the hint of an accent in the English. Malcolm and I frowned quizzically at each other as I tweaked the tuning, because two things were remarkable. One was the high quality of reception given the high level of sun spot activity, and the other was the even handed and unexcitable way in which the subject matter in the broadcast was being treated by those in the studio. Malcolm and I sat glued to the radio set.

Then the programme was over. A link reader announced the news at fourteen hundred hours GMT and stated that you were listening to Swiss Radio, and he quoted the frequency.

Malcolm and I looked at each other in amazement.

But not half as much amazement as we did a couple of minutes later.

After the news of an airline disaster somewhere in the world, the news reader continued to intone in vaguely Schweitzer-Deutsch accented English.

"The four British hostages held in Libya for almost nine months can expect to hear good news tomorrow, Sunday, when it is expected that they will be told of their release."

We just looked at each other.

"Well, fuckin' 'ell!" Malcolm understated.

I let out a long low exhalation.

"Come on," he said. "Let's tell the others."

"No," I said firmly shaking my head. "We've only heard it once, on a station that we don't know anything about. It's not corroborated. We can't take the risk of telling Alan, only to find that it isn't true."

"What about Michael?" said Malcolm.

"I think we ought to wait until we have some kind of confirmation," I said.

"Aye, OK," he said. "What's confirmation?"

"We appear - mark, we only appear - to have reliably got a credible radio station that we can actually hear," I started. "But I would like to hear it from the BBC."

An hour later, we came back to try to find Lilliburlero. We couldn't, so I quickly retuned to Swiss radio again. Nothing was said about us.

An hour later, we came back again to try to find Lilliburlero. We couldn't, so I quickly retuned to Swiss radio again.

This time the bulletin was repeated.

It was time to tell Michael. "Michael," I solicited delicately. "Would you mind if we come in for a minute, please? There is something we would like to chat over with you."

Malcolm and I went in and sat with Michael.

"We've got something to tell you that we think might be interesting, Michael," I started. "And we'd like your opinion on it."

"OK," said Michael, nodding his appreciation of the signal of deference.

I told him about the news bulletin. And told him that we had come to him only after we had heard it a second time for a bit of corroboration.

"Was it on the BBC?" Michael asked.

I told him no, Swiss Radio - that was why we wanted to ask his opinion.

Now we had his attention.

"Oh, if it's on Swiss Radio then it must be true. Swiss Radio relies upon its reputation for integrity. They wouldn't broadcast anything unless they were quite sure that it was true," said Michael lucidly and confidently.

We all sat back.

"Have you told Alan?" Michael asked.

Malcolm and I shook our heads. "Not yet."

"Oh, dear! That man," said Michael, to my faint alarm. "He really is too much ..." and he started to laugh.

He laughed and laughed. I was concerned that he had cracked.

But the laugh went all the way to his eyes.

"Good God," I thought. "He's made it."

"We'll let you know if we hear it on the BBC," said Malcolm, and we left for our own room.

The following day, radio reception was a little better. I took the opportunity every hour to use the continuous music of Lilliburlero, beloved of oppressed peoples the world over, to tune in to the BBC World Service - the nearest approximation to the truth. Following a day of continual disappointment, I finally struck gold.

The seconds of silence that followed Lilliburlero dragged on. Then, in beautiful BBC tones, the announcer said, "This is the BBC World Service. The time is fourteen hundred hours Greenwich Mean Time. There now follows the news, in the World Service of the BBC, with Mel Oxley."

And in Mel Oxley's impeccable tones, the first item was the confirmation that we had been looking for. The bulletin even listed us individually - honorific, Christian name and surname.

Years later of course, Kate Adie told me that she had insisted that, quite unusually for the BBC, our names be inserted into the news bulletin so that, if we were to hear it, there would be absolutely no doubt about who was being referred to.

"You tell him," I said to Malcolm.

"Aye, OK," said Malcolm, and he went off to tell Alan.

Alan reacted non-committally. We had been here before. To an extent Alan was right. He had, after all, been sentenced to a medium term in jail.

Malcolm and I were sitting on the grass outside the villa. Malcolm was dismantling something.

"Why didn't you tell me about this as soon as you heard it on Swiss Radio?"

I was tired of this, and told Alan to shut up. Even as I spoke, I rose to my feet in anticipation of trouble.

"Right, that's it," he said. "I've had just about enough of you, and I'm going to teach you a lesson. I wasn't in the RAF for two years for nothing you know."

"Come on then," I said and took off my sun glasses and put them on the nearby window ledge behind the wrought iron bars, to avoid getting an eye injury in what was almost certain to follow.

Alan took a swing at me as I was finishing putting my glasses down. But I was already on the move and he only barely connected.

I replied and caught him full on the bridge of the nose.

But much more important than doing any real damage to Alan was to stop this nonsense dead. The last thing we needed now was to allow the Libyans to see us scrapping amongst ourselves.

I took Alan full across the throat with the inside of my right, upper arm and crashed with him to the ground with my arm around his neck, strangling him and pinning him to the floor to get us out of sight of some Libyans who I knew were further up the compound.

We fell flat. I had to insinuate my hand between Alan and me and extract his hand from my testicles. "There," he said triumphantly. "I told you I wasn't in the RAF for two years for nothing."

Having extracted his hand with some pain to myself, I told Alan several times to pack it in. But he wouldn't stop. He just wouldn't stop. So I let go of him and simultaneously pounded the bridge of his nose twice more with the flat edge of my tightly rolled, right fist. He rolled away and curled up.

I stood up, and backed away three paces from his motionless body. "Now pack it up!" I shouted at the point of a finger, and turned and walked into the villa.

At about ten o'clock that evening, I had just got into bed, buoyed up by some of the events of the day, and deeply disturbed by others.

The last movements of the day had already been completed so I was a bit surprised when the outer door was unlocked and footsteps were heard.

Malcolm jumped up. A few seconds later he was back to get me.

I dressed and joined Malcolm in a deserted room on the opposite side of the corridor. Deserted that is except for a rotund, unshaven man, in his mid forties and a uniform jacket bearing major's insignia on the epaulettes. He was seated on a chair two thirds of the way into the room, with his legs crossed, and his chin supported by the fingers of his right hand, motionless and without fuss, and remained so until Malcolm and I had settled.

In broken but careful English, he started to tell us the good news. But I had heard enough already and got up and went back to bed.

Malcolm came in about twenty minutes later, and asked me why I had done that. I mumbled something about disappointment before, that I would believe it when I saw it, and in any case, that I was not going to sit around and play charades with a bunch of shits, however senior, who had just deprived me of my liberty, my wife and my children for nearly nine months.

Malcolm then told me what the major had said.

We were going to be released tomorrow. We had to be up and ready to go for nine o'clock. Pronto! Then we would be taken into the city, where we would be handed over to Terry.

We went and told Alan and Michael, who failed to react.

We went to bed, careful to set the alarm on my Casio for a sensible time in the morning.

At the BBC in London, all was set for a grandstand broadcast of the release via a satellite link that Kate Adie had set up and paid for in Tripoli. Pat was at the BBC, ready to respond to a running commentary by Frank Bough, compère of BBC Breakfast Television, as the televised release unfolded. Viewers all over the country tuned in to see the long awaited event.

At the People's Palace in Tripoli, all was set for a grandstand press conference to gain maximum publicity for the Libyans of the release. Everybody was assembled. Kate Adie and the BBC, Brent Sadler and the ITN, Hugh, various Libyan officials including a senior representative of the Foreign Affairs Department, and Terry Waite into whose custody it had been agreed that we would be handed. A large buffet of fresh sandwiches and cakes, brightly coloured fruit drinks and tea and coffee had even been laid on.

At the prison outside Tripoli, we rose promptly as planned, showered, dressed, groomed ourselves, and gathered our belongings. I took a beta blocker and we sat on our respective beds clutching our possessions, and waited. At about twenty past nine, an officer came. We rose to go to the cars. But instead of cars, the officer called out two of us by name. I looked quizzically at Malcolm who had not been called, and was escorted to the office.

The release was off.

Until tomorrow.

Please be ready to leave at the same time tomorrow.

I was furious. But I let my shoulders drop when, in spite of a couple of perfectly reasonable attempts on my part to find out why, absolutely no explanation was forthcoming, and amidst restive body language from all the officers and even Secret Police Man, I was constrained to return to the villa and tell the others what I had just witnessed.

About half an hour later, at ten o'clock, the representative of the Foreign Affairs Department stood beneath a huge portrait of Colonel Gaddafi in revolutionary pose, at the press conference in the People's Palace, by then going out live by satellite to London, and announced that, "Following recent unforeseen circumstances, it has been decided to postpone the conference." And looking at Terry, he added a restive, "I would like to see you, Mr Waite," and turned, with Terry and Kate Adie following him. The three left the conference room by a pair of high, double doors, somewhat to the side of where he had been standing to make the announcement.

Kate Adie reported to London that the release had been called off because of the unveiling of the WPC Fletcher Memorial on the Friday, and the opening of the trial of the four Libyan bombers in Manchester, today, Monday.

Terry Waite looked weary as he said on the BBC, "Feelings run high at a time like this. Keep calm. This requires patient work."

Pat was bitterly disappointed. "The timing of the unveiling of the memorial was awful," she said. No reason was given for the delay, but the memorial was thought to be insensitive.

Pat went on, "Well I'm appalled. But not really surprised. No I'm not over reacting." And when pressed as to whether she thought that Terry could still pull it off, she replied that her hopes always were with Terry Waite.

In the villa I told the others that the release was off until the following day. The general reaction was, "Well, that's it then." We ate breakfast, occupied ourselves in our own ways and got on with another twenty four hours of anxiety. But it was also clear that none of us was interested in taking any further news of our imminent release seriously. And if we did take it seriously, we weren't going to let on.

Over night, Ron Brown, a British MP, asked to go to Tripoli. He had said on a number of occasions that a swap of prisoners was in order, and he was on his way to Tripoli to say the same thing again.

Tuesday morning, 5th Feb, at the BBC in London, all was set once again for a grandstand view of the release. Frank Bough was once in the studio, and Pat was expected. But with no broadcast of any sort yet being received from any Tripoli press conference, Frank Bough moved onto other news and magazine items.

But before he did so, Kate Adie from Tripoli reported that there had been no clear indication of why there was a delay, but that is was now clear that the events in Britain had caused the problem. Everybody was waiting to see if the release would go ahead, and whether this was just a last minute hitch or a prolonged prevarication. But, having made their point, so to speak, the Libyans were now prepared to go ahead with the televised release.

We by contrast were not.

The key in the outer door was turned. I pulled the blankets up over my ears. Breakfast arrived. Malcolm grabbed some food and got back into bed to eat it under his blankets.

At nine o'clock promptly, the officer came. He was horrified to see us still in bed, apparently asleep, and having made no attempt to be ready. He told us three times that we were supposed to be ready. Malcolm and I, at least, just silently rolled over and pulled our covers further up over our ears. The officer padded a rather swift way down the corridor and could be heard pacing across the track.

Two minutes later, and following some muffled bellowing, he was back with a senior officer.

"You are come, now," he said, calmly but firmly.

No-one moved.

His following and subsequent words moved from questioning why we weren't up, to entreaty, to near panic, as it became clear to him that none of us had any intention of dignifying another potentially false start by even getting out of bed.

The officer was hopping back and forth from one foot to another. Then he left with the junior officer in tow.

But, having made our point, so to speak, Malcolm and I were now prepared to go ahead with the televised release.

With no time to groom, and only enough to grab the daily beta blocker and possessions, we found ourselves being driven at breakneck speed along cleared roads to the People's Palace, where we quickly, if solicitously, shepherded into an office.

The huge, polished desk was busy but not cluttered or untidy. A wall unit stood from floor to ceiling. In a passable imitation of rosewood, it dominated the room from behind the matching desk. A substantial, short wave radio set purred intelligibly away, at shoulder height on the wall unit. From somewhere close to the radio could also be heard the crackle and squelch of VHF voice transmissions.

As the four of us entered, assistants with eyes discreetly downcast, found upright chairs for all of us to sit in, and carefully arranged them in a neat arc, a diplomatic few feet away from the desk.

The polished, wooden door to our right reflected in rosewood hues the daylight that shone through an open casement window to the left. The curtains fluttered lightly.

Finally, the two men standing behind the desk raised their heads and smiled well practised, faint, unassuming, dignified and brief smiles with an incline of the head and lowered eyelids. Their tasteful, narrow pinstriped suits, Windsor knotted ties and crisp, white shirts, echoed the clean lines of their French cuffs, their coif and their manicure.

They shook hands with some of us, and we all sat down.

The senior of the two welcomed us to the People's Palace. He invited us to smoke if we wished. We did. He then looked at each of us in turn, addressing us correctly by name as he did so, and waiting for an affirmative from each before moving on.

When he got to me he extended his right arm to pass a blue object, I took my passport with a flicker on my face to indicate the astonishment that I was registering in my head.

He then told us simply but directly that today, with immediate effect, we were all to be released.

"We are free?" said Alan, asserting the question with every tired and twitching muscle of his face.

"Yes," he said. "All of you are free."

"How immediate is "immediate"?" I asked.

And looking me a gentle business like look in the eye, before looking to his left and nodding, he said, "As soon as you walk out that door."

The radio signalled the hour. As if on cue, the door opened a little.

Kate Adie stuck her head around the door with eyes ablaze, and scanned the four of us.

"What's happening?" I said.

"You're going to be released," she clipped out. "I'll talk to you in a minute." Kate turned, looked out the door and nodded a clear affirmative to someone.

Malcolm and I looked at each other. Kate Adie had said it. It must be true then.

And Kate was gone.

The senior official continued. He told us that when we passed through the door, we would be handed over into the custody of Mr Terry Waite, who was currently sitting in a press conference where the fact of our release was being announced to the world's press, even as we were sitting here.

"No," I said.

"Please, Mr Plummer," he calmly entreated, inclining his head, and looking directly at me. "In one minute you will see for yourself." And he continued to look at me until I nodded a silent "OK".

With that, he rose. The door opened as if by magic, and following the offer of handshakes which some took and I refused, we were shown out of the office. Beyond the door was a small sea of faces that included that of The Intelligent One, Tweedle Dee. They regarded us neutrally. I simply ignored them. The owners of the faces proceeded to usher us towards a pair of high, double doors.

While we had been sitting in the office, being formally notified of our release, a media circus of journalists, camera crews, aides and officials - some twenty people in all - had started only a couple of rooms away, exactly as the senior Libyan had stated.

At the BBC, Frank Bough introduced Pat, Jean Waddell, one of the Iran hostages from 4 years previously, and Mayer Othman, who Frank introduced as a journalist and a Libyan. Mayer Othman was blinding in his diplomacy when he said as almost his first comment, "Well, I would like to make one correction. I am an Arab journalist, but I am not in fact Libyan."

The satellite link came up, and the studio was filled with a faded Technicolor portrait of a young Colonel Gaddafi in revolutionary pose, hanging on a wall somewhere above the heads of Hugh, his new, second consul, Richard Beeson and a seated Terry Waite.

Mayer Othman said that it looked almost certain.

Pat said that it sounded hopeful.

Frank Bough said that the food had been ready yesterday and that the whole lot had been cancelled at the last minute.

Frank saw Pat looking anxiously at the screen, and asked her what Terry was like.

With months of practice, Pat avoided the direct question. "Terry can make something funny that would otherwise be very nasty."

She went on to say that on the occasions that she had seen me over the nine months, she thought that I had borne it very well, considering. "I think Robin saw the whole thing as a challenge. It has certainly proved that with the raising and lowering of expectations."

At the moment the transmission failed, and the BBC went to different story.

Then the transmission was back up again.

In Tripoli, the representative of the Foreign Affairs Department, Mr Mohammed Alhijazi who, only twenty four hours previously had announced to the world's press that the press conference had been postponed for twenty four hours, started into a patient and detailed statement of the events leading up to the televised release of today, which was being accurately and precisely translated by Kamal, seated next to him. Around the vast, oval ring of a table, at which conference delegates would naturally be seated were, on Kamal's left, Richard Beeson, Brent Sadler, Kate Adie,

Smokey Joe from the Telegraph, a pretty blonde reporter in jeans who had come out from England with Brent Sadler and, after a considerable gap, Alan Florence and Malcolm Hicks for ITN and, around the other side of the oval, a BBC crew. To the right of Mr Alhijazi sat Terry, concentrating on every word that was being said, and taking notes with his left hand. Then another BBC camera followed by a horn rimmed, bespectacled Libyan incongruous in Burberry scarf, and then Hugh.

In his speech, Mr Alhijazi lengthily recalled in great detail the intervention of King Hassan II of Morocco, President Nyerere of Tanzania, the Greeks and the Italians, Mrs Thatcher, the Anglican Church, the Archbishop of Canterbury, and Terry Waite himself - as well as the intervention of many "brothers and friends".

"In response to all these endeavours, the Brother Leader would have liked to release the British prisoners.

"But since the authority is in the hands of the Basic People's Congresses, all he could do was to prevail on the People's Congresses to discuss the issue when dealing with foreign policy which the Basic People's Congresses discuss under the item of the Anglo Libyan relations.

"The Leader hoped that this item would be given a high priority in appreciation of contacts made by the brothers and friends, and in appreciation of both the Anglican Church and the British people.

"Indeed, the Basic People's Congresses responded and gave the item priority in their deliberations. This was done in the belief that lasting relations are between peoples because of their keen desire to maintain good relations with the British people."

Mr Alhijazi then went over again those whose interventions had been taken into account when discussing this item, and continued by recounting the mechanism by which votes are submitted and counted, indicating a total of 2107 Basic People's Congresses.

The People's Congresses' recommendations for release had been:

272 (12.9%) in favour of releasing the four without conditions

1752 (83.16%) in favour of release with conditions

The main conditions were:

1. Britain should undertake not to support stray dogs, to hand them over, and to stop antagonistic acts against the Libyan people;

2. British Government to work for release of the Libyan prisoners in the UK;

3. The Anglican Church to undertake to look after Libyan students in Britain and to endeavour to secure release of Libyan prisoners;

4. British Government to stop anti-Libyan propaganda channelled through British media;

5. HMG to undertake to treat Libyans in accordance with international law.

Six People's Congresses had voted against the release and 77 had expressed no view.

There then followed what Frank Bough in London described as a confused explanation of the workings of direct democracy and the reasons for delay in convening today's press conference.

"Since direct democracy respects the minority opinion which cannot be ignored, as six congresses insisted not to release the prisoners, notwithstanding the majority view, we were compelled to defer your invitation until today."

Then, very matter of factly and with no suggestion of climax, Mr Alhijazi blandly said, "As the majority were in favour we can say that the decision is to release the prisoners and henceforth they are free to stay in Libya or to leave for any other country."

Pat bit her lower lip in order to quell the worst excesses of a grin that had started to creep from ear to ear.

Frank Bough said to Mayer Othman, "They are free?"

Shaking his head, Mayer said, "As of this moment." And, referring to Mr Alhijazi's delivery in Arabic, "He quite clearly said that."

Frank said, "The delay is now explained by the six congresses - that they wanted to take into consideration the views of the minority."

Frank said to Pat, "So after all that, he's coming home."

Pat turned her head and said, "He's not home yet."

Mr Alhijazi went on to say yet again that the decision was in response to intervention of brothers and friends and out of regard for the Church; he rejected accusation of Libyan responsibility for the St James's Square shooting and claimed that the British Government had ignored a Libyan call for a joint investigation to establish the facts - the British Government had instead attempted to exploit the incident for their own interests. Mr Alhijazi finally hoped that this step would be reciprocated by the British People, the Government and the Church.

Terry announced that he would like to reply. Mr Alhijazi told Terry to get on please.

Terry did get on. But he was damn sure that he was going to tread the diplomatic niceties that were his hallmark, and then give some solemn assurances regarding the conditions, which he himself had only just these few minutes heard.

In reply, Terry brought greetings to the General People's Congress from the Archbishop, recalled the relationship of trust established over the last four months of his religious and humanitarian mission, observed that the break in relations had affected many Libyans and Britons individually and concluded that the prime concern of the church was to show care and compassion for those of both sides who had suffered and to try to build bridges of understanding between the two countries.

Mr Alhijazi spoke to an aide, who left the conference hall.

Frank Bough said to Pat, "We hang on of course in the hope, and it may well be a vain hope, that we will see your husband, and the other hostages might appear unless they're in an ante room or behind the set."

Pat ran her left hand up through the back of her tightly curled hair and tossed her smiling face to one side - then recovered her composure.

Then she gasped.

The four of us were ushered through the high, double doors into the vast hall, littered with a number of very intense people, and three, very focussed camera crews, to the high pitched whistle of electronic flash guns recharging their capacitors, and to the tune of Terry carefully intoning an impeccably well worded reply.

Alan gave a grinning, thumbs-up sign to one of the BBC cameras.

Kate Adie mouthed enthusiastically to me, her head nodding, her eyes radiating, and her body language very positive.

We did not know what the speech was saying or what Kate actually mouthed. But it didn't matter. We already knew what the proceedings were about.

Pat looked beautiful.

As we insinuated our bodies through the narrow gap between the oval table and the wall that was lined with more bodies, Terry stood up, leaned forward and, without engaging us, shook hands with each of us in turn. Upright chairs were found and the four of us sat behind Terry, in a close arc. Someone produced a packet of cigarettes, and we crossed our legs, cuddled our handbags, and gratuitously smoked. And in giving some very carefully worded assurances in reply to the stated conditions, Terry trod a diplomatic and legal tight rope all the way to the conference's conclusion.

With barely a flicker of acknowledgement of Terry's niceties, Mr Alhijazi stood up and left, and the conference was over.

Terry started to give us a précis of what had just passed, but I cut him short and told him of our meeting only a few minutes previously. Terry raised his eyebrows. Michael and Alan nodded concurrence with me, and Malcolm and I just looked at Terry. It was difficult not to smile. But Terry told us of the conditions and that it was important that we were very careful even now about what we said because the biggest fear was whether the Libyan's intended to prevent our repatriation until they had assurances on the five conditions stated.

By the time I had wriggled out from behind the oval ring, Kate had made her way to the BBC camera team, as was busily telling them the next item of business.

I worked my way around to the ITN crew, shook them all by the hand, and thanked them for their support.

Then I went around to Kate Adie. As I approached her, she turned to face me and smiled, and then took half a pace forward to receive me as I put my arms around her. I pulled her to me and hugged her. There was nothing useful to say. Except,

"Thanks, Kate."

A melee followed which slowly traversed its way through the Palace. In the midst of the madding crowd, cameras and tape recorders were shoved in our direction.

Michael said that it was not an experience he would like to repeat.

Terry placed a restraining hand upon a smiling Malcolm's shoulder, but could not prevent him from saying that he had had some assurances from Dr Mohammed here.

When Kate asked Alan if he had a message for his wife, Alan covered his face for a moment so that he could just get Carole into his mind, and then said, "It looks like we're out now. Just wait 'til I get home!" and laughed to Kate.

I kept resolutely away from the journalists.

We squeezed like tooth paste out of a tube into another large hall in which were laid out a number of tables with a large buffet of sandwiches on them. But then I noticed that the edges of the bread were curled, having sat there for twenty four hours.

Referring to the large jugs of red drink on one table, I said, "I don't suppose that's wine in there." Almost immediately I found myself surrounded by journalists.

"What's been happening?" said one of them.

"OK. Turn that lot off," I said, referring to the tape recorders. "Are they all off?" When I had heard a general affirmative, I started to describe the recent machinations.

I had only been talking for about ten seconds, when I noticed a flashing light on a tape recorder.

"Is that on?" I remonstrated.

And Smokey Joe replied feebly, "Yes but it's only for my personal use."

"What are you stupid?" I demanded. "I clearly said to turn that lot off." A buzz of assent went around.

"Oh, fuck it. That's it!" I said, and walked off to find Malcolm.

There was no joy at the party. I refused to speak to any of the Libyans, and couldn't bring myself to eat any of the curled up food. Besides, it was clear that Terry and Hugh we eager to get all of us out, before any real journalistic disaster befell, and we were gently guided in the direction of the door. The journalists followed us as we went down the marble steps and stepped into the cars - Terry in the big black one at the front, others of us in the XJ6 in the rear. With an inscrutable wave to the cameras, we were off.

Hugh drove us to the Bab al Bahar Hotel.

In the car, I said to Hugh that I was concerned about a few things. They probably knew where I lived in England. I told him I was concerned that they might come after my wife and children. Hugh eyed me from the steering wheel and told me that, no, the Libyans didn't make war on wives and children.

Hugh told me that he would be in England the next week. I invited him to Sunday lunch. He accepted - especially upon my mention of a rather good thirty year old.

By close of business that evening, Hugh had confirmed to the FCO in London that Terry had given satisfactory assurances on each of the five conditions, and Hugh did not believe that these five points would become obstacles to our early repatriation. However, the Libyans would be looking to Britain for a positive response in the weeks ahead. It was expected, he told the FCO, that we would leave with Terry by B-Cal direct flight to London on Thursday, the 7th of February.

"Get to your rooms," said Terry. "Call your loved ones. Charge it to the hotel. Don't-don't go anywhere. Take-take a nap. And I'll call you for lunch." He looked around at us. "Is everybody happy with that?"

Kamal walked a few paces distant from me, as the house boy showed me to my room. I had not quite stuck the key in the door when Kamal came close and spoke softly.

"You want girl?" said Kamal, looking into my eyes.

I avoided his gaze.

"You like girl?"

We weren't out of Libya yet.

"You don't like girl?"

He wanted an answer.

"Yes, I like girls."

I had to stop this before he offered me a boy or a dog.

"You want..."

No! I do not want a boy! This was getting out of hand.

"Er, anything!" I riposted. "Girls to Grandmothers. Sixteen to Sixty!"

The translation took a few seconds inside his head. Then he uttered a staccato of laughter, chuckled and narrowed his twinkling eyes as he repeated my proclivity.

Then, " "Tell my wife, tell my company, tell the whole world, 'I have done nothing wrong!' ","" he mimicked, enigmatically. His face was saying, "Didn't you know? You were always going to go free."

I let out a diplomatic snort, and fought open the door handle. I stepped into the bedroom and shut and locked the door. I exhaled quietly, thankful for the solitude.

I quickly familiarised myself with the room, and then phoned Pat.

After all this time, there was very little to say. This is what we had spent nine months fighting for. And now we had achieved it. That was a result.

"If you can meet with Triumph and Disaster, and treat those two impostors just the same..."

But Pat was bubbling like a school girl.

"We're supposed to be leaving on Thursday," I said. "I don't really want to talk detail on the phone."

Pat told me not to worry about that because she would get it all from her end. And she bubbled away about the arrangements. Everybody would be at Gatwick. There was going to be a press conference which you have to be ready for, Robin. Everybody in the street was so glad I was coming home. Everybody had been wonderful. Even her Dad was looking forward to seeing me. My brothers would be there too. The press and TV had been to the house. The children had been fascinated by their equipment, and asked the journalist so many questions that the journalists could barely do their job. At school, Katy had watched a video recording of the entire hostage release. Ross had been driving his pedal car with more than his usual volume of pride.

"Thanks," I said. "I'll see you at Gatwick."

"Plumsie," she said, and with a sincerity that I had never heard before. "I'm so glad you're coming home."

I ruminated and thanked her.

Then I added, "I'm not out of Libya until I'm sitting on the tarmac at Gatwick."

Pat solemnly assured me that she remembered that.

And we said goodbye.

Then I phoned Ian Ridout. I was at the Bab Al Bahar.

I put the phone down, drew the curtains, took my shoes off, and lay on the bed.

We assembled in the hotel lobby. We had long ago given up setting our own timetable and now looked to Terry for a lead. "Shall we eat?" he chuckled. "I-I think we ought to eat," he advised. "Yes, let's eat!" he decided. "We're going to eat!" he commanded.

And we walked into the rapidly filling, hotel restaurant.

"Shall we go over there and sit down?" he chuckled. "I-I think we ought to sit down," he advised. "Yes, let's sit down!" he decided. "We're going over there to sit down!" he commanded.

And we sat at the one remaining table that would take five.

Richard Beeson joined us. We scrunched up to make room. I stole cutlery for Richard off the next table. And Malcolm stole a chair.

We helped ourselves to the buffet. And picked over our portions. None of us had any appetite. Except for Terry. Who ate for all of us.

"Now in a few minutes," intoned Terry, "We're going to have a press call. They might ask some tricky questions. You will be careful what you say, won't you?"

"Nope," I said, disingenuously.

"No?" he replied.

"Terry," I looked at him. "You're the man that's getting me out of here."

"OK," he said.

After lunch, we sat in the hotel forecourt for the BBC.

When I was asked what it was like each day, I quoted from the Hitch Hikers Guide, saying that each morning when I woke up, I used to scream for two minutes when I realised where I was. It wasn't strictly true, and Terry gave me a admonitory movement of his head. But the reality was that for several weeks, I had inwardly screamed every morning until, I'd got control of myself. But Terry didn't understand that. After all, he had never actually been held as a hostage, had he?

Kate Adie asked Alan how he'd cut his nose. Alan explained gallantly and elaborately that he had stood up under one of the projecting wrought iron cages outside the building while exercising one morning.

Terry told us to go to our rooms and stay there until he called for us. "You won't leave your rooms will you, Robin?"

"No," said I, looking him in the eye.

We sat in the main salon at the Ambassador's Residence. The furniture and decor, exactly as I'd remembered them, were elegant but of a period that I could not place. A billiard table sized mirror hung over a fire place big enough to park a small car in. The soft furnishings and carpets were sumptuous and the overall impression was of a substantial town house fit for a queen.

Hugh opened a bottle of cheap champagne - cheap - to clear the dust out of our throats. I quickly cleared the dust out of mine, as I eyed up the chilled Brut Imperial, which Hugh must open next - and duly did. God bless the Diplomatic Bag.

We moved from the huge salon into the sitting room. The room was laid out as I had never seen it - dimly lit, and with the furniture grouped, theatre style, around a large television set, situated before the fire place.

Once we were all settled, we watch the video collection.

The technical crews from the BBC and ITV had assembled outtakes of the entire news coverage of the entire hostage affair. And invented a few bits of footage of their own.

The two hours of professionally edited tape was a manic depressive, roller coaster ride of hysterical satire from Spittin' Image and others, and deeply disturbing BBC and ITN news reports; all interspersed with news footage of our wives, children, sister, and other relatives, in interview, studio and Church House.

Between uncontrollable laughter at the satire, and chest burning despair at what had gone on around us unbeknownst, lurked the continuous thought, "For Christ's sake don't let the Libyans get their hands on this lot."

Emotionally frazzled, yet only half way through the video montage, I ducked out to get a sandwich. The kitchen table was laden with an array of food, quite surprising for Libya. After several minutes of perusing, I sampled the colourful and plentiful buffet.

My plate complete, I turned towards the door. The slow deliberate pace of someone taking charge of the room as they entered it was altogether too familiar to me. I froze. Well groomed hair, pretty makeup, and the line of the breasts covered by a discreet, light, woollen sweater were all underpinned by skin tight levis over a well rounded bum. I recognized Brent Sadler's companion.

She continued to slink towards me until she saw that I had caught her eye, whereupon she carefully steered a path away from me and around to the opposite side of the table.

She raised her hands from her sides, and opened and spread them. The spread continued up her arms until the only obvious things to look at were her breasts. The rising hands each performed an outward semicircle until they rested, fingers outward, palms down, on the table. She lowered her weight slightly, raised her chin and inflated her lungs to capacity.

"You must be Robin," she breathed, and smiled.

I let out a silent breath.

"Why must I be Robin?" I enquired blankly.

"I recognised you from your description." It was like Cider With Rosie.

"Then you know I am Robin," I played. And then tightening the reins, with, "Who gave you the description?"

She faltered. And changed tack.

"I hear you've been charged with spying," she began again, playfully.

"What do you want?"

She stopped trying.

"I thought that you might like to do an interview with me," she stated more professionally but a little less like Rosie.

"You can do an interview with the four of us. I'm sure Terry will help you sort it out," I said a little less stiffly.

"Oh, no!" she said. "I want to do it with you."

"I'm sure you do," I said.

"No," I continued, shaking my head and disengaging.

She tried a couple more times before I'd got to the door. At each attempt I turned politely and answered her neutrally. Then I sauntered back to the others.

I sat and ate, astonished and annoyed that, by her style of approach, it was clear she had not had the first idea of what we had been through for the last nine months.

Back at the hotel, I phoned Terry in his room. I needed to talk to him but not over the telephone. No, it could not wait until the morning.

"Why didn't you tell us you were sitting there?" I asked, referring to his silent entry into the sitting room at the Residence, and then even more silently seating himself only behind everybody else.

"Oh...," demurred Terry.

"I thought the whole point of being at the Residence was that we were going to have a party. It was a pretty subdued affair."

"I didn't want to get Russell all excited," said Terry.

I inwardly despaired.

"You could see what he was capable of when we got back to the hotel, after only a few drinks, couldn't you?" he said. He pulled the Noel Coward dressing gown closed over his legs.

After our quiet drink and the video session at the Residence, we had returned to the Hotel. We might have been expected to go straight to our respective rooms and discreetly disappear until breakfast time the following day.

But Alan led a one man charge. His clattering sandaled feet pounded across the marble floor of the hotel foyer in a bee-line for the reception desk, where he proceeded to engage a member of staff on the topic, presumably, of his alarm call for the following morning. The instructions must have been delivered at least three times, the last two of which were at the point of one wagging finger. The whole continuous harangue, which could be heard echoing off the marble walls all the way up the staircase, was powered by alcohol laden breath.

"OK. I can see what mean," I agreed. "We're not out of Libya yet."

"What-what do you want?" said Terry. "I've got to phone the Archbishop in a few minutes."

I told him of the fight between Alan and me. I told him that it had been important to subdue Alan rather than let the Libyans see us scrapping amongst ourselves.

I mentioned that, in spite of my best efforts, I had managed to get hurt and I was afraid that I might have a Torsion of Testis. I explained the paramountcy of early diagnosis and treatment, to avoid a rather unpleasant result. I needed a doctor. Terry told me to go back to my room and stay there.

At eight o'clock the following morning, a British, expatriate GP was knocking on my door.

He asked a few questions and pushed and pulled a few things, then told me that no, I did not have a torsion. I told him of the Inderal tablets and the chest pain of a few months back, and he listened to my heart.

He lowered the stethoscope and drew breath to speak.

"Soft systolic murmur, probably functional," I said.

He looked at me, nodded his concurrence and put his toys away. "How old are you?" he said.

"Thirty four."

He prodded the musculature of my arm.

"You are in pretty good shape, considering what you've been through," he said, looking me in the eyes. "Pretty good shape indeed." He smiled. We shook hands. "Good luck," he said, and left.

I ordered room service breakfast as Terry suggested.

Almost immediately, Ian Ridout rang.

I could offer him some breakfast. Boiled eggs.

Ian spent a few minutes bringing me up to date on the latest diplomatic moves as he understood them, particularly what British Telecom had done to get me out. I listened without comment.

We covered some administration that consisted of selling my saleable assets left in Libya, settling my company loan account, granting me all my accrued leave, days off and overtime, and my 25% ex gratia payment for contract completion

For all the while that I had been in detention, all my accumulated days off and leave would be credited to me. I would even get my 25% ex gratia payment for additional hours worked.

I would like the small briefcase full of my audio cassettes. Would he bring it?

Ian nodded his head furiously. Would tomorrow be OK? Yes, I'm sure it would, breakfast again? Yes, why not.

"I do have a question," I said.

"What's that?" Ian snapped out.

"How did you get my passport?"

"One of the admins in the office is a calligrapher," he said. "Your signature was difficult, but after an hour of practice, he managed it."

"That's not the point," I went on. "In addition to everything else, I was also the tax hostage."

Ian told me that the admin had done my signature to get me registered as tax hostage in the first place. Ian took the view, he told me hesitatingly, that since the Libyans were already holding me as a hostage, then I might as well be the tax hostage too. There was no point in preventing an additional BT employee from leaving Libya as well, he explained. So it was an administrative convenience to register me as the tax hostage.

"That still isn't the point," I said. "Who is currently the tax hostage? Who volunteered to be the tax hostage in order to get my passport out?"

There was a long silence which I refused to break.

Without looking up, Ian said, "I did."

Breakfast over, we stepped out of the hotel. Terry, Malcolm and I formed the usual loose group, with the other two somewhere close, and Hugh and Richard Beeson in tow. I saw Kate Adie approaching. I caught her eye and greeted her. She greeted me back but looked busy. I stepped aside to allow her to pass. In doing so I realised that Brent Sadler was seated in a car in the hotel driveway almost beside us, along with his technical crew. The unpressured milling around gave the feeling of a happy family and nobody appeared to feel the need to speak. It was nice just to be together.

Without warning, Brent tried to leave the hotel. He quickly started the car, and was promptly addressed by Kate through the driver's side window. An argument started between them which rapidly grew heated. I asked Terry what was happening, and he dissembled. By now, Brent had stated very clearly that he was going, and Kate had stated equally clearly that he was not.

Brent put the car into gear and revved the engine as he let up the clutch. The car lurched forward, and I felt compelled to step smartly a few paces further onto the pavement. On turning back to face the car I was astonished to see Kate, who had somehow leapt around to the front of the car, leaning on the bonnet with outstretched arms, blocking the car's path. Brent threw the steering wheel to the right and attempted to steer around Kate. But Kate was having none of it. The car lurched forward several more times as Brent tried to bully his way past Kate. Brent reversed the few feet that he could, trying to get a better angle to pass Kate, who, red faced, pursued the car until she had it trapped, whereupon she let go with the most incredible tirade of invective. I was stunned. I felt the blood drain from my face. They must have heard her all over Tripoli. Such a female tongue lashing roots husbands to the spot, and I was no exception. Even Terry was slacked jawed as he disengaged any regard of the scene.

None of us dared look at anyone else. We "men" just withered.

Cornered, Brent gave up. I'm glad Kate was on our side and not against us.

Feminine complexion restored itself to Kate's face, and ruddiness replaced the pallor in mine. Being quickest to recover, I asked her what the problem was. She told me very calmly that she had set up a satellite link exclusively for the BBC, in order to do a live interview with the four of us now that we were out. Terry interjected with a worried, "No, no!" Ignoring him, Kate continued to me that at the precise moment that she was turning up to take us to the interview at the satellite earth station, she discovered that Brent Sadler was intending to co-opt the satellite slot to do an identical interview for the ITV.

With what I thought was egalitarianism, I suggested that in the mess we were all in they could just share the slot, couldn't they? Danger flashed across Kate's eyes and her voice rose to persuade me point blank that this was a commercially competitive scoop, on which Sadler was trying to out scoop her. It was a scurrilous and unprofessional thing for him to have attempted and was totally devoid of integrity. No, there would be no sharing. I nodded obediently, and stood back. Even Sadler by now was looking shaken and sheepish.

We all drove to the satellite earth station to try to sort something out and do the interview. But with the usual Libyan muddle, nobody was available at the earth station, the satellite link was not up, and the interview affair fizzled out before our very eyes.

So we progressed back to the hotel.

When we got there, the place was crawling with photographers from the UK tabloids. Kate was nonplussed as to where they had all materialised from, or even how they had got into the country, found us at the hotel etc. Something was wrong that she wasn't saying. So with some effort I managed to separate her from the rest of the crowd and put it to her. She said that we were in danger of allowing the tabloid photographers and hacks access to us. She was afraid of what self serving distortions they might attach to our version of events - and we weren't out of Libya yet. She was soon to be proven right.

The hacks wanted a photo call. They decided that the hotel rooftop would be suitably away from distractions, and we all went to sit on top of the hotel roof. Kate's caution was festering in my ears. My anxiety was heightened as I saw the diplomats and everybody else being carefully eased away from us, and we soon found ourselves alone with the journalists on the rooftop. I was getting as worried as Kate had been. I took a decision to allow the photo call and any attempts at interview to proceed only so far as the journos did not encroach on dangerous territory.

The photographer from the Daily Express was by any standard lacking in subtlety. He seated us in poses that looked as though we were tossing away our L-plates after having passed our driving tests. Such trivialisation of a situation so dangerous was too much. These idiots plainly had no regard for what we had been through or what was still at risk, even if they had ever known and, unknown to me at the time, went on to print some unflattering, unhelpful and potentially jeopardizing remarks about Terry. I drew the line.

I got up and said to everybody that we were going. Alan objected and wanted to continue being interviewed. I insisted that this was an idiotic trivialisation of what had happened and, in any case, that Terry wanted us. That clinched it and Alan came. Even Malcolm had been relaxed about the photo call, which worried me.

I found Kate and told her what had happened. She was relieved that the photo call had been truncated and that anything we had said was suitably anodyne. Then as quickly as it had emerged, the media circus disappeared. The four of us found ourselves more or less alone. We slid into boredom. We went back to our hotel rooms. I lay down on my bed and caught a siesta.

I was awakened by an urgent tapping at the door.

I put on my shoes and skipped frenetically to open it. Malcolm slid in, pushed the door shut, brushed past me and flopped onto the spare bed. He lay with his eyes skyward and an arm across his forehead.

"What's wrong," I asked.

"Alan," said Malcolm.

"Aye, he's going to get us into trouble," I mused.

"He's done it," completed Malcolm.

"Done what?"

"Ah divvent kna," Oh, God! Geordie - At a time like this.

"What's happened?" I persisted.

"Divvent kna."

"Well, you must know something, otherwise you wouldn't have come up here."

"Have you got a cigarette, Robin?"

I opened a fresh packet of twenty, put two in my mouth, lit them both, and passed one to him. I then proceeded to bleed some sense out of him.

In the end, it appeared that Alan had upset a member of the hotel staff who was now raising Cain.

I telephoned Terry.

"I think it's important that we keep calm and stay in our rooms," said he.

I asked what had happened and got an answer that assumed a knowledge in me than I didn't have. I hung up.

"For Christ's sake, Malcolm. What's going on?"

"Alan's flashed someone," he said matter of factly.

"Oh, don't!" I replied.

"Don't what?"

"Don't say that."

"Why not? It's true. We're gonna be here for ever, man."

I phoned Terry again.

This time I got a coherent story.

Alan had been relaxing in his hotel room, as had the rest of us.

Alan had been occupying his own, bizarre world in his hotel room, as he had at the last prison.

Alan's world included the need to attire himself much as he had done at the last prison. The attire consisted of his buff coloured cardigan, worn back to front with all the buttons done up at the back.

But, as at the last prison, Alan had neglected to don any other attire, and the cardigan was not quite long enough.

So when Alan had answered the door of his hotel room to the young, Tunisian chamber maid, the chamber maid had freaked out, and embarked upon a repeated chorus of, "I do not know if I will ever be able to forget this," while dancing a tarantella around the hotel corridors.

The hotel management was doing all it could to hush up the incident. As foreigners themselves, the hotel managers knew the damage that this could cause, particularly in the light of who we were. Management was trying to placate the maid, with little success. She was vaunting her status as a modest Muslim and as a victim of this predatory infidel. If this got out, it was a story that would run and run.

I don't know who we were the more nervous of finding out - the Libyans or the tabloid hacks.

Terry was right. Of prime importance was to keep out of sight.

"Terry, why don't we just get out of here?" I said on the telephone.

"Oh, there's a bit of a delay getting visas to leave the country," he replied casually.

It was possible, but it didn't sound right. The Libyans would by now waive any formality to get rid of us, Hugh had said so. But Terry had got us this far and we'd trusted him up until now, so I let it ride.

Kate and the other journalists were chatting and taking their ease by the hotel reception desk.

The reliable journalists were possessed of an alert and clear eye even when they were taking their ease.

Alan, it would seem, took a similar view.

The same clarity of eye was possessed of some of the corps of secret policemen that lined the lobby wall opposite the journalists, and who surveyed all.

Alan, it would seem, took a similar view.

It mattered greatly. For Alan had profound intelligence to impart - knowledge so dangerous that it must be imparted only to those who were utterly reliable.

Alan sighted Kate from across the lobby.

He sighted the secret policemen as well.

Now he had to cross the death zone, unseen, to impart his fearful intelligence.

He crouched slightly to lower his profile, went up on tip-toe to ensure silent movement, raised his hooked hands to under his chin to ensure invisibility, and scuttered across the deserted centre of the lobby floor, pausing every few metres and looking left and right to ensure that no-one had seen him, right up to Kate Adie and the world's press.

With eyes darting left and right over the top of two hands placed to channel his voice to the ears of Kate, and Kate alone, he said in a hoarse whisper, "I have to talk to you in total privacy - right now!"

"Well, I'm sure that that can be arranged," re-assured Kate. And without a flicker, she enquired, "What about?"

"I know the identity of the next person who is going to try to assassinate Col. Gaddafi," said Alan.

I had a taciturn breakfast of boiled eggs with Ian Ridout. He duly brought me my briefcase of music cassettes. He also brought a large brown envelope of other, small, personal effects. The envelope bore the words "no cheques" on the outside. He also brought my Panama hat.

We shook hands. Ian left. I never saw him again.

Dressed in my Marks and Spencer suit trousers with the immense dog bite in the back of the left leg, a beige, long sleeve polycotton shirt with the collar turned up against the cold, the now world famous chequered cardigan, and my Panama hat, I bagged the front seat of the Jag for the drive to the airport.

I loaded up my suitcase. Getting out of Libya was now in sight and, in spite of my best efforts and nine months of practice, I was beginning to get the bit between my teeth. On leaving the hotel, I misread the layout of the entrance way, and drove my baggage trolley straight into a cattle grid laid across the broadest part of the entrance to the hotel, despite my having read the sign that showed the correct route for trolleys. My trolley shuddered to a halt. Stupid Libyans. Who puts a cattle grid across the entrance to a hotel? My Panama hat flew off the top of the pile of luggage and onto the ground. Then as I was loading my suitcase and music cassette briefcase into the boot of the Jag, my Panama got caught in the boot lid as Hugh shut it. I rolled the hat up, and put it away before it became a liability.

Then we drove to the airport in the XJ6. A camera crew of oversized men sat uncomfortably in the rear, while I enjoyed the confidence of gliding along in the white, bullet proof, British Ambassadorial Jag, with its three quarter inch thick, bullet proof windows, and Hugh at the wheel.

Check in was routine, and our progress through TIP was accompanied by an impeccably uniformed and smiling member of British Caledonian. I reserved a seat next to Malcolm.

Terry was a little more anxious than usual, but I put that down to the same bit that I had between my teeth.

"We'll just go straight to the VIP suite. And I think it's best if we just stay there until we're called for the flight."

The prospect of VIP treatment was at best incongruous when compared to our recent nine months of treatment in one of Colonel Gaddafi's "hotels".

The "VIP room" turned out to be dingy, about twelve feet square and furnished with seats that had long since lost their integrity. We breathed out and settled down until the flight was called.

It was the press corps who noticed it first. Alan had vanished.

When Terry realised he was missing, irritation showed. With a roll of his head and an indiscreet sigh, he asked everyone in general, and me in particular, "Where is he now?"

Malcolm volunteered that Alan had probably just gone to the toilet.

But Malcolm was not acting on instinct this time; he was just trying to be conciliatory. Alan was up to something. He had not given one of his typical statements of intent before disappearing.

Terry left. A few minutes later he was back, looking very worried. A brief search by the press corps had failed to find Alan. Terry said how worried he was that something sinister may have happened to Alan.

For the sake of completeness, I asked Terry what he thought might have happened. Through continued irritation, Terry pointed out that Alan was the only one who had been formally sentenced by the courts, and that the Libyans might have changed their minds about letting him leave the country, after all.

Somebody mentioned that one of the diplomats appeared to be missing also. By the time we had done a head count, it was clear that Alan and Richard Beeson had indeed disappeared.

Wearily, Terry asked, "Does anyone have any idea where he's gone?"

A voice stated that someone had said he had gone to get his money from the bank.

"Oh, no," said Terry. "Where's the bank?"

"Sabratha," said the voice.

"Where's Sabratha?" asked Terry.

I stood up and said to the newsmen, "Look, can you turn that lot off?" They didn't. Or at least if they did, on past performance they couldn't be relied upon to leave it off. I put my back to the journalists and faced Terry.

Alan wanted his money. Money was the reason he had come to Libya, as it was with most of us. I had been getting paid into a UK bank account all the while I was captive. Alan had not. His family were in dire financial straits. No-one could blame him for wanting to get his money. He had, after all, almost nine months' untouched pay in his bank account, and this was his last hope of ever getting the money out. He had been quite adamant that if there was any chance of getting to Sabratha he was going to take it.

So now that we were checked in, he had vanished, presumably with the diplomat and his car, to get his money.

"How far is Sabratha?" asked Terry.

"About sixty kilometres," I said. "It's the first real town to the West of Tripoli along the main coast road. It would probably take an hour to get there, a few minutes in the bank, and an hour back again."

"Do you think he'll be alright," asked Terry, starting to relax.

"The coast road is crummy," I said.

He could always have a puncture - a constant liability on this, an un-reroaded part of Libya - and, with the lunch time rush approaching, God alone knew what hold ups he would incur. Still, he was leaving from the airport, and not the city centre, and he would be returning away from the flow of the lunch time rush in Tripoli. So his chances of making it there and back uneventfully were about as good as any - all other things being equal.

Terry nodded and breathed out an "OK".

By now the hacks were getting impatient at being left out for so long. The word was out and cameras and tape recorders were rolling. I disengaged myself from Terry a split second before I was pushed aside by a cameraman.

Seamlessly, Terry intoned into the camera lens, "I-I don't think there's anything sinister going on." And, more in hope than expectation, he slid his gaze across the lens, and caught my eye.

We settled down for a long and increasingly uncomfortable wait.

The airport buzzed. Eleven o'clock.

The clock ticked. Eleven thirty.

The Muezzin called. Twelve o'clock.

The day got warmer. Twelve thirty.

From somewhere within the airport I heard the strains of Lilliburlero. One o'clock. I wondered who either had such good taste or who was so keen to monitor our progress.

Our reverie was broken by shuffling feet which heralded the pounding gait of Alan's arrival. In his wake was Richard Beeson, still impeccable in collar and tie and smiling as if he had just left a christening.

Alan was alight with blazing eyes and manic beam - some facial strain now eased.

"Sorry I took so long," he growled, long since unable to force the smile.

"What happened?" I enquired.

"I went to the bank to get ...." he started.

"Yes. We know that, but what took so long?" I asked.

"I had to sign all the bits of paper," he replied.

"What, for your money?" I pursued.

"Yes."

"You did get it then," I finished, as much in relief for us as for him and his family.

"There must have been a lot of bits of paper," jumped in Malcolm.

"There were. That's the whole point. That's what took so long. I had to sign in triplicate for every payment that had been made into my account for almost the last year. They wouldn't release the funds until I'd signed for every entry. I must have filled in sixty pieces of paper."

Even allowing for a slight exaggeration, this accounted for the nearly three hours that he had been away.

"How do you have the money," I added conversationally.

"In my pocket," he smiled.

"No. I mean is it in Dinars?"

"God, no! Sterling! When you're terminating a contract in Libya, Libyan law allows you to draw your balance in hard currency. That's why I was so keen to get to the bank if at all possible. This is going to make a big difference when I get home," he triumphed.

And, even through the mad dog eyes, Alan was visibly very pleased with himself. And in spite of the nerve racking three hour wait, I suppose, it was difficult to begrudge him the justification.

We sat around for a few more hours. There was nothing to do and Terry wouldn't let us go anywhere. We stayed in the cramped "VIP" room. It would test the patience of any normal person. We by contrast were used to waiting. Finally, Terry said it was time to go and we went to board the 'plane. We were subject to the last of the formalities, immigration and customs, as is any other passenger, "VIP" status notwithstanding. Our passports were checked, our tickets were requested. I have no idea who produced the tickets but they were more than usually quickly found to be in order.

In my passport was a final exit visa. So I was ordered to surrender my pink ID card. I handed it over without a look at the man who requested it, or a word in his direction.

Customs checked our suitcases for bombs. Just before my case was loaded onto the baggage handling equipment that would take it away to God knew where if we were unlucky, I demanded some tape to bind the catches. Upon returning the roll of tape, I thought on whim to do the same to the audio cassette case that I was going to take on as hand baggage. It took me two or three goes to get the roll of tape for the second time, and I made no attempt to make myself understood in Arabic.

Malcolm asked me why I was taping up the tape case. I couldn't account for it. But by this time I was spoiling for a fight, and I wasn't going to let a small bag coming undone stand in the way. I bulldozed off towards the gate. But I got not three paces when a very determined looking, and heavily moustachioed Libyan barred my way. I looked at his eyes only for long enough to gauge his physical intention and upon looking away from him he peremptorily asked, "Why you no like Libya? Why you want to leave Libya?" I didn't know whether to laugh or cry. I observed that I had never said that I didn't like Libya, which was true. I didn't know whether the others were behind me for support, but I was not about to be detained by this fool. I went to step around him. He moved to block my path and repeated the question. I went to step the other way and as he moved again across me, I stepped to walk straight through him. He backed down. I just kept walking and learned a lesson, however unreasonable, that I have never forgotten - in foreign airports just keep walking until somebody stops you.

The remainder of TIP was a blur, and somehow we were on the plane, being ushered into First Class. It didn't look like first class – it was too big. We were put into seats against the starboard bulkhead, the farthest possible from the door, with no-one seated in front of us, and two lean expats already seated directly behind.

We sat there as the cabin filled to completion, and waited for pre-flight checks, expecting to hear the engines start at any moment.

They didn't.

Hot towels appeared that were very welcome. Glasses of orange juice appeared – doubly so. But all this presaged a delay. Finally, someone from the cockpit came on the tannoy and confirmed that there had been a delay and that we did not yet have clearance for takeoff.

"So we're just doing some technical checks," came the breezy, Hamble voice. This was par for the course, I thought. Malcolm, seated next to me at the aisle, was unmoved. Terry, seated one row ahead, also at the aisle, raised his head and rolled it from right to left as he let out a silent "Oh."

But we continued to sit. The expected fidgetting from numerous, impatient passengers did not materialise. Almost all sat peacefully, out of months of practice at giving nothing away while still in Libya.

Then, after half an eternity, the tannoy came on again to say that we had been given clearance to leave, and that we would be pushing back in a few minutes. A minor frisson went through the cabin. So did the first glass of champagne - starting with us ("Robin, can I help you to a drink?"). Somebody knew who we were. The pre-flight checks now seemed interminable. But then the engines started, and we pushed back. You could almost hear people willing the aeroplane to get airborne.

And then we were. The cessation of the trundling of the tyres on the tarmac was probably the most welcome sound I have never heard. As the undercarriage went home into its bays with that peculiar scooping sound, I felt excitement as I began to believe that we had actually made it. Then I reminded myself of the promise that I had extracted from Pat. We are not out of Libya until we are sitting on the tarmac at Gatwick.

The announcement, fifteen minutes later, that we were out of Libyan airspace was not, to my surprise, accompanied by the usual cheers and applause and, under guidance from Terry, I had to stifle my own attempt at cheering.

Once ties and seat belts had been slackened, seat backs raked, and the first glass of champagne had had the desired effect, the captain came back on the tannoy. He announced the flight number, destination and cruising altitude, and that he was particularly happy to welcome on board the four hostages who had just been released following nine months of captivity. The cabin erupted. It might have been opening night at Glyndebourne. First I ignored what I thought would be a minor courtesy. Then I frowned slightly as the depth and passion of the applause persisted. Then I raised my now empty champagne glass into the air and turned and looked across the cabin in acknowledgement. Only then did the applause subside.

"Robin, can I freshen you up?" came the solicitation from the exquisitely mannered East Lothian Air Steward.

My glass was refilled.

We began to relax. There was no more to be on guard about. But in the absence of being permanently on guard, I did not so much relax as fall into a void.

"Robin, excuse me," said the Steward, and refilled my glass.

"Robin, do please excuse me," said the Steward, and refilled my glass again.

"Robin, allow me to excuse myself," said the Steward, as he served me lunch. It was probably chicken. It was delicious. It was accompanied by a topping French white.

"Robin, might I be allowed to excuse myself," said the Steward, and refilled my glass.

"What is this?" I enquired. He raised both a delicate finger and a delicate chin into the air, and swept away. A minute later, he was back.

"Robin, it's Meursault," he elided, refilling my glass. The label read 1982.

"Robin, let me ask if I might be allowed to excuse myself," said the Steward, and cleared my plate and refilled my glass.

"Robin may I enquire if I might be allowed to excuse myself," as pudding was served with more of the '82.

For length and originality the interruptions were unexcelled in courteousness. But wine was taking its toll and I was grappling to maintain my concentration to the end of each apologetic interruption.

Then it was coffee and liqueurs, and dinner was finally cleared away - followed by more drinks.

We must have had Herculean bladders – or that or we were severely dehydrated following our hours at Tripoli airport. No-one appeared to go to the toilet.

We changed seats with one another.

Terry sat next to me and I expressed my anger for the very first time. As on previous occasions when he felt that it was not appropriate to discuss something, he didn't join in conversation. I let it go.

Terry suggested that we watch the amount we drank on the flight. Bearing in mind that we still had a press conference to undergo on our arrival at Gatwick, we would have to keep our wits about us. I assured him from my point of view that he needn't worry how much I had. I was already mentally preparing myself for it.

He asked me what I was going to say. I told him that I would answer any question obliquely. It would be pure obfuscation. I wouldn't drop any of us in it. Not after what we had just been through. He asked if I thought that Michael and Malcolm were going to be OK at the press conference.

I said, that, yes, Malcolm would not say anything of any substance, and Michael would stick to the party line.

"What about Alan?" he solicited. We discussed the state of Alan and quickly concluded that his presence at the press conference would most probably be something of a liability.

"What do you think we ought to do," said Terry. I observed that this was England, and you can't just lock a man up to prevent him from talking. Terry pointed out that Alan's behaviour was by now very odd, and that he had demonstrated himself capable of almost anything. If we didn't watch out he was still capable of getting us all killed. It sounded a little extreme, but I agreed.

"Look," I said. "If you're that worried, why don't you radio ahead, get two psychiatrists on standby and get him sectioned as soon as we land. That avoids one potentially difficult situation even if it creates another."

Terry agreed the distinct possibility, although he added that it seemed a bit tough to do that just to keep Alan out of the press conference. I added that if Alan was not prepared to stand down voluntarily, then we might just have to do that.

"Look," I said. "Why don't we..."

"...just tell the press" interrupted Terry, "that he won't be attending the conference because he's too ill. And tell Alan too."

"Exactly," I affirmed.

"I'll talk to Alan," said Terry.

"No," I replied. "I think you have to make the decision for him."

And that's what Terry did.

To lighten the conversation, I asked Terry with some interest how on earth we managed to get first class accommodation on the flight. The cabin was full. He told me that he didn't think it was that difficult. On the subject of who paid for the seats, so that we could convey our thanks, he told me that he didn't think I ought to worry too much about that. The conversation was over.

I saw a friend of mine several seats over. Of course I hadn't seen him for almost nine months. He was a member of the diving club. I got up and went over to chat to him. Even now as I got up I realised that I was still looking around me very circumspectly and moving very slowly. The instinct not to cause some trigger happy revolutionary to shoot at me was still very strong, and I wasn't to lose that instinct for months to come. In fact I don't think I've ever quite lost it. I went and spoke to my friend. He told me that the diving club had all been very concerned when I disappeared. I said that that was nice of them to show such interest. Oh, no, he went on. They were all quite nervous because I had known so many of them, and nobody had any idea what I might say to the Libyans if they questioned me, or who I might implicate. They'd even dismantled the diving club compressor room, hidden the equipment and shut down all diving for months. A not unreasonable fear, I observed to myself, but nobody in the diving club knew me very well if they thought I was going to implicate anyone. I didn't feel there was any point in trying to enlighten him. It was pointless now because it was all over and, anyway, I just didn't have the energy. I did attempt to reassure him of my silence however, by telling him that by the time October had come around, the Revolutionaries could have broken every bone in my body and I wouldn't have told them my middle name. He smiled, but he didn't know. It occurred to me at this point that it was odd that he should be travelling first class. I mentioned it. He earned good money, he told me, it was his money to do with as he liked. Why shouldn't he fly First? Absolutely right. It takes all sorts to make an expatriate. "Oil industry, isn't it?" "Yeah. Two weeks on, two weeks off." "Twelve hours a day?" "When I'm on duty." "Then you bloody deserve to fly first class." We laughed and shook hands. I wished him good luck for his return to Libya after his two weeks' leave. He told me not to remind him of it. That wasn't for another two weeks yet.

I stood up straight, caught the eye of another expatriate who I had vaguely seen around Tripoli and we exchanged brief waves and nods of the head from opposite sides of the cabin. On the way back to my seat, I caught the eye of another expatriate for a split second before he lowered his eyelids. I read from the barely perceptible smile that he knew who we were but I couldn't remember seeing him anywhere in Libya before. He was seated directly behind our seats. He was very fit. "That's the best sound of the lot isn't it?" I opened. He looked up. "That stuff about 'Ladies and gentlemen we are now out of Libyan airspace.' I mean," said I. He smiled a bare trace of a smile. "Oil industry, is it?" I enquired. He shook his head, while the man next to him ate his food and continued to ignore me. I was wasting my breath. It takes all sorts to make an expatriate. Not a wine glass in sight either. Some funny characters on this flight. I returned to my seat, directly in front of them.

Malcolm went up to the flight deck for fifteen minutes. The captain had placed a radio telephone call, and Malcolm was talking to his wife. It was curious, but I felt vulnerable and incomplete without him and, quite irrationally, jealous that somebody else had a higher claim on him. I was going to miss him. We had made a great team together. He is confident that, indirectly, I'd saved his life, and I am just as confident that I couldn't have made it without him. Whatever the truth, we were both here, alive, basically sane and out of Libya.

I felt deflated. The rest of the flight was boring. Boredom was something I was going to have to get used to over the next few months. Life was going to be pretty uneventful from now on. Still, we had the press conference to go.

And then, after circling around Gatwick airport for what seemed an eternity, we touched down in darkness. The sky was heavily overcast but the whole airport was ablaze with light, reflected in huge pools of surface water from rain that had poured relentlessly for most of the day and was still falling. Terry had suggested that we not kiss the ground after stepping onto the tarmac. He was quite right, of course. None of us was the Pope and, after all, our arrival was not going to be a big media circus, was it?

The aircraft rolled gently to a halt.

Except for us, the first class passengers disembarked, followed by those in the main cabin. We were then asked to sit in the main cabin for a while. We knew not why. But this was England. They could arrest me for not having a valid passport if they liked. They could even stick handcuffs on me if they wanted. This was England - Habeas Corpus and all that. And we were on the tarmac at Gatwick. An immigration official boarded the aircraft, and checked our passports right there. It wasn't obvious and he didn't let on, but their purpose was to avoid an uncontrollable crush in the terminal as we tried to get through immigration. He asked if I was carrying any duty free alcohol. I just looked away. Formalities complete, we all stepped out into the ink black night - Michael, Alan, me, Malcolm, Terry, Richard Beeson, an air hostess, and the two taciturn expats from behind our seats in first class. The airport floodlights blinded us to everything in front of us and we had to pick our way carefully down the stairway for fear of slipping or falling. Malcolm turned up the palms of his hands to indicate to Terry the state of the English weather after all we had been through. Alan nonchalantly posed, leaning on the stairway hand rail, and waved a slow, casual wave to the bank of photographers that he guessed correctly were out there in the gloom, to show how casually he was taking all this. My desire to get away from all this and out of the rain before any disaster befell us at the hands of Alan, began to show and I tried to step around Alan. However, he read me perfectly and pounced to stay just ahead of me. As Michael trod the tarmac, first among us, a photographer called out for him to kiss the ground. To his credit, Michael concealed himself behind a genial wave and called back, "I'm not the Pope. I'm not the Pope." Ludovic Kennedy later commentated that we all come down the companion way in our own various ways.

Once on the tarmac, it followed that as a group we would give the press a photo opportunity, rain notwithstanding. And while we were stood there Alan did just that. He withdrew a cigar from within the folds of his clothing and, with studied nonchalance, proceeded to light it, directly under the port engine of the aircraft. I had difficulty in concealing my horror and fury at the recklessness of his showing off and the potential for causing a fire that could easily kill us all even at the last knockings. I turned my head looking at, what I hoped was the terminal and set off once again in the hope of avoiding being caught in a fireball of aviation spirit. Alan once again tried to impede my progress.

Terry took my cue, and we left for the terminal to a disconcerting barrage of motor wind, single lens reflex cameras from the stand erected especially for the hundreds of photographers in front of whom the aircraft had pulled up. The walk to the safety of the terminal building was a blur.

And then there was my family. A brief hug with Pat who clung to me like never before, and a kiss for Katy, aloof and beaming like the cat that got the cream. Ross and Chris jumping up – almost climbing up me in order to get a cuddle.

Then there was my Dad and Janet. I could not understand why Janet was there. My brother Barry explained that Dad and Janet had got married.

"Hello, Robin," said Andrew, and Barry introduced me to two youngsters.

One, Margaret, was in floods of tears. Not knowing that Margaret was Janet's fourteen year old daughter but seeing her crying as she attempted to address me, I took her hand. Then while still trying to figure out who she was and what was going on, I was introduced to Steven, Janet's seven year old son, bemused and smiling.

In the midst of this mêlée, I found myself constantly on the move instinctively to avoid being hemmed in by a crowd of unknown people or being shot at by who knew who else that might among them.

Pat was dissolute and avoided my gaze.

One of the men from my crew in Libya was there with his wife. They both came to greet me. I appreciated that no end.

Alan Florence and Malcolm Hicks, who just happened to be duty ITN crew that evening, stood impassively by as they rolled their camera. They had been told in draconian terms by the Powers That Be where they were to stand, and that they were to remain rooted to that spot for the duration of the reuniting of the families. I almost raced over to them and joyfully and enthusiastically shook them by the hand and hugged them. They both raised the palms of their hands and gave innocent looks to the Powers That Be as if to say, "We didn't move." Slack jawed, the Powers That Be were now searching for hankies to wipe the egg off their faces.

I addressed a young, uniformed police constable to let him know of my support in the midst of the murderous strikes that had beset England over the previous months.

I thanked a senior police officer for the show his men had put on to receive us safely.

George Newns and Mike Peace ghosted in. Heads down in a practiced posture of inoffensiveness to match their practiced interpersonal skills. Mike suggested that I be brief in the press conference that was to follow. Didn't they know what I had been through?

"We've got some help to get you out of here if need be," he said. I resented the threat.

So Special Branch was here. The suits, the ties, they'd all just had their bloody hair cut. In this country we all tend to obey the law. There isn't any business of "you do what I say or your days are numbered". It's staring, data processing eyes, that in many cases have never stared death in the face. And you can tell the difference.

Andrea walked right up to me and kissed me a big, firm smacker on the lips. "That's for the one Pat gave Malcolm," she said. The shock and desire had me open mouthed and wide eyed.

The immaculate Richard Beeson stood around with Terry. They both smiled at a job rather well done.

The plan had been that we all assemble and have our photos taken by the press. It was simple enough.

But the scores of photographers started to push and shove each other, jockeying for position or a clear line of sight.

The assembled hostages and their wives and children entered the centre of the floor in a group.

The ensemble was a gift of a photo opportunity, and the photo call suddenly lost any semblance of dignity. Motor wind SLRs clattered with an awe inspiring din, and the hostage group looked dazed. The photographers continued to push and shove each other. Heated words were exchanged. Someone fell over.

Alan decided that enough was enough. He walked over to a chair against a far wall, behind the photographers. Standing on the chair, he bellowed at the World's Press to stop all this nonsense at once, and proceeded to give them the Word of the Lord about good manners and patience, and that they would all get what they wanted if they would just behave themselves for a few minutes – all at furious decibels and at the point of a wagging finger.

This was a photo opportunity too good to miss. The photographers turned, en masse, and pointed their cameras at the now hysterical Alan, and proceeded to punch and push their way to a clear shot of Alan as he continued to harangue them about good manners and orderly conduct. The noise of motor wind SLRs was intimidating.

Alan was horror struck at what he had achieved. With a final homily, he climbed down from the chair and attempted to force his way through the photographers and back to his wife and children. But the crowd of photographers was too dense and they scented blood. Tempers were now lost, they proceeded to punch and kick each other, and Alan was trapped in the middle.

I shouted to Pat to grab Ross, as Terry scooped Christopher up in his arms. I could barely hear myself think above the din of the cameras, and shouted to all Plummers and Terry to get back against the wall, now! Terry, squatting, with his eyebrows slightly raised; quizzical Christopher sitting on Tel Waite's thigh and encircled by Terry's left arm; Pat with her back to the wall, in the casual embrace of her husband, Ross between squatting Pat and me for protection; and Katy standing full height at the back against the wall with a smile on her face the size and colour of a slice of water melon, just delighted to have her Daddy back.

Terry pulled Michael in, who also squatted, faintly uncomfortable in the protective embrace of Terry's other arm.

Then one cameraman saw us. Then another. Then another. Then another, until the whole cohort of sixty odd photographers was snapping its deafening way towards the first editions. Alan, quite forgotten, our grouping made it into the national and regional broadsheets and tabloids the following morning and onto the front page of the British Telecom internal newspaper that month.

And we still had the press conference to get through.

The noise started to die down. Terry and I read the timing and stood up simultaneously. I started to ease the family towards a double door more or less beside where we had created our crouched group, but Pat said that she wasn't coming into the Press Conference - that there was a suite of monitors for the families to watch us on. So I kissed Pat and each of the children, and told them that I would see them in a few minutes.

"Where's Alan?" I said.

"Oh, don't worry about that," said Terry with the characteristic, aloof raising of his countenance into the nearest void. But thinking better of it, he looked down into my eyes, smiled and said, "His family's got him. I-I've briefed Carole ... she agrees. He won't be in the press conference."

My blood pressure dropped.

Through the double doors, we sat on upright chairs. Malcolm, Michael, Terry, me.

The world's press arrayed themselves in ranks before us, not deep but wide, in order to give the maximum number of people a shot at the chairs with a camera.

The clean, emulsioned walls and the elegant, but understated furnishings were in stark contrast to the yellowed and gaudy fittings of press conference halls of late.

The acoustics were good. Even if one spoke quietly, every word could be heard.

Terry started with one of his engaging and narrative but innocuous preambles that got the journos writing stuff that had already been published. But it set a tone of moderation and it showed who held the reins of the conference.

Then the first journalist piped up. "It's very good to see you all home and looking so well."

We voiced our thanks.

Then, "How did you feel throughout the time of your captivity, Michael?" he directed.

"Insecure," said Michael, with emphasis. "Just very ... insecure." And he shut up.

Well done Michael. His immaculate shirt, impeccably knotted tie and sharp blazer were a long way from the rumpled diffident of the previous nine months.

"What was the worst bit, Malcolm?" cried another journo.

"It was all the worst bit," said Malcolm, looking about him. "Just ... you know ..." and slipping the ball to me, he turned and said, "Robin?"

I caught the ball and kicked it into touch. "The worst bit was when the toilet paper ran out."

A ripple of laughter went around the press corps, which I followed with a beaming smile, until my gaze came momentarily to rest on two surprise attendees, innocuously propping up the wall by the door, through which we had entered. That took the smile off my face. George Newns and Mike Peace looked for all the world like two owls - their heads dipped in motionless deference, but eye balls upturned to look out from under lowered eyelids. The overcoated, senior managers of the Libyan Coaxial Cable Project in London were plainly doing what I suspect they had been very clearly instructed to do from the very top of the company. Make sure Robin doesn't blacken the name of British Telecom during the press conference.

Then Stern magazine thundered its incisive, Germanic way to the heart of the press conference.

"Were you properly treated?" articulated a stout, goatee bearded copywriter, who looked as though he played tuba in an alpine village brass band at weekends.

"Yes," I said.

"How can you say that you were properly treated when you were held in solitary confinement for nine months?"

"We were properly treated," I said, avoiding his gaze.

Res ipsa loquitur.

And the tuba player spluttered with exasperation, as I let the thing itself speak.

Terry was satisfied that the press conference had run a successful course and that there was no point in pushing our luck.

So he drew it to a close with a typically gallant valediction.

The press corps had to run to meet their copy deadlines, and the journos started to switch everything off.

I called out, "Hold on, we're not finished yet. Switch that lot back on." And some of them did.

I saw Terry draw an anxious breath. I shuddered to think what the two owls were thinking.

"I'd like to say 'thank you' to about a hundred and fifty authors whose books we read," I said. "We sat up some nights reading the Hitch Hiker's Guide to the Galaxy," I continued. "I even did all the voices including Marvin the Paranoid Android.

"I would also like to say some words of appreciation of the way that you, the press, have in general handled our case. You might be interested to know that we got the FT about once a week from the 1st of September onwards, and spent a lot of time watching the price of gold go up and down."

The journos groaned suitably.

"But of particular interest to us was to see the stock exchange quotation of the Daily Express take a nose dive.

"I see also that Australia beat India in the Test," said I, as the room became increasingly quiet. "And in Britain's latest international," I said, slowly turning to Terry, "I think the referee was Man of the Match."

The whole press corps erupted into a surprising burst of applause as I thought of the Libyans trying to translate that one into Arabic. I shook a smiling Terry's hand that had come around to meet mine.

And then it really was time to go.

We got out of our chairs.

First, I shook hands with Michael and congratulated him for sticking to the party line. Then with Malcolm, who, having said nothing of substance, blew out a sigh, then smiled at me and said, "Thanks, Robin."

We moved back into the room where the photo call had taken place, and while I looked for Pat and the children, I found myself being greeted by my brothers.

Andrew pulled out some cigarettes and we smoked, with our backs to the wall, all of us just glad to be alive and together. I clutched my cigarette and my handbag, and avoided anyone's gaze.

A few seconds of smoking, laughing and the odd photo or two, and it took Andrew to observe that someone was trying to attract my attention.

About twenty feet in front of me, in an impeccable suit and tie, was a clean shaven man of about my age, making an open handed attempt to engage me.

I stepped away from my brothers and, while still advancing on him with my arms by my sides, asked what he wanted with no more than an upward flick of my head.

"Would you like to do an interview with Selina Scott?" he enquired very politely.

But right there, right then, I felt a left hand curl its way around the inside of my right elbow from behind, and an attempt to lead me away from the young man.

Initially, I thought it was my brother, Andrew, but the body movement didn't feel like him. So, whoever it was, it was clear that they had absolutely no understanding of what I had been through in the last nine months and that, now I was back in England, I was not going to stand for anyone putting their hands on me and telling me what to do.

"Getchya hands off me," I said levelly and convincingly, still looking at the young man, who bridled.

"They" let go.

"Who's Selina Scott?" I said.

"I am," purred Selina Scott, as she walked her feline walk across the last ten feet of floor towards me - her great, big eyes, fixedly tried to bore holes in me as they looked out from under magnificent eyelashes and a huge cascade of blonde, blonde hair.

But Special Branch was at it again.

"Getchya hands off me," I repeated more slowly, with more decibels and with more gravel than before, while I still looked at this apparition gliding across the floor towards me.

Special Branch let go.

"No," I said to Selina, neutrally, looking straight into her eyes.

Selina Scott raised her eyebrows and her chin, widened her eyes and formed her mouth into a perfect 'O', just about the right size to receive a drinking straw.

"No?" she purred musically, and turned her chin back down in admonishment.

"No," I confirmed. "If you want to do an interview with me, go and see Terry, and I'm sure he can fix one up for you. If he says it's OK, then I'll do the interview."

"I did one with your wife, Pat..." she tried.

"That is as may be..." I said neutrally. "We've made a decision not to do any interviews. I'm sorry."

Selina started to speak again. As she did so, I stepped half a pace forward to shake her hand. But she took a comparable step backwards.

"Ah," I said under my breath. And "I've got to go, now." And went to look for Pat.

As I turned around, I saw only my brothers, and George Newns and Mike Peace.

"Who took me by the arm?" I said to my brothers.

"We didn't see anyone," said Andrew.

"But you were only standing ten feet behind me," I said. "I mean I know there was a crowd."

They both looked at me and shook their heads from side to side.

Christ! These blokes are good. I thought.

The drive home was interrupted only by a couple or three stops to get the children snacks and water. The BT chauffeur was a man in his middle twenties, polite, unctuous and a good driver. This was just another job to him. In what I thought was the generous manner of Terry, I tried to engage the driver in conversation. He was pleasantly monosyllabic and concentrated on driving. He did his job well, but didn't talk to his passengers. Inside, I was still expecting the feeling of pressure and of being utterly alive. The feeling wasn't there. The children made noises as if they wanted to ask questions but didn't know what questions to ask. Pat was silent. She too did not appear to know what to say. Mike and George followed in a second car, and a third car followed them, for which no explanation was in evidence.

In the silence, I remembered the wording in the front cover of my passport: "Her Britannic Majesty's Principle Secretary of State for Foreign and Commonwealth Affairs Requests and requires in the Name of Her Majesty all those whom it may concern to allow the bearer to pass freely without let or hindrance, and to afford the bearer such assistance and protection as may be necessary." A fat lot of good that was.

When we got home, the third car did not approach the house, but I invited my chauffeur, and Mike and George into our house, if only to get them out of the cold, crisp, February night air. I offered them refreshments which they refused, and the little gathering fizzled out. I showed everybody out, and turned to my wife and children. We got out the champagne, looked at the sitting room, highly and secretly decorated by the neighbours with witty cartoons and slogans, that I appreciated a lot.

Pat and I drank the champagne and went to bed.

THE END

NOW LET ME TELL YOU WHAT HAPPENED

The following day Katy and Ross went to school. Christopher spent the morning on my lap showing me what he had been doing and jabbering to his Daddy. He had recovered from his defensiveness of his mother at Gatwick when he had been heard to say, "Who's that strange man kissing my mummy?"

Then the phone started ringing. The Cambridge Evening News, the BBC, The Times, The Telegraph, and the gamut of local and regional papers. Appointments were made for all of them.

A neighbour came around briefly and left a video tape of BBC and ITN news items that she and her husband had recorded since the 1st of September.

Another neighbour who, along with her husband, had kept an eye on our house every other day or so that Pat and I were in Libya came and handed back the keys, and wished me well. She also gave us a welcome home present. 1 large fruit bowl - off white inside, plum coloured outside. I thought it was beautiful.

No-one stayed long. That was very gracious of them.

I started to watch the video tape.

Then the BBC arrived, set up their lights, warmed up their camera lenses, took the phone off the hook, and re-arranged the furniture. During the interview, they asked questions that permitted a narrative reply from me and, although they were searching, none of the questions was truly dirty. They got what they wanted.

As I ushered them out the door, I saw to my surprise a phalanx of smiling photo journalists flocked on the pavement a respectful twenty feet or so from the front door, and wrapped up to the ears in duvet jackets. A couple started to take photos and others clamoured to ask questions. I raised my left hand and told them to, "Hold it, gents!" and said that they should let me just get the BBC into their cars and away, and then I would speak to them. As good as my word, I quelled the rush by saying that if they would just be patient, I would answer all of their questions that I could, and they could all take photographs. Some twenty minutes later, they had got what they wanted and some made a swift but orderly retreat presumably to make the early editions. I got talking to those who remained.

Despite the cold, they were warm and generous and, having established from their questions that I was in fact alright and that they had got the essential news interest, not in any respect pushy.

By the end of Saturday, I had watched the entire three hours of news items, recorded by our neighbours, Alan and Sue Marr.

The television news reports gave an indication of the danger that we had been in. And I was catatonic as I absorbed just how much greater had been the danger than I had known. Even allowing for the fact that Kate Adie had made a decision, against every professional instinct, to deliberately not report at the time, certain, potentially explosive facts about our situation, I found myself alternately wriggling on the sofa and trying to remain glued to screen. And, throughout the three hour tape, whenever I felt myself back in Libya, or even contemplated ever having to go through that again, my lower lip started to tremble as it would for another four months to come.

But the facts of our ordeal sat in sharp contrast to the lack of knowledge and understanding among friends and journalists of what I had actually been through.

So when I woke up on Sunday morning I was on an emotional roller coaster ride.

I answered the doorbell to find a smiling Hugh, his pretty daughter and his lovely, slim fiancée.

At my behest, Pat had cooked, to her usual high standard, roast pork, and spotted dick and custard.

Over lunch Pat told me how angry she and all the other wives had been about the appallingly bad timing by Mrs Thatcher over the unveiling of the memorial to WPC Fletcher. Mrs T must have known how annoyed the Libyans would be and she must have known how likely such an act would be to disrupt negotiations just as they were at their most critical time and when anything could have gone wrong. "It was just like her to sabotage Terry Waite's effort right when it looked as though everything was about to succeed," she said.

"It wasn't surprising that the Libyans didn't let you go on the Monday and held you back for another day. It wouldn't have surprised any of us if the Libyans had changed their minds completely and kept the lot of you. God, that woman makes me angry."

I said that I thought Mrs Thatcher had a lot of guts. And her timing was absolutely brilliant. Here was a leader of the free world sending a message to Colonel Gaddafi that it was of no importance to the free world what games he and his regime played. No-one was taking a blind bit of notice. It was a brilliant piece of brinkmanship that at the last minute she could stick it right up the Libyans for everyone in the world to see, and still the hostages got out of Libya.

That might be true, Pat pointed out, but she, Pat, had understood that the real reason why Colonel Gaddafi finally decided to let us go, and this was not a matter of public knowledge, was that he wanted something that was more important to him than keeping us as hostages.

"Apparently his father had been dying of cancer," she said. "The only useful treatment his father could get was in England. And the only way Big G could get a visa for his father was by first releasing the hostages. That's how you got out."

Simple as that?

Hugh nodded.

I poured the thirty year old.

Then, Pat told me that she had seen a satire of our release in Private Eye or Spittin' Image or something. In the satire, someone had asked Colonel Gaddafi under what conditions he would release the hostages. Gaddafi had replied that he would release them only on the condition that they all came and shook hands with him.

THE END

NOW LET ME TELL YOU WHAT <u>REALLY</u> HAPPENED

Col Gaddafi actually did want to see us after we were freed. Not only did he want to see us but he was not going to let us out of the country until he had had a public meeting with us in the full glare of the world's media and press, which would satiate his manic desire for publicity.

But let me start at the beginning.

Throughout the whole of our captivity we had been held by a revolutionary committee dedicated to using us as hostages for the release of the four Libyan terrorists arrested and remanded in custody in Britain. Doug Ledingham was held as a hostage to put pressure on British Caledonian to continue operating in Libya. George Bush had been held just to push up the ante, and because the revolutionaries thought that they might make some propaganda out of his name.

However, throughout the whole of our captivity there had been a body of moderate opinion within the Libyan administration, that was opposed to the whole idea of hostage taking and who could see that the initial kidnapping and subsequent detention of the hostages would serve little or no useful purpose. These moderates also recognized after a while that our continued detention was becoming an international embarrassment and an obstacle to improved international relations, or, indeed, to international relations at all. The moderates included people within the administration in such exalted places as the Ministry for Foreign Affairs and the Justice Ministry. Some of these moderates were reliable and honest men, one of whom turned out to be a very powerful man, and who told of where these revolutionary idiocies were getting Libya.

After our earliest interrogations, it was plain that we were being held on the flimsiest of evidence, and the traditional legal authorities would have nothing to do with us virtually from the word go. This meant that at least one other of the hostages and I were being charged with and tried for espionage by a Revolutionary Court on evidence that would not hang a cat.

The moderates, some within the administration and therefore with some considerable clout, knew that we had become an embarrassment. Colonel Gaddafi himself had been pushing for weeks to get us out. He had indeed decided in December that we should be released, but no-one in the Revolutionary Committee holding us was taking a blind bit of notice. More emphatically, the Committee holding us positively would not let us go and a power struggle developed over a number of weeks, which effectively begged questions about who actually ran Libya. The theoretical answer to that was, of course, that the Revolutionary Committees ran Libya. This was after all established in Colonel Gaddafi's own Third Universal Theory and enshrined in his treatise on the subject, The Green Book. But the Committees were beginning to run out of control, which was not supposed to happen, and Colonel Gaddafi was increasingly not fully in control.

Thus we, the hostages, were at the centre of a power struggle that all came to a head at the weekend of our release. One of the moves made by Colonel Gaddafi in the power struggle was to abolish the Revolutionary Courts because of their persistent and damaging misuse of power. We were being held by a Revolutionary Committee, and two of us were being tried by a revolutionary court. But because the traditional legal authorities had already declared that they would not and never were going to touch us, and the revolutionary courts had been disbanded by Colonel Gaddafi himself, there was in fact nobody to try us and we were left in a limbo created by the usual Libyan muddle. There was also no-one left who could officially rule that we could go home. This now left a further problem in that the Libyans, and Colonel Gaddafi in particular, would not arbitrarily let us go home. They are surprisingly legalistic and would not move with out due legal process. And now no due legal process existed.

The power battle took a turn with Colonel Gaddafi trying to persuade the Revolutionary Committee to authorise our release. This would have been a legal release. But they refused to do so. This meant that we were stuck in a power vacuum over Sunday, Monday and Tuesday and Colonel Gaddafi had to resort to other means.

An announcement was made on the Sunday that we were going to be released on the Monday morning. On hearing the announcement in London, Kate Adie chartered a jet from Gatwick and, on arrival in Libya, arranged for live television coverage of the release, which would be complete with a lavish party of cakes and fruit juices and the whole media circus with which we had become familiar. The expected televised release was also much trumpeted in Britain. An army major came on the Sunday evening and told us of our impending release. But nothing happened.

The raging power struggle culminated on the Sunday night in a real fight when the Revolutionary Committee dug in its heels and refused to release us. Colonel Gaddafi simply hadn't threatened them enough. Things came to a head when nothing happened on Monday, 4th February, 1985, the day we were supposed to be released.

During the whole of Monday there was a real row going on between Libyan factions. The Libyan department of Foreign Affairs was steaming at the refusal. The Justice Ministry was absolutely furious. Monday night, was a truly dramatic time with lots of activity going on, very fast and determinedly. Some very powerful people had finally had enough and issued a stream of orders to mobilize the army. It had got to the stage where something had to be done. The hostages had, for any number of reasons, got to be released. The Revolutionary Committee had to be restrained. It was necessary to threaten them much harder than thitherto. The army would be required in great numbers to do this. But such an operation could not possibly be allowed to become public knowledge, for then it would be known that Colonel Gaddafi was not fully in control. So it all had to be kept totally secret from the world's media which had assembled its full glare in Libya for the much publicised release.

That night the army was mobilized and people all over the place were being rounded up. It was necessary to round up members of the Committee and anyone else who might know of the defiant stand taken by the Committee against Colonel Gaddafi, or who might attempt to continue the power struggle or make a public fuss about it. The army was thus compelled to sit on the members of the Revolutionary Committee and continue to do so until we were out of the country. Getting us out of the country was now, clearly, the biggest imperative, lest the secret operation become public, or anybody changed their mind.

We were only released from detention on the Tuesday because Colonel Gaddafi threatened to shoot the Revolutionary Committee if we weren't.

But in fact it was a condition of the release that it must be on television, and we still had the televised release to go through yet. Kate Adie engaged in some real activity to get a satellite link up in time for the Tuesday morning broadcast. This was all the harder to achieve because of the disappointment of the previous day, and she had a hard job persuading all the right people that the link really was going to be needed and used on the Tuesday. She also said to the Libyans that she was not going to go live on air until she had guarantees that we had in fact been released. She was not, she told them, going to lose face for a second time over the waste of media build up and the satellite link.

As the time for the televised release approached, Kate still had no guarantee of our release. And Colonel Gaddafi had cleared off...

Frantic activity was still to follow. It was only when the entire media circus had been assembled in the People's Palace, and the satellite link was up, and Frank Bough and Pat were sitting in the studio in London, where the BBC News was being extended for the first time since man landed on the moon, and the speeches announcing our release were actually being delivered in the great hall of the Palace, and the covers had been taken off the party buffet which had been sitting in the heat since the previous morning, that Kate Adie finally got the guarantee she was seeking.

Kate had told her contacts that she wanted to verify our presence at the televised release as a condition of going live. One contact told her of the location of some men who were being released that day, but whom he had never actually seen. He would personally take her to see them, but she would have to identify them. At that point, unknown to anyone except this contact, we were being told formally of our release, sitting in the office close to the Great Hall where all the bally-hoo was going on, when Kate, with her contact out of sight behind her, stuck her head round the narrowly opened door, and we saw each other. She had her guarantee, and she went live.

The delay in releasing us was accounted for by the Libyans telling the world live on television about the six Congresses that had voted not to release us. But the army was still secretly sitting on the Committee members.

We should have got a flight out of Libya more or less immediately if nothing else had happened.

But Colonel Gaddafi wanted to meet us. He actually did want to see us, in public.

This came to light after we'd arrived at the hotel, when Kate was told by a contact that Colonel Gaddafi wanted to meet "them". Kate put the meeting off. She said that the men had extremely mixed emotions in their present state, particularly Alan and Michael. "In fact the only person, Robin Plummer, who has got his brain in the right place and all his faculties intact, would probably kill him. He is, very rightly, extremely angry about the way that he has been locked up for this length of time for no reason and if the meeting went ahead he would probably jump on Colonel Gaddafi and strangle him," she said.

But Kate was told, please, to come now. The aircraft was waiting to take us all to Sirte where Colonel Gaddafi was waiting in his tent to have the public meeting in front of the world's media.

Kate went bananas. She stormed at her contact, stormed out, phoned Colonel Gaddafi's men and said, "No!" She spent one and a half hours putting her foot down. But Colonel Gaddafi had made it a condition of our leaving the country that we attend the public meeting. Kate said absolutely not. We would probably get to Sirte by air alright, but with the usual Libyan muddle, there was no guarantee that we would get back again for a scheduled flight out of Libya, or indeed get back at all. It could take weeks to organise a return flight from Sirte. Anything could go wrong. The army was still sitting on the Committee members. Suppose one of them escaped? Suppose one of their friends got wind of the secret operation and subsequent restraining exercise? Suppose one of them got out to Sirte and shot the hostages? Suppose Colonel Gaddafi changed his mind? Suppose one of the tabloids at the meeting with Colonel Gaddafi tumbled what was going on and said the wrong thing? "They could be absolutely relied upon to fuck it up, fuck it up!" said Kate. Even as we were standing there at the hotel, one breech of the current secrecy could have a howling mob down around our necks and then the hostages might never get out of Libya. "No, I'll come to Sirte," Kate said. "I'll give him his media publicity, but there is only one thing for these men now. Get them out, out, out! And not only that, it is a condition of me giving him his media publicity that I will not go to Colonel Gaddafi until they are actually off, out of the country."

So frightened was Kate that any one of a catalogue of things would go wrong, that she, herself, got on and organized an aeroplane for us, among other aspects of our journey home. Further, the FCO had authorised Hugh in guarded but unmistakeable terms to try to arrange our departure to another destination, say Rome or Valetta, the following day, the 6th of February. They even authorised him to pay for the air tickets if that would help. But Colonel Gaddafi remained adamant that we would not be allowed out of the country until we had attended a public meeting with him. And Kate remained equally adamant that we would not attend one. The promise of massive media coverage of a public meeting with Kate Adie was still the offer to Colonel Gaddafi, but only on condition that we were out of Libyan airspace before the meeting took place.

But every remaining minute we stayed in Libya, every wrong move made in a hotel doorway, every unwitting slight, misplaced word, whiff of alcohol or breech of protocol would have us in danger of being recalled. The army was still sitting on the Committee members.

Even two days later on the Thursday when we were finally sitting in the British Caledonian jet on the tarmac at Tripoli waiting for permission to take off, Colonel Gaddafi still would not allow us to leave without a meeting, and permission to take off was denied.

Kate Adie was sitting at the table eating egg and chips when the telephone rang. Her contact answered it and hung up. He dialled a new number and handed the phone to Kate. "Ask who this is," he told her. "Tripoli air traffic control," came the reply. Taking the receiver back, Kate's contact delivered a message in Arabic and then in English. We were cleared for take off. Then we were airborne, First Class. Then we were out of Libyan airspace and everybody slackened their ties. Then the champagne flowed and we were attended to by the Scottish steward. Kate, who should have been on the flight with us in order to scoop our return for the BBC, had gone to Sirte for the Colonel Gaddafi press conference as promised, and now had some explaining to do to her boss when she finally got back to England, a very long time after we were sitting on the tarmac at Gatwick.

THE END

POST SCRIPT

Robin

I would like to be able to say that Pat and I lived happily ever after, but it was not to be.

The hostage situation changed both of us but we changed separately and not together. The two of us struggled for eight further years to try to overcome the changes that had happened to us and to our marriage. We eventually got divorced and sadly, three further years later Pat died at the age of 42 of complications surrounding Multiple Sclerosis.

Remarried to Rachel Russell, a talented, one time musician, Stage Manager and later Event Organiser, we have a musically gifted daughter, Rhiannon, who plays cello, piano and, like her father, anything else she can get a tune out of.

Malcolm

Malcolm's marriage also failed. He went on to live with a new partner outside of the UK, and moved on even from there.

Malcolm became a welding inspector and formed his own company.

I stayed with him for a long weekend break on each of two occasions, and we still exchange Christmas Cards.

Michael

I understand that Michael returned to Libya to teach English. Other wise I have lost contact with him.

Alan

I spoke to Alan once on the phone. Otherwise I have lost contact with him.

Doug

Doug still works in the airline industry. I make contact with him every few years.

Hugh Dunnachie

Later served at the British Embassy, Dubai, as Consul-General in Perth, Australia and later left HM Diplomatic Corps. I have lost contact with him. Thanks Hugh.

George Anderson

After 4 years in Libya, George was given a soft posting in the Solomon Islands. He later served at the British Embassy in New York, and soon died of a heart attack. His dear wife later remarried. Thanks George.

Thanks for reading A Brush With Madness. Robin Plummer, Royston, Herts, 2010.
Copyright © Robin Plummer 2010

www.ABrushWithMadness.com

AND WHAT OF NOW?

Most of this book is written from memory - reliably so, on account of how indelibly the events were imprinted on Robin's mind. The correspondence among government departments and diplomatic missions, which helped to confirm Robin's memory, was acquired under a Freedom of Information Act (FoI) request. The FoI request, however, took over 11 months to get a final reply because all the government papers about the hostage situation had to be sifted by HMG to ensure that nothing prejudicial to the now greatly improved relations with Libya should be released.

The children, and very much they are children no longer, persevered. Each has become a very productive member of society. I am immensely proud of what they have achieved.

Katy, BA(Hons), PgDL - solicitor.
Ross, BA(Hons), MA with Distinction - advertising campaign film producer.
Christopher, promoted and decorated - two army tours to Iraq.

Robin runs a small, international consultancy business, specialising in Turnaround and Recovery, and has travelled to or worked in over 50 countries, including many of the world's hot spots. He has never been back to Libya.

Robin still practises aikido, and sees his children as often as possible.

Visit www.ABrushWithMadness.com